THE
FORGOTTEN
SISTER

THE FORGOTTEN SISTER

Caroline Bond

CORVUS

First published in Great Britain in 2019 by Corvus, an imprint of Atlantic Books Ltd.

10 9 8 7 6 5 4 3 2 1

A CIP catalogue record for this book is available from the British Library.

Trade Paperback ISBN: 978 1 78649 368 2
E-book ISBN: 978 1 78649 369 9

Printed in Great Britain by Bell and Bain Ltd, Glasgow

Corvus
An imprint of Atlantic Books Ltd
Ormond House
26–27 Boswell Street
London
WC1N 3JZ

www.corvus-books.co.uk

To Chris, because it's about time he got a mention!

THE BEGINNING

A newborn baby is a vulnerable thing: soft-skulled, thin-skinned, best watched over, for fear of damage.

But this little girl is alone.

She sleeps peacefully on the floor, in front of the fire, covered by a slightly grubby shawl. The shawl rises and falls gently in time with her breathing. There's a thud in the room above, something dropped and cursed over. Footsteps pattern the ceiling. Her eyes flutter open, revealing glossy black pupils that can see very little, only a blur of light and dark. Shadows pass over her like birds across an open sky.

She's awake now.

In the tiny, coral whorls of her ears the sounds upstairs are muffled, soft-edged as if she's still in a world of water. Her arms and her legs wave, but she no longer floats; dry land is so much harder to navigate. Her feet get caught in the fine mesh of the shawl. She kicks and manages to free them, but she cannot move, she cannot roll over, cannot even turn her head. She is where she is; in a safe place or in harm's way? She cannot know.

All she can do is feel.

She feels the rub of the babygrow against her skin and the pinch of the wound on her belly. She feels the soft nap of the blanket beneath her head and the heat of the fire. And she feels the loss, the absence, the sudden, violent removal from the warm flesh that once folded her in.

And so she cries.

Her small, shocked lungs expand as she forces out one startling cry, then another; high, hard, angry yelps that fill the room, pierce the walls and ricochet up the stairs. They proclaim her presence, her needs, her wants, her demands.

Perhaps she is not so helpless after all.

But no one comes.

She stops. Her eyelids squeeze shut. She waits, learning anticipation or disappointment. Then she takes three short, desperate gulps, drawing in the unfamiliar air.

She tries again, louder this time, more desperate.

Comfort comes out of nowhere.

Fingertips brush her cheek. Soothing, tentative, but real enough to break the spiral. She listens to their message. The touch tells her that she is safe and not alone.

It is enough.

Prologue

THE HOUSE phone was ringing, which was unusual. Grace ignored it. She carried on stacking the dishwasher. The people she knew – the people she loved – rang her mobile. It would be a sales call. They had a cheek. Friday nights should be sacrosanct. The answerphone kicked in, mercifully cutting off the noise. She set the dishwasher running.

Through the kitchen window she could see Tom ambling round the garden, hands in his pockets, head bowed, inspecting his precious lawn. He looked at ease, relaxed – happy even. Grace felt her own shoulders loosen in response. It was still a lovely evening. They should make the most of it. She fetched a bottle of wine and some glasses and slipped on her flip-flops, intending to join her husband. They could sit out, enjoy the warmth, maybe talk things through again, see if they couldn't come up with a different tack; their current approach plainly wasn't working. Or perhaps not – perhaps *not* talking about Cassie was what they needed.

Grace heard the answerphone stop and reset.

She pushed open the back door and was about to step out into the fading light when the phone began ringing again. It sounded louder, more insistent. A chill rippled through her. She shouldn't have ignored it the first time around. It was tempting fate to ignore a ringing phone. She crashed the wine and the glasses down onto the counter and hurried across the kitchen, stumbled and lost a flip-flop. She kicked off the other in frustration. The soles of her feet slapped across the unforgiving hardwood floor. It suddenly felt very important that she reach the phone before the caller gave up. She snatched at the receiver, nearly dropping it in her haste. 'Hello.'

'Mrs Haines?'

She could tell, instantly, that it wasn't a call centre. 'Yes?' Her breathing echoed back at her through the handset.

'Ah, good. I was having problems leaving a message. I think there's something wrong with your answerphone.' Grace wasn't interested. The woman carried on. 'Could you confirm your home address and date of birth for me, please?'

'Sorry, but what's this about?' Her question came out more sharply than she'd intended, worry taking precedence over politeness.

'If you could just confirm your address and date of birth, please, then I'll be able to explain.'

Grace relented and gave her personal details. Balanced on the edge of panic, she looked round their hall, taking in its reassuring ordinariness. Tom appeared at the kitchen door.

The voice came back on the line. 'Thank you. I'm sorry to inform you that your daughter's been brought into A&E at the General Infirmary.'

Grace took a shallow breath. She'd imagined this phone call often enough over the years, endless nightmarish permutations of dreadful accidents and life-changing injuries, conjured up out of the overwhelming instinct to protect her children. But the reality was different. The reality was worse.

'Mrs Haines? Did you hear me?'

Grace managed to respond calmly. 'Yes. Sorry. What's happened? Is she all right?' Of course she wasn't – she was in hospital. 'I mean, how badly hurt is she?' Tom raised his hand to his face, obscuring his expression.

The woman said, 'I don't have that information, I'm afraid. I'm just the booking clerk. I've been given your contact details and asked to request that you come in.' There was a pause. The remote soundtrack of other people's traumas reached down the line and insinuated itself into their home: a child crying, a raised voice, the muted but urgent peal of a siren. 'Mrs Haines? Are you able to attend?' There was a touch of impatience in the clerk's voice now.

'Of course. Yes. We'll be there as soon as we can.'

'Thank you.' The line went dead.

Grace carefully replaced the receiver, delaying, for a moment, the imperative to deal with what the woman had said. She looked at Tom.

'Cassie?' he said, although he didn't really need to ask – he already knew.

Chapter 1

FOUR MONTHS EARLIER

RYAN HAD asked Cassie to wait for him after her shift finished. Her parents had asked her to come straight home.

She'd said 'yes' to him and lied to them.

She sat on the wall that separated the hotel from the park, enjoying the last rays of sunshine. This late in the evening it was quiet, only a few solitary dog walkers around. They criss-crossed in and out of the shadows in a complicated pattern of amicable avoidance. It was entertaining to watch – from a safe distance. They were far enough away for Cassie not to feel anxious. No chance of an over-exuberant puppy jumping up at her or some bad-tempered yapper appearing out of nowhere, teeth bared. Cassie didn't like dogs – any dog – big or small, cute or ugly. She didn't see the point of them and, more honestly, they scared her, with their unpredictable affection and equally erratic aggression.

The sun felt good on her face. She closed her eyes and let the warmth seep though her skin. As she basked, her mind turned to Ryan. She wondered, idly, which of the shelters they'd use, probably the one at the top that looked out across the city. Not that they paid much attention to the view. It was a long walk, but the hack up there was worth it, because the top shelter had one distinct benefit: it was private.

Cassie shifted her position, happy for the time being to wait. It was nice to sit outside; the quiet was soothing, after the noise and hassle of evening service. Cassie hated being a waitress, at the beck and call of fussy diners. But as much as she disliked the work, she enjoyed the money. The job also had the benefit of getting her out of the house and away from the non-stop prying of her parents. Last-minute lunch services and additional evening shifts – there was always a credible cover story, should she need one.

There was still no sign of Ryan.

Cassie swivelled round to catch the last of the sun on the other side of her face; as she did so, the kitchen door banged open. Her heart rate quickened, but it wasn't Ryan. It was Freddie, one of the waiters; nice-looking, nice-smelling, nice manners, with a very nice gym-bunny body to go with it. Cassie watched him open a can and take a long drink, celebrating the end of his shift. The can glinted as he raised it to his lips, providing her with her own, private Diet Coke Break. Ryan couldn't stand Freddie. He hated his posh voice and his cockiness. Cassie knew that it irritated Ryan that she found Freddie funny, which somehow made her laugh just a little bit louder and longer than was strictly necessary whenever he cracked a joke. It was all part of the new reality that Cassie found herself operating in. She'd thought the physical changes that had happened at high school were the biggie – the periods, the boobs, the mad mood swings that made her want to murder her mum one minute, then climb onto her knee the next – but she'd been wrong. It was learning what to do with her body that was the revelation. And that had really taken off since she'd started working at the hotel and had met Ryan.

Ryan Samuel Newsome, dark, wiry, sometimes crude, often moody, inked – and wanting more – not a brainbox, not a great talker, or listener for that matter; basically not her type at all. And yet...

With Ryan, Cassie was discovering that the pathetic hook-ups that used to happen at school were a pale imitation of the real thing. With him, there was the pull and the push of fierce sexual attraction. It was a physical thing, not explained by logic. Addictive, exciting and at times almost scary.

The pull was fascinating.

Cassie was very conscious of the power she had over Ryan. She saw how his eyes tracked her in and out of the kitchen: her and no one else, not even Sophie, who was prettier and far slimmer than her. Cassie liked to watch his reactions when she spoke to the other staff, especially Freddie. She loved how she could distract him by the simple act of wearing a black bra underneath her white work shirt – add in a slow stretch, and it was almost cruel. She could feel Ryan's hunger pulsing through him when he was near her. It was a massive turn-on. In fact, Cassie wondered – sitting there quite happily, on her own, on her wall, in the sun – whether she didn't actually enjoy the pull more than what came after; whether the chase wasn't better than being caught. Either way, it was changing the way she felt about herself and everyone else.

The sun left her face and edged further down her body. The door opened and Ryan finally emerged.

Time for the push.

There was the briefest nod of acknowledgement between Freddie and Ryan, then Freddie tossed his can in the bin and walked off, watched by Ryan, who stood perfectly still, as if unable to move until Freddie was out of his orbit. Cassie was just about to shout 'Hi', when she suddenly, inexplicably, decided against it. Instead she swung her legs over the wall and dropped down the other side, where she crouched, out of sight, uncertain why she was hiding from him.

From her secret vantage point she had a clear view of Ryan's confusion. He looked round, thrown by her not being where she should be. He glanced at his phone. Nope. No text. He scanned the car park, searching for her, obviously thinking that she'd stood him up. Perverse as it was, she stayed hidden, enjoying his uncertainty. He paced away, then turned and walked back, and in that moment she caught sight of the look of raw, furious disappointment on his face. She felt a sudden, sharp, uncomfortable surge of panic. But now she had a problem. She could hardly pop up from behind the wall, like a jack-in-a box; she'd look like a complete idiot. She was trapped. There was no option but for her to shuffle along behind the wall, through the scrubby fringe of grass and the weeds, keeping her eyes peeled for dog crap, doing an awkward kind of bear-crawl, until she finally made it to the gap in the bricks. Once there, she crouched, waiting for the right moment to appear... She could pretend she'd just been for a walk in the park. When Ryan turned away for a second, she stood up.

When he turned back round and caught sight of her, the darkness in his eyes cleared and he smiled.

They were breathless by the time they made it to the top of the park and the sky was turning pink. Cassie knew she couldn't stay long, but she also knew she couldn't say that to him, not yet. Ryan headed for the shelter and she followed him. They'd used up all their topics of conversation on the way up through the trees, so they sat side-by-side looking at the shadows, without talking. The park was virtually empty now, the dog walkers all gone, except for a lone woman in Lycra, who was jogging laps of the bottom path with her Westie skittering along by her side. From a distance they were little more than a splash of neon-pink and a dab of dirty white, tracing circuits in the fading light. The silence that stretched between Cassie and Ryan was taut with expectation.

It was Cassie who made the first move. She owed him that much. She put her hand on his thigh. They both looked at it. She waited, enjoying the tension beneath her fingertips. Then, without a word, she slid her hand down his leg towards his knee, enjoying the feel of his muscles flexing in response to her touch. Ryan's breath quickened. Then, achingly slowly, she trailed her fingers along the inside of his thigh, back up towards his crotch. Ryan put his hand over hers and guided it higher.

There was no need for conversation for the next hour as the purple sky turned black.

Chapter 2

TOM LET himself into the house and threw his keys in the bowl. He was on domestic duties for the evening, Grace was away in Reading with work. The house was quiet, which was a change, but a welcome one. Cassie was out, working a midweek shift at the hotel, with their permission, which meant it would be a nice, chilled-out evening, without the drama that his eldest child had a tendency to generate of late. The fact that Ryan would be hanging about at the hotel, ogling Cassie while she worked, was, however, quite a high price to be pay for an evening of peace. Tom was bemused as to why his bright, articulate, opinionated daughter was so enthralled by a lump of such exceptionally average masculinity. The couple of times Ryan had called round to pick up Cassie, Tom had been so underwhelmed he'd thought she was joking – that she might be parading Ryan in front of him as a warning rather than as an actual boyfriend – but apparently not. The lad seemed to have some sort of hold over her, though Christ knew what. Sex, probably. Damn it, she was only seventeen, and she was his daughter. It was too soon. Tom hated the thought of it. In truth, he hated the very existence of Ryan, and the thousands of others like him, lying in wait for both his daughters.

Tom could feel himself tensing up. No, not tonight. Cassie was coming straight home after her shift, she'd promised; she'd have no time to be getting up to anything. He was going to take Grace's advice and let it be. She was sure Cassie's infatuation with Ryan would run its natural course. He hoped his wife was right.

He hung up his jacket and eased his feet out of his shoes, divesting himself of a tedious day at work, and of his anxiety about Cassie. Tonight he was determined to focus on his youngest daughter. Poor, easy-going, 'never a drama – never mind a crisis' Erin, who risked being forgotten, by virtue of being so low-maintenance. He assumed Erin was in her bedroom, doing her homework, as she so often was. He headed upstairs, hoping that he'd be able to lure her away from her books for a few hours, get her down to talk to him, maybe even help him prepare the meal, but when he reached the landing he paused. Her door was ajar, but her desk was empty. He was just about to shout 'Hi' when he caught sight of the soles of her bare feet at the end of her bed. He peeped into her room. She was lying on her side, completely still, her cheek resting on the open pages of one of her school books, fast asleep. Tom backed away from her room, leaving her to nap.

In the bedroom he dug out a pair of shorts and one of his comfy old T-shirts, a Grace 'favourite', the Chicago Bulls one with the peeling logo. As he pulled it over his head he started thinking about what to cook and whether he wanted a beer or a glass of wine. He had every intention of going downstairs once he'd changed, but instead, on a whim, he found himself heading up to Cassie's room, taking care to avoid the creaky stairs.

Cassie's 'den' was on the third floor. It extended from the front to the back of the house, a luxury of space and light. It was one of the reasons they'd bought the house ten years ago, plenty of square footage for their family to grow up in – happily. Tom didn't venture up to Cassie's room very often these days, mindful as he was of respecting her growing need for privacy and separation, but he was familiar with every stick of cursed-over flat-pack furniture in it. The Ikea vibe was strong, lots of funky Scandi storage solutions, grey paint and the obligatory swinging light bulbs, but in amongst the assertion of modernity and borrowed identity there were crumbs from the past: the row of children's books on the shelves, the dusty teddy on the top of the wardrobe, the plastic hippo on the bedside table.

Tom sat on the bed, feeling nostalgic for the old house, the old routines and the smaller spaces that used to exist between himself and his children.

Cassie's tablet was on the floor beside the bed, charging. Tom picked it up, intending nothing more than to look at the cover, a vermilion-and-black spider's web design, which on closer inspection revealed itself to be a dreamcatcher. It must be new. Her last one had had cartoon rabbits on it. He had bought it for her, thinking she'd appreciate the cheesy humour. She'd obviously grown tired of it. He opened the cover, intending nothing more than to see whether her tablet was fully charged – wasting electricity, a teenage-girl Olympic event. It was. He lightly touched the screen, intending to glance at Cassie's choice of apps. The screen immediately asked him for her pass code. Without thought, he tapped in 1 – 2 – 0 – 4, her birthday, and was surprised when the screen opened; some things in her life hadn't changed. He briefly scanned her pages, hunting for clues to this new, emerging incarnation of his daughter, but the apps told him little, other than that she was as mired in the same social-media web as every other teenager, which – curiously – reassured him.

He shifted his position on the bed and barely touched the Internet icon, intending simply to check that Cassie hadn't been spending all her allowance on make-up. She hadn't, though there were plenty of searches for exorbitantly expensive eyebrow pencils. She'd also googled a shop that repaired hair-straighteners and, reassuringly, found at least a little bit of time to do some homework, if the search on American Civil Rights was anything to go by. But there was one other search that definitely wasn't 1960s US politics-related – family-planning clinics in their local area.

Tom closed the cover and dumped the tablet back on the floor, scalded by the insight into his daughter's life that he'd had no intention of discovering.

Erin woke, having not thought she'd been asleep, to the absolute certainty that there was someone in the house.

She lay still, her heart thudding, neither flight nor fight winning. Had she locked the back door behind her when she came in? She couldn't remember. Had some lad in a hoodie with a habit slipped through the side gate into the garden, peered through the windows and seen enough to make it worth his while? There was definitely someone upstairs. She could hear them moving around in her parents' bedroom, searching for valuables, not caring how much noise they made, thinking the house was empty. Erin didn't move, too frightened that they would hear her. The 'awkward' second drawer in her parents' chest of drawers squeaked as it was yanked open.

Then her dad swore, softly.

It wasn't a drug-dependent burglar about to attack her and leave her sprawled in a pool of blood, like a character in a TV drama. It was her dad. Of course it was. Erin unclenched and waited for her heart rate to steady. She was an idiot. She lay with her face stuck to her book, the horrid gluey taste of adrenaline coating her tongue, feeling stupid. Her dad came out onto the landing and she waited for him to barge in and make one of his chronically unfunny jokes, but instead of coming into her room, he went upstairs. She heard his footsteps cross the floor overhead, then silence. And then more silence.

Erin unpeeled her face from her book, pushed herself upright and listened to her dad, doing absolutely nothing, in her sister's bedroom.

✳

An hour later, Tom dished up dinner. They ate in the kitchen. Erin did her best to keep her father occupied with anecdotes about the new maths teacher with the personal hygiene problem. After they'd eaten – a huge bowlful of spag bol, with lots of cheese on top – and cleared up the kitchen, she made an effort and followed her dad into the lounge. He didn't seem to want to be on his own. The only 'compromise TV' they could find was a natural history programme, but after five minutes of watching thousands of tiny, newly hatched turtles playing 'chicken' – and losing – across a six-lane highway in Hawaii, Erin couldn't stand it any more. She excused herself and went back upstairs to have another go at her art homework. The minute she left the room she heard her dad switch over to the History Channel for some sepia Second World War footage of mass death and destruction. That was bound to cheer him up.

Her homework was a reinterpretation of Munch's *The Scream* and it wasn't going very well. The background colours were warring with the figure in the foreground and the perspective was off. Erin felt that with every mark she made, she was making it worse. As she worked, the picture grew darker and muddier, but she persevered, hoping that if she just kept going, somehow it would come together. She struggled on without interruption for over an hour, with the exception of a couple of texts from her mum, who was going through a chronic phase of emoji overuse. There was nothing from Cassie; there rarely was these days. And, thankfully, there were no more excursions upstairs by her dad.

Cassie got back later than normal. Erin had already been lying sleepless in her bed for nearly an hour by the time she heard her sister try and sneak into the house unnoticed. She failed. The lock was on a spring mechanism and, as always, it made a loud rattling noise as the door shut. Simultaneously, the sound of the TV cut out.

Erin lay in the dark and waited. She heard footsteps. Cassie made it across the hall, but not up the stairs.

'You said you'd be back by quarter past ten.' Tom's voice, full of suppressed irritation, was very clear. Erin waited for her sister's response.

'It was busy.' Cassie's voice was equally clear. But it wasn't the words themselves that were the problem, it was the tone.

'Cassie, you have to stick to what we agreed.'

Erin pushed herself up in bed and listened.

'It's only half an hour, what's the problem?' Cassie's casual, but deliberate defiance echoed around the hallway.

'It's closer to an hour; it's gone eleven p.m. Anyway, it's not the time that's the problem – it's doing what you said you'd do. Or at least texting, if you're going to be late.'

'Oh God, Dad. Can't you give it a rest!' Cassie's footsteps made it onto the stairs.

Tom's voice went up a notch. 'Cassie! Please don't walk away from me when I'm talking to you.'

'I'm tired. I'm going to bed,' she replied. No hint of apology or compromise.

Tom's next question was the one guaranteed to light the blue touchpaper. 'Were you with Ryan?'

There was a long, long pause.

Cassie's response, when it finally came, was loud, firm and final. 'No.'

Erin heard her come up the last few stairs, cross the landing, go into the bathroom and close the door. The minutes ticked by. The loo flushed, the tap ran, she came back out. The landing light clicked off, plunging the house into darkness. Cassie thudded up the stairs to her den and shut herself in.

Conversation over.

Erin sat hunched up in bed, breath held, still waiting for her dad's response.

But there was nothing – just the unmistakeable and unnerving sensation of him standing, silently, at the foot of the stairs in the dark.

Chapter 3

CASSIE NEARLY backed out of it. She put it off for more than a week, picked the Tuesday to definitely go, then conveniently couldn't, because 'something important' cropped up. The Thursday was a bust as well, but on the following Monday she caught the bus into town after college, on her own, with every intention of going through with it.

The place was nothing special. It was a modern, two-storey building that could have been an office, but for the sign outside offering podiatry – whatever the hell that was – a dental clinic, a baby clinic and Cassie's destination, the sexual-health and family-planning clinic. Even from way across the other side of the road, the sign made Cassie flush and feel hot. She watched people coming and going for at least ten minutes before screwing up enough courage to cross over and hurry through the automatic doors. Even then she could have backed out of it – was actively considering it – but the woman at the reception desk chose that precise moment to look up, smile and say, really loudly, 'Can I help you, love?' It was purely Cassie's inability to come up with a deflecting response that saw her being directed up to the first-floor waiting room, the one on the left, not the one on the right, *unless she wanted her corns seeing to*. Even then, Cassie could have not sat down and not waited for her turn. But she did.

The whole exercise had become a sort of test, a self-imposed challenge. It wasn't about Ryan, not really. It was about her growing up, making her own decisions. She hadn't told him what she was doing. He would have got the wrong idea; well, not wrong exactly, but he would have got excited, very excited, and the invisible red lines that she'd so carefully drawn around her body would have been wiped out in an instant. Cassie wasn't sure she was ready for that, not yet. She liked the tension at the edge of what he wanted and what she would allow. She liked that the power was in her hands. But she also knew she was going to relinquish it, eventually, probably sooner rather than later, and when she did so, she wanted to be prepared.

Her parents should be proud of her for being so responsible, but she seriously doubted they would be.

'Cassie Haines?' a voice bellowed. Cassie leapt up and dropped her bag. She felt like a complete chump as she gathered up her stuff and followed the woman through into the consulting room. The website had promised that all the doctors at the clinic were female, but for a minute Cassie could have sworn that the person sitting at the desk was a man. Cropped hair, a big jaw, no make-up, bad jeans and a bland shirt. A bloke. Cassie stopped, two steps into the room.

'Come in. Please.' The Amazon indicated an empty chair.

Cassie sat down, clutching her bag to her chest.

'Now, how can we help you today?' On closer inspection, it was a woman – just. The he/she doctor waited patiently while Cassie stutteringly explained what she wanted. The following ten minutes were awkward. She stared at a point beyond the doctor's left ear as she answered the questions about her intentions and her decisions. They seemed very keen to establish that Cassie knew the meaning of consent. She reassured them, more than once, that she did. The doctor was actually quite good. She was straightforward, helpful, un-judgy. She nodded, a lot, as if agreeing that Cassie was making a wise and sensible decision. Before too long they were onto which were the best methods of contraception to avoid pregnancy and which were better for protection against STDs. 'You need to keep yourself healthy as well prevent conception,' she advised. As the doctor talked, Cassie felt the screwed-up sensation in her gut ease.

Then a form was produced. The doctor clicked her pen. 'I just need to ask a few last few questions about your medical history, specifically on your mother's side. It helps us decide which device might be best suited to you. There can be a familial link to certain risk factors with some of the methods.' The pen was poised ready to fill in the box. 'Is there any history of breast cancer in your family?'

Cassie answered, 'No', but as the doctor started to write down her answer she realised she couldn't say that. 'Sorry,' she blurted out, feeling stupid and unsettled, 'I don't know.'

The doctor scored through her original answer and scribbled DN on the form and continued. 'Any history of strokes/ embolisms? That's blood clots?' she clarified.

Again Cassie had to answer, 'I don't know.' Her voice grew fainter.

'Obesity or diabetes?' Another box to be ticked.

'I don't know.' Her response was barely audible.

The doctor, sensing her discomfort, seemed reluctant to ask the next question. 'And the last one: any mental-health issues that you are aware of – depression, schizophrenia, paranoia? Don't worry if you don't know; many of our patients haven't a clue about their family's medical history.'

Cassie didn't answer.

Mercifully, the doctor stopped probing. 'Well, like I said, it's not too much of a problem, but I'm afraid we're obliged to ask. I think we have enough to be getting on with. It might be good, however, if you could speak to a family member before your next appointment; your mum perhaps – if you feel you can – so that we can have a full record.' She straightened the papers on her desk and seemed all set to proceed, but Cassie couldn't cope with any more.

She stood up. She wanted out, and fast.

'Cassie? Are you all right?' the doctor asked.

She wasn't, but she couldn't tell them why. The concern on the doctor's face only made it worse. Cassie panicked. 'I'm sorry, I think I need to think about it some more, before I decide what to do. I'll come back another day, maybe.' And without waiting for a response, she walked out of the room.

Head down, cheeks burning, she hurried across the waiting room, down the stairs and out of the building. In her rush to get away from the clinic, she ran across the road without looking. She was rewarded by the blast of a horn, and a very unfriendly gesture from a white-van man, who shouted some obscenity at her through his open window. The shock tipped Cassie further into confusion. She suddenly hated Ryan for landing her in this position, in an area of the city she didn't know, on her own, being asked questions she couldn't possibly answer.

The sight of her bus approaching at least gave her a focus. She ran to the stop, got there just in time, paid and headed up to the top deck. Distance, that's what she needed; distance and some space to breathe and compose herself. Unfortunately, the bus was busy. Cassie swayed to the back, targeting the only double seat that was still free. The bus pulled away as she claimed it. Within seconds the clinic had disappeared from view, but the shame lingered, slick and oily on her skin.

Cassie watched the streets and shops grind by, waiting for the embarrassment to fade; which it did, slowly, only to be replaced by something worse. She felt as if someone had grabbed hold of her and shaken her. She clung onto the handrail, desperate for the juddering sensation to settle. Until she'd stepped into that bloody clinic, her adoption had been an interesting but inert fact in her biography. She had been adopted as a toddler, so what? It was an irrelevance. An acknowledged part of her history, but something with no bearing on her everyday life. She rarely thought about it. Now she couldn't stop. The doctor had woken up the reality of her adoption and sent it crashing around her brain, knocking over the familiar furniture of her life. She willed it to stop, but it wouldn't. The truth was that she knew nothing about her medical history, because she knew virtually nothing about her life before her parents. She'd accepted their potted version of her past as if it didn't really relate to her. What was wrong with her? Shouldn't she have wanted to know more about her biological mother? It should have mattered. *She* should have mattered.

Cassie twisted and turned in her seat, struggling with the sudden awareness of her own ignorance. Only one thing was certain: her adoption now had the shadow of her actual, birth mother attached to it.

Chapter 4

GRACE WAS worried that Cassie had been abnormally quiet for the past week. Her usual flow of opinions and self-assertion had dried up. She ate with them, when she didn't have a shift at the hotel, did what they asked – which was a relief – and appeared to be doing some work for college, but she seemed absent, distracted. After every meal she either retreated straight upstairs to her own room or to Erin's, closing doors behind her. It left a void. In the evenings it was almost as if they didn't have children. Tom was relaxed about it, privately enjoying this quieter, less combative version of his daughter. He was pleased that Cassie was home more. Secretly he was hoping that she'd ditched, or been ditched by, Ryan. There had been no sign or mention of him of late. If it was a break-up – fingers crossed – and she was a little down, she'd survive. Ryan had looked eminently replaceable, to Tom. But Grace was concerned.

So when Cassie was running late for work on the Saturday morning, Grace went up to her room, knocked and tentatively offered her a lift. Grace hoped that the time in the car might give them a chance to talk. For a second she thought Cassie was going to turn her down, but then she shrugged and said, 'Okay, yes please.'

Grace crossed the room and sat on the bed as Cassie rushed

around, shoving things into her bag. When she'd got her stuff together, she flumped down on the floor in front of her mirror and started dragging a comb impatiently through her hair. Grace winced as she watched. The rasp of the comb announced the damage that Cassie was doing. Grace risked taking another small step – by offering to help. Again Cassie surprised her by agreeing. Grace took up her position behind her daughter on the floor, picked up the comb and began working it through Cassie's hair, a section at time, carefully, lovingly. Patience paid dividends with hair like theirs. Beneath her hands she could feel energy crackling through her daughter, the thrum of a thousand unspoken emotions, but Grace told herself to ignore the clamour. She concentrated on the task at hand and on the curve of Cassie's skull beneath her fingers, working efficiently and gently.

Her touch seemed to have the desired effect, or perhaps it was the familiar smell of the oil and the comfort of old routines. Whatever it was, the vibe in the room softened and Cassie submitted willingly to her mother's attention – just as she had fourteen years ago, when Cassie was Cassidie, and Grace was yet to become a mother.

A steam-filled bathroom, with condensation trickling down the window.

The dark night outside.

Jane, Cassidie's foster mum, on her knees alongside the bath.

And Cassidie, splashing around happily with her toys, chattering away to herself, despite the presence of a virtual stranger in the tiny, airless bathroom.

The bedtime visit was a crucial step in the carefully choreographed 'getting to know you' ballet of the adoption matching process; a deadly serious dance that was destined to determine the shape of the rest of all their lives. But that night it looked just like a child getting ready for bed, with her *current* mum and her *potential* mum, neither of who was her *real* mum. It had all been so deceptively normal, so seductive, so hypnotically peaceful.

The bubble of calm shattered when Jane tackled Cassidie's hair.

'I warn you, she doesn't like having it washed,' Jane said, and she wasn't joking. Slippery as an eel, Cassidie twisted and slithered around the bath, as Jane endeavoured to lather her hair. It was an onslaught that swiftly escalated into a full-blown battle. Jane persevered, ignoring the tears and full-volume wailing, scrubbing away with a vigour that made Grace feel tearful herself. To rinse the suds away, Jane dumped three bowls of water straight onto Cassidie's head, to the pitiful strains of 'No, no, no, no!' Then she whipped a towel around Cassidie and scooped her out of the bath. Tough love meted out with no coddling, and no conditioner.

Thankfully, Cassidie seemed to survive the ordeal without too many ill-effects. She calmed down quickly, sniffing away her rage, as Jane tucked her swiftly and efficiently into some faded Winnie-the-Pooh pyjamas; a hand-me-down pair, Grace guessed, from one of the many foster children Jane must have scrubbed clean and put to bed across the years.

'All done and dusted,' Jane announced as she gently shoved Cassidie towards Grace. Jane immediately turned round and started chasing plastic ducks in the draining bath water. 'Off you go! Mummy Grace is going to get you into bed and read you your story tonight.'

Grace froze, disabled by inexperience and the overwhelming need to get this right, but Cassidie simply blinked, pushed a strand of dripping hair out of her eyes and put her hand out, accepting the handover without complaint.

Holding Cassidie's small hand nervously, Grace led the still-damp child to the bedroom at the front of the house, swiping a hand-towel on the way. There she lifted Cassidie up onto her bed and started gently drying her toes. Cassidie chuckled and retracted her foot. Grace traced the corner of the towel across the soft sole of her other foot. Cassidie jerked her leg away, laughing out loud. The simple pleasure of being close to Cassidie's warm, soap-clean body was so powerful that Grace had to take a few deep breaths to steady herself. The years of aching for a child melted and pooled in her heart. This was what she had wanted all along; this was what she'd never stopped pining for, despite all the evidence that God really was *that* cruel. To be a mother. But then she foolishly went and spoilt the mood by asking, 'Do you want Mummy to brush your hair for you?'

Cassidie shook her head and tucked her chin down onto her chest, revealing just how much of a haystack her hair was. Who could blame her for her reluctance, after Jane's military shampooing regime? Afro hair really did not respond well to full-on assault; it needed gentle taming. After a moment's thought, Grace told Cassidie to wait for her. She went downstairs, grabbed her handbag and hurried back into Cassidie's bedroom. She had to dig around for a few seconds inside her new, cavernous, 'all eventualities catered for, now that I have a small child' bag until she found what she was looking for – her comb. Cassidie eyed it suspiciously and edged a little further away, clearly unwilling to let anything with such big teeth anywhere near her. Grace decided that 'show, not tell' was called for. With Cassidie solemnly watching, she reached up and pulled the comb through her own hair, forehead to nape of the neck in slow sweeps. Cassidie bottom-shuffled across the duvet.

Then Grace hunted in her bag once again and tracked down her little tub of hair conditioner. She unscrewed the lid and the smell of coconut filled the room. Cassidie inched closer. Grace smeared some of the oil on her fingertips and ran it through her own hair. By now Cassidie's hot little body was pressed up against her. Grace let her hold the pot and sniff it. 'It's called Hair Pudding,' Grace said. Cassidie grinned and stuck out her tongue, going for a lick. 'No, honey. It's not the kind of pudding you eat. It's for your hair. Look.' She took the towel and tentatively rubbed Cassidie's hair, feeling her bumpy little skull beneath her fingers, then she took another dab of the conditioner and smeared it onto her palms. Cassidie shuffled around, tucking herself into the V of Grace's legs, and submitted to her touch.

The room settled into a drowsy quiet, as Grace worked through the thicket of Cassidie's hair. As she combed and oiled each section, Cassidie's head grew heavy with sleepiness under her fingertips.

'Mum, I'm gonna be late.' Cassie jerked her head away and Grace's hands fell into her lap.

Despite Grace's hopes, Cassie was unforthcoming on the short journey to the hotel. Grace tried to get a conversation going by keeping the tone light and avoiding any direct questions. She certainly didn't ask about Cassie's relationship with Ryan – its state or stage – though she longed to know. As she drove she breathed steadily and prayed silently that love would somehow miraculously translate into communication. In the absence of any cues from Cassie, Grace chattered on about her own sisters' many boyfriends when they were growing up, mixing in plenty of sensible advice with some funny anecdotes. Cassie barely seemed to listen. The stories certainly failed to raise a smile. Grace was rapidly running out of time – the hotel was only on the High Street – so she risked a direct approach. 'We're just a bit concerned. You've been awfully quiet these past few days, not yourself. Are you worrying about something?'

Cassie brushed off Grace's concerns like crisp crumbs, pointing out that *they kept telling her to concentrate on college more than her friends, so she was. They should be happy.*

In the end Grace was reduced to offering up the never-ending gift of all concerned parents: unconditional love, with a side order of non-judgement. 'I just want you to know that if there's something troubling you, you can always talk to me. You know that, don't you? And I mean *anything* – even the things that might feel a bit uncomfortable or awkward. I might be able to help.'

Cassie finally looked at her mother properly, and during the pause Grace waited, willing her eldest child to confide in her. But, as the silence stretched out and became uncomfortable, she began to fear a more serious revelation – real heartache or actual recklessness. Cassie put an end to the silence with her usual robust bluntness. 'Mum, leave it. I'm okay. Please, stop fussing.'

Grace had to give up and back off.

They sat in the traffic on the High Street on the last leg of the journey, without speaking, Grace grieving for the little girl who had trusted her so quickly and so completely, and Cassie feeling choked by the impossibility of dragging the ghost of her birth mother out of the shadows into the brightness of the present.

Chapter 5

CASSIE WORKED without concentrating. She got two orders wrong and forgot to request a gluten-free special. All of which irritated the head chef, Len, a fact that he made perfectly clear by giving her a very public bollocking in front of the rest of the staff. Ryan kept catching her eye as she ferried plate after plate of food from the hot kitchen into the nearly-as-hot restaurant, but his sympathy was of little help. She was told to smile – *It might never happen* – twice by guests, and topped off her poor performance with a show-stopping finale: dropping cheesecake, cream-side down, into a diner's lap. The man in question was actually very understanding about it, declining the offer to cover his dry-cleaning costs that Cassie was instructed to make, along with a full apology. That he was nice only made it worse.

She couldn't wait for her shift to finish. She'd agreed to meet Ryan after work; she didn't particularly want to, but neither she did she want to go home, and Ryan had been nagging all week, moaning about how much he'd been missing her. As she collected her last order off the pass, he told her that he had a surprise for her. In the mood she was in, she couldn't even fake interest.

At last her shift ended. She yanked off the stupid apron that all the waiting staff were made to wear and dumped it in the laundry bin on her way out. Ryan would be at least another half-hour; Len was a pain about making sure each station was thoroughly scrubbed down after service. Ryan bitched about it, all the time.

Cassie went into the loo in the shabby staffroom and set about putting herself straight. She kept make-up and deodorant in her locker at work. She hated smelling of food. As she reapplied her make-up, she stared at her face in the crackled glass. The visit to the clinic had robbed Cassie of her ability to look at herself and not see the differences. Her features now seemed to stand out more prominently, not as facets of a normal face, but as individual, disassociated elements – none of which were inherited from Tom or Grace. It had been happening all week, this growing awareness of how the fragments of her life didn't fit together properly any more. Every time she looked in a mirror, it seemed to mock her. The lips she liked, the dark eyebrows that she spent hours taming, the nose she hated and tried to minimise. Skin, bone and gristle, none of it determined by the parents she knew, none of it a match to her parents – or to Erin.

Avoiding her own reflection, Cassie made do with a quick slick of mascara, lip-liner and gloss. She stepped away from the mirror, sprayed a cloud of body-mist into the air and walked through it, towards Ryan and his thoughtless realm of sensation and desire.

He was standing near the dustbins, grinning like an idiot. Despite herself, the sight of him made Cassie smile. She immediately she felt more sure of herself. Ryan took her by the hand and pulled her along after him. She noticed that he'd put on some aftershave and changed into a clean T-shirt – small gestures that softened her heart.

'Right, close your eyes,' he said. He looked as excited as a little kid. 'Go on.' She obliged and he led her forward, laughing at her hesitant steps. She let him guide her. 'Stop! No, this way a little bit. Yeah, just there.' He came and stood close behind her, placing his hands over her eyes, his breath warm on her neck. She could feel his heart beating through her back. 'Ta-dah!' He lowered his hands and she opened her eyes and found herself looking at a dark-red Golf.

She was genuinely surprised. 'You bought a car?'

He nodded, jangling the keys like a trophy. 'Come on.' They climbed in and belted up. He over-revved the engine, showing off. 'Where to?'

'Anywhere that's not here,' she said, settling back into the cracked leather seats.

'My pleasure.' He accelerated out of the car park.

The drive-in at Krispy Kreme wasn't really what Cassie had in mind, but at least it wasn't work and it wasn't home. They sat with their drinks and a box of doughnuts balanced between them, spraying sugar crystals around the inside of the car. Ryan had treated them to the full dozen, letting Cassie pick her favourites. She could tell he was on a high about the car, showing her what all the switches and buttons did. It was sweet, the way he kept brushing the crumbs off the dashboard like a fussy housewife. As he swallowed his last mouthful of dough and smiled at her, she felt a pang of guilt. She'd been keeping him at arm's length for the past week. He'd texted her, repeatedly, but she hadn't been in the mood. Her responses had been short and to the point. No chit-chat, no flirting, no affection whatsoever. And she'd not sent him a single photo. That had been cruel.

The car was warm. With the music playing and the sun glinting off the other vehicles in the car park, it didn't feel such a bad place to be after all. It felt safe, and for that Cassie was grateful.

Ryan wiped his fingers on a napkin, put his hand on her knee and stroked her leg. Despite the resultant smudge of chocolate on her jeans, Cassie didn't move away. She took another bite of doughnut and let him touch her. As his fingers massaged her leg, she began to relax. She licked the frosting off her lips – slowly – fully aware of how closely he was watching her. But when he slid his hand higher up her thigh, she shifted position. He took his hand away, immediately. She rewarded him with a smile.

Pull and push. It was all part of the game.

But tonight she wanted more from Ryan than just mindless lust. She wanted him to comfort her and talk to her. She wanted him to recognise that she was sad and to make her feel better. She popped the last piece of doughnut into her mouth, willing him to get it right.

'Do you want to drive somewhere else?' he asked.

She knew exactly what he meant. He meant somewhere out of the way and conducive to getting it on. She sighed. It was obviously going to be up to her to get a conversation going. 'No. Here's fine. So... what's new, apart from the wheels?'

'Not much. Getting used to this baby.' He actually stroked the steering wheel – lovingly, like it was a pet, or a girl. He must have caught the look on her face because he stopped abruptly, embarrassed. He shifted his attention back to her. 'Who dropped you off at work today?'

Cassie balled up her napkin and shoved it into her empty cup. 'My mum.'

'Oh.'

'What do you mean, "Oh"?' Cassie asked, poised to take offence.

'Nothing,' Ryan replied. 'I just didn't know who it was.'

The atmosphere in the car shifted.

Cassie stared at him for a moment. 'What? Wasn't she what you were expecting?'

That's when Ryan got it completely wrong by answering, quite innocently, 'Not really. I just never knew whether it was your mum or dad who was black.'

After that he drove her home.

Chapter 6

THEIR HOUSE was quite big, but it seemed even bigger to Erin when Cassie was out. The three of them, put together, seemed to make less noise than her sister did, or used to. Because something was up with Cassie, Erin could sense it. The way she was staying close to home, not going out with her mates, doing as asked, without any snarky comebacks, was new. And it was weird how she kept seeking Erin out, then not saying anything, just hanging around in her room. When Erin asked her if she was all right, Cassie simply shrugged and said she was fine. But it wasn't normal – and Erin hated it when things weren't normal. The imbalance unsettled her.

She rolled off her bed and went into the bathroom, the only room in the house with a lock on the door. Even in there she could still hear the hushed mood, a kind of uneasy lull. It felt like the type of atmosphere they built up in films – just before something really bad happened. Erin knew these were exactly the sort of thoughts that she needed to keep to herself. None of her friends could hear the 'souls' of their homes. She put the toilet lid down and sat on it, looking down at her bare feet. Thin-toed, bony, ugly, out of proportion, like so much of her. Erin felt that her body was growing at different rates, almost overnight! She'd get up some days, and clothes that had fitted her the day before no longer did, shoes that were comfortable suddenly began to pinch. She didn't even fit into the house properly any more; shelves and cupboards and sharp corners crowded in, connecting with her skin, biting little chunks out of her. She felt like Alice in Wonderland, but without the magic potions.

To calm herself, Erin picked up Cassie's make-up bag and rested it on her knee. It was gaping open, too full of products to be zipped shut. She started looking through it, aware that she shouldn't, but comforted by the touch of her sister's things. She uncapped a tube of concealer and rubbed a little onto her hand, followed by a tiny blob of foundation. It was expensive. Cassie wouldn't want her wasting it. She blended them together as Cassie had taught her, watching the uneven tones in her skin blend and fade into something smoother and featureless. Happy with that one tiny patch of flawlessness, Erin brought her hand up to her face and smelled her sister on her skin. It was a soothing thing to do.

Suddenly she heard the front door bang, her dad shout, 'Hi, how was it?' and then footsteps clattering up the stairs. Cassie, back from work.

'Crap,' Cassie yelled as she passed the bathroom, her voice loud.

Erin jumped. She crammed everything back into the bag and shoved it onto the side. Cassie's footsteps continued up to her bedroom, and the breath-held quiet settled back on the house. Erin stepped out onto the landing. Three options: back to her room and her art project, downstairs to her dad and his eager need to chat – which wasn't happening – or up to Cassie.

She took the stairs, up.

Cassie was standing in the middle of her room, attempting to push open one of the skylights with the handle of a tennis racket. There was a proper pole-thing to do it with, but Cassie never bothered using it. Cassie jabbed the racket at the window, but it glanced off the glass. She tried again, harder, but to no effect. 'Fuck!'

Another unsuccessful stab. 'Fuck!' She stabbed at the catch, growing frustrated. 'Fuckity f—' Without warning she suddenly hurled the racket across the room, and herself on her bed. Erin stood by the door, uncertain whether she should offer to help or whether that would only irritate her sister even more. The consciousness that whatever came out of her mouth mattered rendered her speechless.

'Well, either come in or sod off. Don't just stand there.' Cassie was obviously in a foul mood. Erin surprised herself by turning round to leave. 'Sorry.' Cassie's voice lost its sharp-edged aggression. Erin faced back into the room. Cassie refused to look directly at her, but scooched over on the bed to make room for her sister. 'I'm sorry. It's been a crappy day. Work was rubbish. It was really busy. And Len, the chef, was nasty to me, in front of everyone.' Erin held her ground. 'Then I dropped cheesecake on this bloke. Right in his crotch. It went all over his trousers.' Erin didn't smile. 'And Ryan is an idiot.'

It was the peace offering of a Ryan insult that swung it. 'Do you want me to open it?'

'Yes,' Cassie said. 'Please.'

Erin fetched the pole from the corner and pushed open both of the skylights, quietly and efficiently, letting a breeze into the room.

'Thanks.' Cassie took off her shoes, kicked them off the edge of the bed and sat, flexing her aching feet. She patted the space next to her.

Erin sat on the bed and studied Cassie, looking for some clue to explain the change in her sister. She found none, only a tight façade of fake okay-ness. It was confusing and so frustrating. 'Cass, what's wrong? And please don't say, "Nothing", cos I know there's something.'

Cassie said nothing.

For a long time the sisters sat side-by-side, in silence, neither of them being able to find a way to reach out to the other.

✳

The day Erin 'the miracle' was born, everyone cried.

Four-year-old Cassie didn't understand why. She remained dry-eyed at the hospital as the baby was handed from one weeping relative to another. It was like a very weird version of Pass-the-parcel. Cassie sat on the bed, next to her mum, lost amidst the emotion and noise. The sudden lack of attention was disconcerting. It was as if no one could see her any more. She'd grown accustomed to looking up and meeting someone's eyes – eyes that were always watching her, smiling, encouraging her, warning her. Perhaps they'd forgotten she was there. Cassie poked her elbow into her pale and podgy mother, summoning her back. It seemed to work. Grace gave a little shiver and put her arm round Cassie and hugged her tight. This small act made the weirdness in the room take a few steps away from the edge of the bed.

Cassie decided that the best thing to do was to stay close to her mum, on their island, and ignore the swirling sea of weepy, squeaky relatives. She wriggled her hands into the gap between Grace's dressing gown and her nightie, kneading her fingers into the warm softness of her mother's body. Once safely anchored, Cassie laid her head against Grace's side and thought about going to sleep. When she woke up, they might all have gone.

'Cassie.' Tom's voice summoned her back. 'Cassie, do you want to hold your baby sister?'

With her face pressed into the fleece of Grace's dressing gown and her eyes closed, Cassie considered this question. Did she? She didn't know. What she did know, because she had learnt, was that when her daddy wanted her to do some something, it made him happy when she did it, and it made him very happy if she did it straight away, with a smiley face. So as much as the safe haven of her mum was preferable to facing the room, she lifted her head, shuffled around on the bed, held her arms out wide, and said, 'Yes, please.' There was a pause, then everyone laughed. Cassie felt tricked. They could see her now, of course, now that she'd done something stupid. Anger coursed through her. She folded her arms tight across her body and frowned. Grandpa laughed again, even louder.

'Hey, it's okay, honey. Dad!' Her daddy's voice held two very different tones at once, soft for her and hard for Grandpa. Her father came towards her, smiling. 'Here. She wants a cuddle from her big sister.'

He bent forward and offered Cassie the rolled-up baby, but Cassie wasn't going to be laughed at twice. She pulled her chin into her chest, keeping her eyes downcast. This whole performance was nothing to do with her. She stared at the scab on her knee, concentrating on the different colours trapped beneath the crusty skin. But her dad was not easily deterred. He surprised Cassie by slotting the cottony lump of the baby into the space between her face and her bare legs. Despite herself, Cassie looked at it.

It was like a doll, an ugly doll. It had a squished-in face and no eyes. Cassie knew this was because it was lying down. She was tempted to tilt it up and see if its eyes popped open, but something made her hesitate. It had a tiny, flat nose and a pouty mouth. She couldn't see whether it had any hair, because it was wearing a little woolly hat. Although it looked just like a toy lying there in her lap, it felt completely different. It was absolutely still, but Cassie could tell it was alive by how heavy and uneven it felt against her legs. It was a strange sensation. She wasn't sure she liked it. She stared down at its face, fascinated by how small its mouth, its nose, its eyes, its chin were. All the same features as hers, but shrunk down to fairy-size.

Cassie wondered what it would feel like if she put her finger up its nostril or in its ear. Would it be soft and squidgy or hard and cool, like a real doll? As if it knew what she was planning, the baby started to squirm – odd, light movements, kitten-like. It gave Cassie a funny feeling in the pit of her stomach. She shifted her leg a little and the baby's head flopped sideways. It obviously didn't like its new position, because it started meowing. Cassie watched its mouth transform into a pink tunnel. She was about to do something to stop it crying, when it was taken away from her, suddenly and without warning. Cassie could tell by the look on her dad's face that she'd done something wrong.

She didn't get to properly examine the baby again for another four days. Though her mother came home with it, as promised, they never seemed to be on their own. The much-vaunted 'routine' that her parents always invoked, to get her to do things, went out of the window and they didn't even seem to care. It was an endless parade of relatives and friends and people Cassie didn't know, who came, drank tea and oohed and aahed over the baby – a lot.

So when Cassie walked into the lounge one afternoon and finally found it almost empty, she was surprised, but happy. She liked that she could hear the clock in the hall ticking, and her mother moving around in the kitchen, banging drawers shut with her hip. Of course the room wasn't completely empty – the baby was in it. It had been left on the floor, on the rug. Cassie walked round it, taking care not to tread on it, then she climbed up on the sofa to get a better vantage point. She lay on her tummy and peered down at it, sucking on the biscuit that her mother had given her for being a good girl.

Its eyes were open; well, at least they were in between blinks. It had on a green dress and tiny cream tights, so it was more obvious that it was a girl. A real baby girl, not a doll. The baby was Cassie's sister, and she was its. Everyone kept saying *sister* as if it was a special word. It wasn't. Cassie had heard it lots of times before on TV, and in books and at nursery. She was also fairly certain that having two of something made it *less*, not more, special. Cassie watched the baby, quite contentedly, for ages, relishing the sweetness of buttercream and biscuit crumbs on her tongue. After a while her mother came into the room and flopped down on the sofa next to her. They both looked at the baby, waving its legs in the air.

'Do you want Mummy to read to you?' Grace asked.

Cassie did – a story in the daytime, she hadn't had one of those for ever. She climbed down, scattering crumbs on the carpet, and went to the shelves where her books were kept. She tugged at one and a stack slid out, splaying themselves across the floor in a really helpful fan. Her parents didn't grasp that it was impossible to pick a book by the narrow bit; you needed to see the picture on the front if you were going to get the right one. She heard a little puff of air escape from her mother's mouth as the books spewed across the floor. It was the sound she made when Cassie made a mess, but she didn't say anything. After some thought, Cassie selected the one about the monster who ate the little boy and no one noticed; and the big one with the dark-green pictures about the monkey who couldn't find its mummy. But as she was passing the books to her mother there was a gurgling noise.

'Oh, for God's sake, not again,' Grace said to the ceiling. She stood up, even though she was supposed to be staying put to read. 'Sorry, poppet. Your sister's been sick again. I won't be long.' And without even looking at Cassie's choices, she walked out of the room. Cassie dropped the books on the sofa. She was never going get a story now.

It was always spitting something up, or crying, or pooping. That was why there wasn't ever enough time any more – the baby gobbled it all up. No wonder it was always being sick. The milky smell it gave off made Cassie cross. She thumped down on the floor and glared at it. At this level it looked quite big, bigger than when she'd been looking down at it, or maybe it was just growing, really fast. There was sick everywhere: in its neck, stuck in its hair and splattered all down the front of its dress; see-through milk with white blobs in it. Disgusting. While Cassie was examining the baby, it made a funny coughing noise and more lumps spurted out of its mouth, then it started coughing *and* crying. Cassie edged closer. Its face changed, turning from milk-chocolate to purply-red, the colour of a new bruise. Despite the sea of sick, Cassie edged even closer. It kicked it legs and cried even louder.

Cassie decided it was time she made it stop.

It was disgusting, but it didn't take too long and once it was over, the baby wasn't crying any more. After she had done it, she sat, cradling her little sister on her lap, supporting her head, exactly as they'd shown her in the hospital, listening to her mum crashing around upstairs, waiting patiently for it to be her turn.

She took a long time.

Eventually Cassie heard her mum clattering down the stairs. 'Sorry, Cassie. Mummy couldn't find the wipes. I'm coming.' A moment later she walked back into the lounge.

Cassie looked up and smiled, shyly. 'She was crying, Mummy, so I helped her.' The baby lay quiet and very still in her arms. 'I sang her "Old MacDonald", she announced, proudly. 'She likes the piggies best.' For moment Cassie thought she must have done something wrong, again, because her mother's face went stiff.

Grace dashed across the room, knelt down and tugged the blanket free of the baby's face. The baby blinked in the light and sucked on its flaky little fist. Grace smiled, but it was a flickery one that didn't stay on her face for quite long enough. 'You've done a fab job. All those yucky clothes, and I'm grateful, honey, but you really didn't have to. Mummy was coming. I was just fetching her some clean clothes. And really, you shouldn't be lifting Erin up on your own. She's only tiny and we have to be very careful with her.'

Cassie looked at her mother, listening, but she didn't agree with what she was saying. Her sister had needed her, and it had been her responsibility to step up.

Grace was still fussing. 'Next time shout for Mummy, okay?' Cassie dipped her head, which Grace took as assent. 'Do you want me to take her now?' she asked.

'In a minute,' Cassie replied. She shifted Erin in her arms, getting more comfortable. The baby blinked three times, then closed her tiny eyes, perfectly content.

Grace smiled properly then, a real smile that reached her eyes and stayed in place. 'Look at you. You're just like a mummy.'

'No,' Cassie said, ever the stickler for things being correct, 'I'm not a mummy. I'm a big sister.'

And she always would be Erin's big sister.

It was still Cassie's job to protect Erin, although nowadays the threats to her little sister's happiness were more complex and far less easily resolved. So as much as Erin kept sitting next to her on the bed, staring, waiting for her to spill the beans, Cassie knew that she simply couldn't. It wasn't right to burden Erin with her growing need to find out about her birth mum. Erin was only thirteen. She was her little sister. She was the person Cassie should be protecting.

Cassie knew that her relationship with Erin was different from the relationship that her mates had with their brothers and sisters. At best, they ignored their siblings. None of her friends seemed to *like* their sisters. Cassie did. She enjoyed spending time with Erin; she felt relaxed around her, somehow better when she was with her, more herself. It was true, they were chalk and cheese in terms of personality, but they were still exceptionally tight. The lack of shared blood made no difference.

Cassie flopped back onto the bed and rested her forearm across her face, pressing down hard, suffocating the overwhelming compulsion to talk to the one person she knew would listen to her.

Time passed and the words stayed trapped inside.

After a few minutes she felt the mattress bounce as Erin came and lay down beside her.

Cassie was vibrating with pent-up confusion and directionless energy, while Erin was wrestling with a burgeoning anxiety about her sister, but both girls kept their thoughts to themselves. They lay side-by-side, self-consciously at first, listening to the muted sounds of the traffic and the stirring of the leaves coming through the open window. After a while their breathing found the same rhythm and began to keep time, moving from fast and shallow to regular and steady, until their hearts were beating in sync. They inhaled each other's scent, a reassuring mix of deodorant and familiarity. It was calming. Their silence had an ease about it, an absence of pressure, that they both appreciated. Cassie felt herself slowly relax. She rolled onto her side, and Erin did the same, each of them getting comfortable. They curled close together, but not touching, warmth radiating between them. After a few moments Cassie felt herself begin to drift. She closed her eyes and drew her knees up to her chest, returning to the position she'd slept in since she was tiny, feeling safe in Erin's company.

Morning-bright light. The sun is smashing around the room, bouncing off the mirror, splashing diamonds across the walls.

She closes her eyes to block out the sunlight and 'sees' the diamonds burning blue and white on the insides of her lids. Beneath her she can feel the buttons and the dips of the mattress. She knows where the spikes and lumps are and where the smooth patches are. It's a familiar map. When she stretches out, she's disconcerted to find there is no one there. She stretches wider, pointing her toes and her fingertips to the far-flung corners of the bed, searching for her.

But she's not there.

She can hear her bones popping as they try to burst through the limits of her skin, but when she twists her head she feels a dull, deep ache, the bruise on her neck reminding her to stay small. She recoils and starts to fret. Where is she? She's always there when she wakes up. Where can she have gone? Why has she left her behind? She never leaves her behind.

Then she hears a voice full of croaky sleep from across the room. 'It's early, Cassidie. Go back to sleep.' Her voice is close, reassuringly so.

She rolls onto her side and does as she's told.

Chapter 7

SATURDAY AFTERNOON. Cassie was out shopping with her mates, looking at tops. She'd been nagged into it by her friends. They were, apparently, sick of her staying in *all the time* – missing one girls' night out, and not 'liking' every one of Aimee's thousands of posts, immediately. The shopping trip had also been encouraged by the unexpected gift of thirty quid from her dad, and by her mum's offer to drive them all into town. There seemed to be some sort of concerted effort going on to cheer her up. She wasn't sure it was going to work.

'Get lost! Not with my tits.' Tegan threw the itty-bitty vest back on the pile and they moved on to look at the dresses. They clacked through the racks, knowing, through osmosis, which dresses to pause over and which to react in horror to. Over the PA, old-school music played. Cassie shifted her bag onto her other shoulder and reached out to touch the fabric of a white sundress that might suit her, an instinctive action. She didn't feel remotely interested in looking at clothes.

The beat changed and the girls moved in a shoal across to the jewellery, leaving the dresses behind. Tegan started rooting through the display, picking out bangles; like a magpie, she was drawn to the shiniest ones. She slipped a few over her hand and held her slim arm up to the light, watching as the bangles slid back and forth with a clatter. 'Ooh. Old-school. I love this. He was fit when he was young.' On the screens a loose-hipped Justin Timberlake appeared, dancing in a light-box.

Cassie picked up a fake pearl drop-choker, looking for the price, but when she turned it over in her hands, the numbers on the sticker blurred. She suddenly felt queasy. Tegan was still there, standing right next to her, yakking on about stuff, but Cassie could no longer hear her; all she could hear was the music. The beat filled her head.

So you grab your girls... She felt someone grab her and lift her up, holding her close – so close she could feel the vibration of their voice in her chest. *Don't be so quick to walk away, Dance with me.* There was the sensation of being spun around, dipping and rising in time to the music. Cassie reached out to steady herself, but her hand connected with nothing. Round and around she spun, faster and faster. Someone's hot breath was on her face, their voice close, mimicking the beatboxing. *Chicka-boom, Chicka-boom... Just let me rock you till the break of day.* Laughter. Hers and the other person's. The voice grew breathless, laboured. 'You're getting heavy.' ... *Dance with me...* Spinning round and round. Then the sensation changed. The hands holding her lost their purchase. She was slipping. Falling.

'Cassie!' Tegan grabbed her and tried to hold her upright, but failed. Cassie's hip crashed into the counter. A stand of earrings crashed to the floor. The lights pulsed and the room tilted violently, as a thousand tiny flashes of silver danced around her feet.

Afterwards, with her head tilted forward, a glass of water in her hand and the girls cooing around her, Cassie felt embarrassed. 'I'm okay,' she kept saying, but they weren't listening. They were enjoying the drama too much. If one more person patted her back, she would scream.

The store manager was fussing as well. 'Try and have another sip of water. Girls. Girls! Give her a bit of space.' They retreated; all of a few centimetres.

'He's coming now.' Ayleah's voice cut through the concerned chatter. Of course it was Ayleah who'd taken charge.

'Who's coming?' Cassie raised her head.

'Your dad. I rang him from your phone. He said he'll be here ASAP.'

No, he hadn't. Her dad would never have said 'ASAP'. Oh, for God's sake, that was all she needed. Cassie put her head back down and tried to block them out. As they fussed around her, she poked nervously at the flashback, or whatever the hell it was that she'd just experienced. It was the first time she'd had one outside the house and, more scarily, it was the first time she'd been completely awake. The others had all been when she'd been on the cusp of sleeping or waking up; indistinct images and feelings that had shimmered briefly and brightly, then faded to a faint echo.

This was a whole new level of losing her shit.

The dreams were why she hadn't wanted to come out with her friends in the first place; why she'd been sticking so close to home, rooting herself in everything that was familiar and that had, in the past, been reassuring. She had no intention of telling her lovely but totally self-obsessed mates that she was having weird dreams about being a little kid. No one wanted to be that special. She hadn't told anyone about them, not even Erin. What was there to say. 'Hey, I seem to be going a bit mad at the moment. I'm having visions.' The music had obviously been the trigger this time.

As her friends continued to flap, Cassie tuned them out and concentrated.

She could still feel the sensation of being held; it lingered within her goose-pimpled flesh – hands holding her close, the smell of another body, warm, tangy with sweat. A shared moment of giddiness and fun: a good feeling. Yes, she was sure that what she'd felt in those few moments, in that past, had been happiness.

What was disturbing was that she couldn't control these blasts of memory. They just came, randomly, out of nowhere. Whether she welcomed them or feared them, she didn't really know. All she did know was that she wanted to be home, away from the screeching and the sympathy. So when Tom finally arrived, she brushed off the competing offers from her friends to travel with her, and let her dad lead her out of the shop by the hand like a little girl. It was good to have him there, anchoring here in the present. But when he went to put his arm around her to guide across the road, back to the car, she shrugged him off, telling him she'd felt faint because she hadn't eaten anything. He didn't insist.

On the journey home Cassie pretended to listen to Tom's suddenly very definite views on the importance of hydration and nutrition, and she made the right noises as he clumsily, but lovingly, dropped in a smattering of remarks about how beautiful she was. But she drew the line when he starting making some truly dodgy jokes about stick-thin models. He was so needy sometimes, so desperate for her attention and her love. She felt confused by her reaction to his kindness, but she couldn't control it. She knew that she was lucky to have two parents who cared, and yet at times it felt like a burden. Their love seemed to weigh heavily, their expectations to exceed her capacity. Tom was still rambling on, trying, but failing, to mask his obvious concern about anorexia – the unmentionable fear of all parents. Cassie couldn't deal with it, so she didn't. She had more pressing concerns. She rested her head back and closed her eyes, waiting for the ghost of her birth mother to rise up again and escort her home.

Tom talked self-consciously and drove carefully, as he stole repeated glances at his eldest daughter. She gave nothing away. Passing out was not normal, being this uncommunicative was not normal, being this secretive was not normal, their whole relationship no longer felt normal – and that hurt. Eventually his anecdotes dried up and an uncomfortable silence filled the car.

Cassie kept her eyes shut, blocking him out.

Tom missed his daughter. It was true that Cassie looked more like Grace's child, but her interests, her competitiveness, her sense of humour and her character were much closer to his. Though they often clashed – they both loved a good argument, and could keep one going for days – there had always been an understanding between them, a respect, even a sneaking admiration for each other's pig-headedness. That bond had evaporated of late. He couldn't even make her smile any more.

As he drove and tried to work out how to rebuild some semblance of trust between himself and his estranged daughter, Tom remembered how, in the beginning, humour had been the bridge that had spanned the gulf between a desperately anxious 'nearly' father and a petrified child.

On the day they met Cassie for the very first time, Tom was a bundle of nerves. It felt like the most important day of their lives – because it was.

They arrived in Stockport way too early, but Tom just couldn't drive any slower; there was too much adrenaline pumping through his heart. They pulled onto the correct street and spotted number seventeen almost immediately. A paved-over front garden with a grey people-carrier obscuring the view of the house, a glimpsed, blue front door, then they were past it. Tom turned left at the end of the road onto an almost identical street of red-brick houses, left again, then pulled randomly into a space. 'I didn't want to park right outside.' He clicked his seatbelt free, an admission of just how early they were. He flexed his fingers and cracked his knuckles, causing Grace to wince. 'Sorry.'

The next hour felt like a day.

With ten minutes left on the clock, they drove round the block again, parked, got out, walked up to the house, edged past the people-carrier and found themselves standing outside the blue front door, literally on the threshold of meeting their child. Before Grace had a chance to ring the bell, the door was opened by a stout woman in her early sixties. 'Hello, come on in, we're all ready for you.' Her voice was high and tight with friendliness. They followed her down a narrow hallway, skirting around a basket full of children's shoes and a bulging coat rack; the jumble of fur-trimmed hoods looked like a nest of foxes. Grace followed Tom into the lounge, where they both stuttered to a halt, overwhelmed by their expectations.

It was a long room – once two rooms presumably, which had been knocked through to create more space. Light streamed through the back window onto a big, dusty TV, two cushion-strewn sofas, an overflowing toy box, an expanse of carpet, an ugly hearth and a huge collection of framed photos. It was a typical family home, well used, comfortable and very, very warm. Tom felt as if he'd just stepped onto a stage set and, despite days of rehearsal, had completely forgotten his lines. He could hear the dialogue and knew that he needed to play his part, but a yawning black blank had replaced his brain.

Thankfully Jane, the foster mum, took charge. 'Sit down. Make yourselves at home. The kettle's on. Now, Cassidie, there's no need to be shy. Look, Mummy Grace and Daddy Tom are here.'

Four small words, never spoken before.

Tom and Grace looked past Jane, searching for the child they'd been waiting a lifetime for. She was on the sofa, beneath the far window, curled up so small that she was barely visible. Her head was buried behind Wendy, her social worker. For a second they all stared at her hunched back and the sharp peaks of her shoulder blades. Her T-shirt was pale blue. It had rucked up, revealing a wide strip of skin. The sun, coming through the window, picked up the downy hairs on her back. The soles of her feet poked out from beneath her bottom. Everything about her position shouted, 'Go away, you're frightening me.'

'It's okay. Really,' Grace said, though it wasn't.

Tom's pulse was threatening to break through his temples, so God knows what the child must have been feeling.

But Jane persisted. 'Come on, Cassidie. Say hello.' At the second command the little girl wriggled upright, and Grace and Tom saw their potential daughter for the very first time. Or at least they saw the top of her head, because she sat with her eyes downcast, one hand clutching a fistful of Wendy's cardigan, the other to her mouth. Wendy chatted to her softly while Tom and Grace perched on the edge of the sofa, unbearably conscious of their bones and their breath, and of the wrongness of their looming presence in the room. Jane smiled at them again. 'Don't worry – it gets easier, I promise. Tea?' As she crossed the room, Cassidie's head lifted and they saw her face.

She was as breathtaking as her picture. More so, more solid, and real, and beautiful; and, obviously, currently very frightened, because when Jane disappeared into the back of the house, Cassidie's expression wobbled. Her compact little body leant after Jane, yearning to be close to the one person she trusted. The urge to reach out and comfort her was overwhelming, but they were frozen by the absolute certainty that if they went anywhere near Cassidie, they would terrify her. It was an appalling, distressing moment – which galvanised Tom into action.

He clambered down onto the floor and shuffled across the carpet, on his knees, heading towards the toy box. Wendy smiled. Tom picked a toy out of the box, a lump of bright, pre-school plastic: four coloured boxes with closed lids, set in a row. He sat on the floor, facing Cassidie, who was still looking anxiously at the door, waiting for Jane to reappear. Tom shook the toy. Nothing. He tried again. Nothing. Then he banged it against the hearth. The noise drew Cassidie's attention. He thumped it again, still nothing. Pure bafflement. Next he swiped it back and forth across the carpet, making a great swishing sound. Still nothing, but now he had her attention. Next Tom tried to prise open one of the lids with his fingertips – no success. He pulled a face of pure frustration. He turned the toy upside down and shook it. No luck. He dumped it down on the floor in front of him and sat back. Defeated.

Cassidie looked up at Wendy, who nodded. 'Go on, show Tom how it works.'

She climbed down slowly and crouched on her haunches opposite him, her expression solemn and uncertain. Tom shrugged and shook his head, as if to say, 'You've got no chance.'

'It's okay, Cassidie,' Wendy prompted softly.

At last her chubby little hands reached out. She pulled the toy towards her and, without a moment's hesitation, pressed the button in front of the red lid. A pig popped out... *Oink!* Tom fell back as if he'd been shot. A smile transformed Cassidie's face. Tom twisted round to address the room, marvelling at her cleverness. 'Did you see that, Grace? This girl's a mechanical genius.' While he wasn't looking, Cassidie reached out and stealthily pressed the blue button. Up popped a cow... *Moo!* Tom collapsed backwards again, all drama and smiles. This time Cassidie laughed, a proper chortle of delight at the game and her role as chief mischief-maker.

By the time Jane came back into the room, the contents of the toy box were spread across the carpet and Grace and Tom were on the floor, within touching distance of their child.

Tom was within touching distance of his daughter now, but he couldn't reach her.

He pulled the car onto the drive and switched off the engine. Cassie got out of the car and walked away towards the house, without waiting for him.

Chapter 8

AS SOON as they got back home from the shops Cassie escaped up to her room, where she crawled into her bed, hugging her secret close. She felt hemmed in by the mounting pile of unanswerable questions. It was exhausting. She lay watching the birds against the slate-grey sky, adrift. She knew that if she closed her eyes and let the weariness in, the images would come.

After half an hour of resistance, she let them.

She wakes.

Her top is soggy. It sticks to her chest as she twists and turns. Breathing is difficult. She's cold, so cold it hurts. A wet, wheezy sound fills the bedroom, like a dog snuffling for food. It's not a nice noise. A bubble forms, pops, then re-forms on the end of her nose. The skin around her nostrils and lips is sore. The dog starts to bark and once it starts, it doesn't stop. Her breath is hard-edged, wedged in her throat. She can't see the dog, but it sounds awfully close. She rolls over, but succeeds only in binding herself tighter in her sheet.

A light clicks on and a voice speaks, shushing them both. She's lifted up and immediately the blockage in her windpipe shifts. Something soft and warm is wrapped around her. With gentle efficiency the gluey film is wiped off her face. There's a brief stinging pain, followed by a rush of air into her lungs. She's held close and patted – soft, regular taps on her back. There's some shouting in another room, but it's not aimed at her.

She knows the sounds that she can, and must, ignore. The barking stops. Her breathing slows and settles. The voice hums and mutters, a series of sounds that begin to form a rhyme she recognises. The taps turn into strokes, keeping pace with the song. 'Round and round the garden, like a teddy bear', a soothing mantra rubbed into her back. She's no longer cold. 'One step, two step.' Her head grows heavy. She rests it against bone and flesh and slips into sleep.

It's a race, but she's in front, and she knows she's going to win – she always wins. Their rubber-soled shoes squeak up the stairs. It's a great sound, full of energy and life and not caring. They run straight upstairs – not looking left. The room on the left is the one that she must never go into. The room that smells different; smoky, almost nice, but not quite. There's a meaty edge to it, like something gone bad. It's the room in the house that is full of dark shapes and deep voices, which have nothing to do with her.

The air whistles through her throat into her lungs. Her heart is racing, fit to burst. It feels good to rush and clatter and make a noise.

But the stairs aren't long enough. The race is over too soon. They are back in the bedroom, inside the trap. The same four walls. The same stale air. The same everything. She is sick of being in the bedroom.

'Again. Again.' She jumps up and down, momentum pounding inside her legs.

'No.' Short and sharp. Warning her.

She edges back towards the door, itching to run some more, back down the stairs and out the front door, away from the house. Far away, as fast as her legs can carry her. And she is fast.

'I said, "No"! That's enough.' There's a pause. 'I ain't messing.'

She knows that she isn't.

She throws herself on the mattress and pretends to go to sleep.

She wakes and immediately knows that she's on her own.

It's dark. The door is closed, but the voices downstairs reach up through the floor – loud voices, 'fucking this' and 'fucking that'. She doesn't like it. She curls up as small as she can, her knees tight against her chest, her eyes shut.

She keeps quiet – like she's been told.

She hides, knowing that a blanket is not enough.

She's on her own, again.

Bored.

She's been bored for ever.

The door is open. Beckoning. She ignores its whispering. She's been told, in no uncertain terms, to stay put. She concentrates on her book, but she's looked at it a hundred times before; its pages might as well be blank, for all the interest they hold.

Below her someone is laughing. Someone laughs back.

Today downstairs sounds happy.

The door is still open. She can't hear or smell the dog.

She goes to stand by the door. The right side of the line.

Downstairs someone claps.

She steps – small – over the line.

Nothing bad happens. Three more steps, out into the open, onto the landing. 'Proper' naughty. But nothing happens. One foot, two feet at a time; one stair, then another stair at a time, edging towards the laughter.

Before she knows it, she's downstairs.

The shock stops her – that and the voice in her head.

But... it's too late. 'Hey, look. A little dude.' Eyes and legs. The room is full of eyes and legs, and hoods. And smiles. And smoke. And they can see her. That is bad. She shouldn't let them see her. She edges back. One of them stands up. He's big. His face disappears, but his voice reaches down to her. 'Hey there, Cutie. Come in and say "hi" to the guys. We don't bite.' The mouths in the room laugh. He reaches out and she remembers, in no uncertain terms, what she's supposed to do if they ever try to touch her.

He might not bite.

But she does.

Chapter 9

ON THE Monday morning Cassie said she felt sick. Her mother obviously didn't believe her, but she didn't challenge her either – she colluded – ascribing her tiredness to a virus. 'It's doing the rounds at the moment. We've had a lot of staff off with it. Another day won't do you any harm.' Her mum fussed over her for ten minutes, before leaving late, with a final injunction to *drink lots of water* and *definitely eat something*.

Left alone, Cassie spent the day rattling around the empty house, trying to make sense of what was happening. She concluded that she really must be going mad. The doctor had asked about her birth mum, Cassie had thought about her and, in thinking about her, she'd conjured her up. It was as simple and as weird as that. The memories were coming thick and fast now. She couldn't anticipate them, or summon them, nor could she block them. The lack of control was deeply unnerving, but it was also kind of thrilling.

She had another mother.

She was not Tom and Grace's daughter.

She had been born into a different life and somewhere, embedded deep within her, there seemed to be fragments of that other existence. What else could explain the images that were rising to the surface of her brain? But with the dreams came a sense of guilt. Cassie felt ashamed that she'd never bothered to find out more about her adoption. It hadn't mattered to her before. Now it did.

Needing something more tangible than confusing half-memories and weird dreams, Cassie began searching.

An hour and a half later she sat at her desk, staring at two photos. They were glossy, square-cornered, glaringly old-fashioned. It had taken her quite a while to find them. She'd shoved them away years ago, with no ceremony or consideration, giving them the respect she'd felt they deserved – namely, none. She'd eventually uncovered them in a box file, on her bookcase, mixed in with her old school reports and dancing certificates. They were the only relics of her past that she possessed.

Picture one was of a chubby little girl, cute, serious, sitting on a woman's knee. The child's fat little fists were clutching a teddy. The woman in the photo was smiling, both arms encircling the child. She was old enough to be Cassie's grandmother, but she was not. Picture two was of the same little girl, but younger – thinner? – still cute, sitting on a different woman's knee. No toy this time. The woman in the photo was also smiling, one arm loosely holding the child. This woman was young enough to be her mother, because she was.

Cassie picked up the second photo and studied it closely. Her mother. She didn't look like an addict. She looked...normal. The photo didn't fit with the portrait that Grace and Tom had painted. The woman was white, slim, light-brown hair with the hint of a curl. She looked about twenty. She was wearing some make-up, but not loads, and was dressed, as far as Cassie could make out, in a T-shirt and jeans. She looked – bland; that's what she looked, blandly anonymous. Nothing like Cassie, not like 'a mother', but not like an apology for a human being, either. Cassie looked at the background of the photo for clues, but found few. The edges of a patterned blanket or throw, a plain wall, the corner of an ugly, fussy mirror. It could have been anywhere. It didn't look like anywhere particularly grim, just somewhere very far away. Cassie felt a strange kind of hollowness when she looked at the image. She should, surely, feel anger or pain, but she didn't. She felt nothing.

She'd not looked at the other photo in years, either. Why would she want to look· at the woman who had fostered her? She couldn't even remember her name. She'd merely been a stepping stone on the way to Tom and Grace. Cassie stared at the photo and felt even less.

Both of the photos were as irrelevant to her as images on someone else's timeline, a glimpse into someone else's life; two unknown women, one who did a little girl harm and one who kept her safe. That she was the little girl was hard to grasp. It was frustrating, and pointless. She pushed the photos away.

Cassie suddenly felt a rush of anger, at herself. She was being pathetic and self-indulgent. This was her past. This was her life. She needed to reclaim control over it. She fetched her phone and set about trying to find some answers for herself.

By the time she heard Erin come in from school, Cassie was feeling better, or at least less useless. Erin's footsteps drifted around downstairs and Cassie waited, impatiently, willing her upstairs. After what felt like an age, Erin finally knocked on Cassie's bedroom door and wandered in, dreamy as ever, still in her school uniform. She was carrying two mugs of coffee and had a packet of Crunch Creams wedged under her arm. She passed one of the mugs to Cassie.

'Feeling any better?' Cassie nodded. 'Thought you might be up for a biscuit.' Erin caught the tail of the wrapper opening with her nail and undid the end of the packet. She passed the first two biscuits to Cassie, then reached for two more. 'What's really up with you? This "feeling a bit delicate" is getting a bit old.' Erin used air quotes.

'Nothing.'

'So you *are* faking it?' Erin prodded.

'No, I just didn't feel like going into college,' Cassie countered.

'Is it Ryan?' For a quiet mouse, Erin could be surprisingly persistent.

'No.'

'Okay. But you're not really a closet anorexic, are you? Bulimia, that I'd maybe believe – at a pinch...' Erin said, watching Cassie dunk her biscuit, 'but self-imposed starvation, I'm not buying it. You do know that Mum and Dad are really, seriously worrying about it, don't you? I bet Mum's already been online looking up the best approach to dealing with it.'

Cassie smiled. 'Yeah, I know. It's not anything like that.' She scraped the cream off the biscuit with her teeth. 'Can you make sure they know I'm not doing anything stupid? Though, let's be honest, I hardly look like I'm wasting away.'

Erin nodded, but didn't move. They slurped their coffee and demolished more biscuits. Cassie felt happy having Erin there in her room, sitting on her bed with her thin hands and her flat chest. Perhaps it was that sense of peace that made Cassie blurt out, 'I've decided I want to find my other mum.' She looked at Erin, waiting to see her flinch or look horrified, or at least register shock, but Erin's expression merely flickered for a nanosecond, as if her emotions were buffering.

She went for a straight question, pushing down the pulse of panic that had flashed through her, at the mention of Cassie's original family. 'Right. What brought that on?'

'I don't really know,' Cassie lied. Erin didn't need to know all the details. 'I just think it's time I knew a bit more about her.'

Erin picked a few biscuit crumbs off the duvet and ground them together between her fingers. 'Right. Have you spoken to Mum and Dad about it?'

'Not yet.'

'Right,' she said, for want of anything else to say.

'Can you stop saying "right", Cassie snapped. She didn't want to delve too deeply into Erin's reserve, but she could tell by the way her sister held herself that she was trying really hard not to give anything away.

Erin met her sister's gaze and corrected herself. 'All right.' Sarcasm as a defence, but at least it broke the tension.

Cassie thumped her on the arm. 'I can't really explain it, but I just feel I need to know about her. That I should know.'

'I get that,' said Erin, 'and you're worried about how Mum and Dad are going to react.'

In all honesty, Cassie hadn't really thought about their feelings, she'd been too focused on why she was so suddenly, so absolutely certain that she couldn't go on, unless she knew what her alternative could have been. 'Yeah,' she lied. 'Do you think they'll freak?'

Erin risked a joke. 'Not freak – that's more your department. They'll be a bit rattled, I guess, but I think they'll understand.'

Again Cassie felt a swell of love for her nerdy little sister. 'So, how do I bring it up with them?'

Erin gave it some proper thought. At last she said, 'I've no idea', and, for the first time in days, Cassie laughed.

Chapter 10

AT WORK Tom applied himself conscientiously to his tasks, but the concern about what was troubling his eldest daughter hummed beneath the surface of his day.

Cassie had taken to her bed, once he'd got her home from the shops. They'd 'tucked her in' like they used to when she was little, with water and tea and toast, and plenty of affection, but they could tell their attentions were unwelcome. He was sure he heard her sigh with relief when they eventually backed out of her room. Tom wasn't a complete fool; Cassie's casual dismissal of her fainting episode as simply skipping breakfast didn't ring true. His daughter was unhappy, and that was as unusual as it was unsettling. He was worried that bloody Ryan Newsome was at the root of it. Tom suspected that he'd completely misread the importance of Cassie's relationship with that lanky, tattooed waste of space, thinking it was nothing more than a flexing of hormones. But maybe, for Cassie, it was love; the painful, illogical, teenage kind that he'd been praying both his daughters would bypass. If Ryan was messing his daughter around, he'd – well, he'd... To be honest, he didn't know precisely what he'd do.

Tom's inability to think of anything to improve his relationship with his eldest daughter drove him out of the office at lunchtime. He set off at a fast pace, dodging the ambling shoppers and zigzagging between the gridlocked cars. He hurried past two passably pretty city-centre parks and at least twenty perfectly sit-on-able benches, on his quest to reach his 'go to' thinking place. The canal. Two job moves had taken Tom further away from his original haven, but he still returned to it occasionally, especially when life became too knotted to be unravelled by red wine and a conversation with Grace. 'His' bench was, thankfully, empty.

Tom sat down and inhaled the nearly fresh air. He gave himself a mental shake. Cassie was down, that was all. Teenage hormones probably. She was also beginning to discover that the opposite sex was a nightmare. It was a painful life lesson, but one they'd all been through. Yes, that was probably all that was troubling her. He was getting it out of proportion. And if Cassie was sleeping with Ryan (he forced his mind to swerve around the question of where, for God's sake, they were doing it), then at least she'd been sensible and taken precautions. Or at least he hoped like hell she had. The lack of control over your children as they grew up was the worst thing about parenthood, and yet it was the thing that no one ever seemed to talk about. He stared out across the canal, looking up from the wet litter to the glass-and-steel cityscape. The view was starkly impressive, as long as you kept your eyes focused on the horizon. Perspective – that's what the canal gave him.

He took another deep breath. He reached inside his jacket pocket and took out the bulky square of paper that he'd been carrying around for the last couple of days like a talisman – though *what* he was trying to ward off, he couldn't really say. He unfolded the paper, smoothing it as flat as it would go on his knee. It had been a long, long time since he'd looked at it properly. There'd been no need. Today there was. He held the creased, tatty sheet. It was made up of pieces of paper taped together to form a ragged jigsaw. Tom looked at it, realigning the fantasy with the reality.

The image of Cassie stared back.

Their perfect daughter. A fantasy sketched out of hope and wishful thinking all those years ago, in that barren hall full of desperation and desire.

Up until a few weeks ago, Tom had believed that their dreams had come true. Cassie had been as close to perfect as any real, breathing, thinking, passionate, funny, stubborn daughter could be. She'd grown from being a lovable toddler into a loving little girl into a lovely teenager; one who was capable of empathy and kindness, with a maturity that was way in advance of her years.

Tom looked at his drawing and felt a wave of sadness – with it came a very clear memory of his mother's funeral. A terrible day, that was made bearable by Cassie.

The morning they buried Sheila, it poured down. The incessant rain made the whole experience harder and more mournful than was fair or humane.

As they gathered in front of the crematorium, the wind picked up and took on an edge of pure spite, ripping and gusting around the clumps of mourners. The sight of one of the ushers struggling to hold a huge black umbrella over Erin and Cassie pulled Tom up short in the midst of a whispered, last-minute conversation with the funeral director. In that moment the swirl of slick, wet overcoats and sombre faces faded away and Tom was left standing in the driving rain, trapped on the wrong side of the hearse, unable to reach his daughters.

Erin looked terrified, dwarfed by the occasion and the sea of adults milling around her. Her hands fluttered from the buttons on her new coat to her throat and back again in a restless, repetitive cycle. Cassie stood close to her little sister, sheltering her from the worst of the rain. She was doing what she always did when she was stressed and out of her depth – she was faking it. At thirteen, she was conjuring up a better impersonation of composure than any of the assembled adults: straight back, chin up, eyes forward, defying the situation.

His daughters.

Sheila's cherished granddaughters.

They shouldn't be alone.

Tom looked around for Grace, but she had her hands full. She was over by one of the cars in the cortège talking to his dad, trying gently, but firmly, to guide him into the chapel, out of the downpour. The back door of the hearse swung open and the pall-bearers positioned themselves, ready for Sheila's last journey. The funeral director indicated to Tom that he should take his place – but he couldn't.

Erin's eyes were huge. She was staring, unblinking but not uncomprehending, at the casket. Her first experience of death. Conflicting loyalties raged through Tom. The funeral director gestured again for him to step up. His mother or his girls?

Just as Tom was about to abandon his post, he saw Cassie bend down and say something to Erin. She turned towards her older sister, a naked expression of panic on her small face, and again Cassie whispered something to her. Then she took hold of Erin's hand and tucked it into the pocket of her own coat, pulling her little sister close to her and away from the coffin. They stayed that way, welded together, as the coffin slid out of the hearse and was hoisted up onto the pall-bearers' shoulders.

The service, when it finally began, was insipidly routine; as lacking in warmth as Sheila had been full of it. The 'celebrant' could not have been more inaccurately named. He read from his notes with as much passion as a bored teacher. He mangled the pronunciation of Aunt Aisling's name and, despite being asked repeatedly by Tom, failed to even mention Sheila's best and stalwart friend of thirty-six years, Kathleen. By the time it was Tom's turn to give the eulogy, he was more incensed than sad.

His mum had only been sixty-seven.

She shouldn't be dead.

He stepped up to the lectern and looked out at the rows of family and friends. The sound of his own blood thudding in his ears was deafening. Sheila had been well liked. It was a good turnout. She would have been pleased to see so many there. What a stupid saying that was. What comfort could his mum have – ever again? She was dead. Tom looked out at their faces, all turned in expectation towards him, and froze. He couldn't do it. His mum really was dead. Gone – for ever. People shuffled in their seats and glanced at each other, waiting. The knowledge that he was expected to perform, expected to give a heart-warming, suitably respectful light-and-shade speech, with a few gentle jokes thrown in to make the congregation feel better, made him want to scream. That's what raw grief was, a howl – not a polite, pre-prepared eulogy. In that moment Tom's dominant emotion was impotent rage.

He looked down at the front row, seeking solace in his family.

Erin was sandwiched between Grace and Cassie. She had her head bowed, one hand holding onto her sister, the other gripping her mother. As Tom watched, Grace tightened her grip on their youngest daughter, pulling her close into her body for protection and comfort. Grace looked at Tom across the top of Erin's head, questioning, kind, concerned. Tom swallowed, but the anger blocking his throat wouldn't shift. There was more shuffling and a smattering of coughs. He had to say something. But he couldn't. He was choked by the solemnity of the occasion and by the sheer wrongness of his mother's brutally swift decline and painful death. He couldn't do it. He was going to let his mum down. The blood rushed and roared in his head.

Then Tom saw a movement in the front row. Cassie. She gently eased her hand free from Erin's grip, stood up and walked, very calmly, across the front of the chapel. She skirted the coffin, climbed the steps onto the dais and came to stand next to him. Once by his side, she leant across him, her hand briefly brushing his, and straightened the pages of his notes – not that they needed rearranging. Then she smiled and whispered, 'It's okay, Dad.'

And somehow, after that, it was.

A cyclist whizzed along the towpath, startling Tom back into the present. The back-draught tugged the picture away. He snatched it back.

Not a perfect daughter, perhaps, but Cassie came pretty damn close.

Chapter 11

THE GIRLS did it that night. Erin was Cassie's wingman. It was all pre-planned.

Cassie made a real effort during the meal, reassuring Tom and Grace that she felt much better, clearing her plate to prove that she wasn't on the cusp of an eating disorder, and being very chatty. She felt guilty to see her parents relax and smile, knowing what she was about to throw at them. As her dad stretched and made to start stacking the plates she said, 'Can you leave that a minute, Dad? I want to talk to you both about something.'

He sat down, clattering the plates onto the table. Grace straightened her back.

Cassie ploughed on. 'I've been thinking about asking you something for quite a while now, but I didn't want to upset either of you.'

'Okay,' her mum prompted.

'It's about my adoption.' Cassie couldn't be sure, but she thought she saw her dad actually relax a little.

'Of course. Anything. You can ask us anything, you know that.'

Cassie looked at Erin, who nodded her encouragement. 'Well, it's just that I feel I want to know a bit more about it.'

'About what?' Always Mr Specific, her dad.

'Well, about my birth mum.' Cassie watched her parents glance at each other.

Her dad ceded control to her mum. 'Of course we're always happy to talk to you about it, but they never provided us with that much detail.'

'Yes, but there must be more than you've told me.'

Grace looked thoughtful. 'There isn't – not really. All we knew was what we were told by the social workers and what was in your file.'

'And?'

'Well, as you know, she struggled to cope – your birth mum – that's why they made the decision to take you away from her.'

Cassie felt a ripple of frustration. She'd heard this before, and while previously it had been enough, now it wasn't. 'But that's so vague. We haven't talked about it in years. What you told me when I was little, that can't be the whole truth. I want the adult version.'

Tom couldn't help himself. 'Why?'

Cassie bridled. 'Do I need a reason?'

'Well, no, what I meant is – why now? What's triggered this now?'

'Does it matter?'

Grace stepped in swiftly. 'No, of course it doesn't. What do you want to know?'

Cassie stalled. What did she want to know? Just more. She wasn't naïve enough to think there was some fairy-story version of her biological mother and her adoption; she knew it was probably going to be bad. But whatever the truth was, it was hers. And... and she needed the facts, to compare with her dreams. A miserable start in life didn't chime with the fleeting but very real moments of happiness that she was 'remembering'. 'Well, for a start, when you say she couldn't cope... what does that mean?' Cassie hadn't been able to forget the doctor's softly spoken questions about family illnesses and mental frailties – her unknown genetic inheritance.

'Just that. She didn't have the skills. She was struggling to look after herself, never mind anyone else. She wasn't feeding you properly. And we were told the house was in a poor state. Not very clean. Cold. Not a good place for a small child. For any child.' Grace spoke slowly, carefully.

'So, she was a lazy cow? They don't take your kids away just because you aren't keeping up with the hoovering. Why couldn't she cope? What was wrong with her?' Cassie could hear her voice vibrating with emotion, but she was powerless to rein it in. Neither of her parents spoke for a few seconds, but Cassie caught Tom glance at Erin and realised that having her sister present was inhibiting their responses. They were giving her the PG-rated version, to save Erin's feelings. A sharp tine of frustration pushed into Cassie's skin. 'Tell me! I have a right to know. If you don't want Erin hearing this, then we can go in the other room.'

Erin pushed her chair back and stood up. 'No. I'll go. I'll be upstairs.' She walked out of the room, her face averted so that they couldn't see her expression. The sense of betrayal burnt in her chest. No one tried to stop her leaving. She pulled the door shut behind her, quietly, already forgotten.

Grace very slowly and self-consciously placed her hand on the table, the upturned palm only a few centimetres away from Cassie's closed fist. It was a gesture of affection. Cassie ignored it. Grace took a breath. 'Okay.' She drew her hand back onto her lap. 'All we can tell you is what we were told at the time. It isn't much.' There was another pause. 'Your birth mum apparently came from quite a chaotic background herself. Her family was known to Social Services. She did well, comparatively, for a while. She finished school, got a job, sorted out somewhere to live, away from her parents and her brothers, and was doing okay. But after a series of casual jobs she ended up unemployed. She started having money troubles, rent arrears, payday loans and suchlike. That's when she had her first...' Cassie didn't see

Tom start, it was so slight a movement, 'brush with the authorities. She got caught shoplifting. There was some sort of altercation with a security guard at a supermarket. The police were called. The shop wanted to press charges. That triggered Social Services getting more involved. They helped her, gave her some support, sorted out some of her debts. They apparently kept her on their radar for a while. It all settled down. She had you a few years later. She wasn't on anyone's list any more. No one thought to check how she was coping. She was just another single mum – one of thousands. Then one day someone reported her, a neighbour, I think it was. They said they had some concerns about what was going on in the house where she was living. Someone visited to check up on her, and on you. She was deemed to be coping. A few more months went by. By then there'd been a number of disturbances at her address. The police got involved. They brought in Social Services, again. That's when the decision was made to remove you.'

Suddenly Tom spoke up, a rush of words. 'Apparently there were people coming and going through the house, at all hours. They found drugs. It sounded like things had spiralled completely out of control. She wasn't looking after you, protecting you as she should have done. You were at risk. Probably had been for a while.' He drew breath. 'I'm sorry, I know it's upsetting, but they did the right thing taking you out of there.'

Grace reached out and took Cassie's hand. 'Cassie, I know it's hard, but you mustn't think badly of her. She had a poor start in life. I don't think it was wilful neglect. I think she lost control of what was going on. It sounded like people preyed on her vulnerability. And I think she knew, deep down – when you were taken away – that it was for the best. She gave her blessing to you being adopted. She never opposed it. Many of them do. Changing their minds months, even years, later. We were warned about it. We were told not to think of you as ours until the court made the final ruling. But she didn't object to your adoption. Not once. If you think about it, that's the most selfless thing anyone can do – put someone else's happiness in front of their own. I believe she wanted you to have the kind of life she'd never had, and couldn't give you.'

'Or maybe she was just glad to get rid of me.'

Grace was about to argue the point, but Tom cut her off. 'It's possible, Cassie, but either way, the outcome was a good one. Wasn't it? Without her, you'd never have been our daughter. We will always be grateful to her for that.'

Cassie suddenly felt tired. Bone-weary. 'Okay. Thank you for being honest with me.' She saw them both relax, ever so slightly. 'Do you know where she is now?' The tension returned to their faces.

'No.'

'Okay.' She hauled herself out of her chair.

It was enough, for now.

Chapter 12

GRACE AND Tom didn't speak about their conversation with Cassie until late that night, when they felt sure both girls were asleep. 'Do you think that's the end of it?' Grace rubbed moisturiser into her elbows, smoothing the cream into her skin in small circles.

'God knows. Something must have set her off. She's always been so disinterested before. At least it explains why she's been so quiet this past fortnight. She must have been stewing about asking us. She'll feel better, now we've spoken about it.'

Grace looked at her husband. 'But we hardly told her the whole truth.'

'No. And we mustn't. We agreed.'

'It feels wrong,' Grace said.

'What good can telling her do? Did you see her face when we were talking? She hated hearing what sort of background she very nearly grew up in. And she is happy – normally. I think it'll settle down. I just wish she'd say what set her off thinking about it.' Tom pulled a fresh T-shirt over his head. 'She hasn't said anything to you, has she?'

Grace screwed the lid back on the tub of cream and shook her head. 'No.'

'Let's wait and see then. Keep an eye on her. Let her ask anything else she wants to.' Tom got into bed, 'But let's not encourage it, either.' He pummelled his pillow into a better position behind his head.

Grace got into bed beside her husband, her expression clouded with anxiety. Tom clicked off the light. They lay side-by-side, reliving their shared but very personal memories of the long, hard path they'd had to travel to become a family, and the decisions they'd had to make along the way – decisions that, at the time, they truly believed were in Cassie's best interests, and their own.

It began in earnest when they put their names down on a sheet of paper on a table in an echoey room in the Town Hall at an 'Introduction to Adoption' session. That was the day they first met Estelle, Kev and Lynne, Di and Mario, Natasha and Sanjuy, Emma and her morose partner whose name no one could ever remember and, of course, the unforgettably irritating Nina and Lewis. People with whom – despite the long hours of mutual soul-baring and the emotional protestations of staying friends for ever – they had long since lost touch. A random group forced together by their willingness to put themselves through the arduous, invasive screening process, just to have the slim chance of adopting some else's child.

The training sessions took place every other Tuesday, between 7 p.m. and 9 p.m. A strict, compulsory schedule, which was blocked out on all their calendars months in advance. People rarely missed a meeting; in fact most of them arrived early, having done whatever preparation had been asked of them. It was important to demonstrate wholehearted commitment at every turn. Only Nina and Lewis seemed indifferent to the rules. They often arrived late, unrepentant and ill-prepared because they considered themselves special. In one very significant respect they were. They already had a child; a foster daughter, *little Gwen*, who came to them as *a tiny dot with a mop of dark hair at two days old*. A child who had been

73

filling their lives with joy ever since. The group, secretly, jealously, collectively resented Nina and Lewis with a passion.

The night of the drawing exercise was no exception.

Everyone was there, settled in their usual places, ready to get going, but Nina and Lewis were *running late* – again – due to some *incident involving Gwen and Nina's best nail polish.* Tom sat checking his emails, trying to distract himself from his rising frustration with the whole painful, painstaking process. Staring at his phone had the additional benefit of allowing him to avoid conversation with the other attendees. The room's layout, with its ominously arranged chairs, was designed to encourage interaction. It was yet another aspect of the sessions that made Tom feel tense. He hated the enforced camaraderie, the sharing, the empathy, the knowing, sympathetic smiles. In reality they had nothing in common, except one thing – their failure to conceive a child.

Grace felt differently. She sat on Tom's left, chatting happily to Estelle, the lone female in their cohort. The lone black female. The lone black, lesbian female. A woman with a steel spine beneath her calm, gentle demeanour. How she was coping with the process on her own, Tom didn't know. He remembered Estelle walking up to the desk at the first meeting in the Town Hall and adding her solitary name to the growing list of couples, looking as relaxed and unconcerned as if she was strolling across a park on a sunny day, with twenty-four pairs of eyes watching, judging, sizing her up. It was a first taste of the scrutiny that was to become a feature of all their lives.

Tom recognised that this access to the innermost truths of other people's souls should have engendered empathy in him – surely that would have been the normal reaction? They were all in the same boat, after all, chasing the same dream: a child to love. That it didn't, worried him. At times, especially when the group was together doing one of the endless self-examination exercises, he worried that this lack of connection pointed to some emotional flaw in his make-up. Maybe there just wasn't enough kindness in him to care properly about other people's feelings. If that were true, what sort of father would he make for a child who wasn't his own? That was the problem with these bloody sessions, they made you second-guess yourself – about everything.

At last Nina and Lewis arrived and they were good to go. Lee, the course leader, called them to order. Matching pairs – more couple's work. Great! Grace immediately asked Estelle to join them, thereby avoiding the usual awkwardness that occurred when they did partnered exercises. Large sheets of paper and startlingly childish packs of felt-tip pens were passed to each group, then Lee briefed them. 'What I want us to spend this evening focusing on is the future.' He left a slight pause. 'I want you to think about the impact that a child coming into your lives will have. A real flesh-and-blood child. It may feel uncomfortable at first, but I want you to articulate your innermost hopes and dreams about that child. This applies equally to you guys.' This was aimed at a questioning Nina and Lewis. 'I want you to talk openly, be honest, put it all down: the ideal age, gender, personality traits, what they will grow up to be. Think about your own lives, your interests, your personalities – what will this child be coming into? What will they have to be like, to fit in?' He glanced at his watch. 'Shall we say thirty minutes, then we'll share?' He turned away from the group and started talking to Steph, the other course moderator.

Silence.

Lee glanced up. 'Oh, come on, guys, how many times have we been through stuff like this in the past few months? The same rules apply: no judgement, no interrupting, no wrong answers, no fudging.'

And so, as commanded, each little huddle turned in on itself and set about disembowelling another soft, vulnerable part of their lives.

Tom, Grace and Estelle were sitting with Kev and Lynne, the oldest couple in the group. Kev, who seemed to dislike the soul-searching as much as Tom, thankfully volunteered to go first, wanting, as always, to get his contribution over with. 'As you guys already know, we want a boy.' Lynne had already drawn a neat outline of a little boy on the sheet of paper, as Kev spoke she added shorts, curly hair and a big smile. 'Young, ideally – maybe up to three or four, at a pinch. We're used to boys. We've got lots of nephews. We seem to breed boys in our family.' Lynne lowered her head over the sheet and kept on adding to her drawing. 'We wouldn't really mind, but I wouldn't have thought they'd offer us a coloured kiddie.' Tom, Grace and Estelle made no comment. 'We'd want a child who likes the outdoors. A robust, healthy type. A lad who'd want to come fishing with me, play football, that sort of thing.'

Lynne finally looked up. 'And I'd teach him to cook. He's not gonna be just a mini-Kev. I can at least move evolution on a tiny bit.' Kev smiled at his wife.

Estelle's wish list was surprising. 'I'd happily take a boy or a girl, I really don't mind, but not a baby. I can't see me doing the baby-thing very well. I wouldn't be patient enough.' Grace's face gave away her thoughts. Estelle seemed to be one of the calmest people on the course. 'No, seriously,' she continued, 'I don't want a baby. Besides…' she hesitated, but only slightly, 'with a child, you'd know for certain if everything was all right – developmentally, I mean. I'd worry with a baby. You just can't know what damage has been done before they come to you.' Estelle continued unabashed, leaving the cold draught of her logic to blow across them, 'Ideally, five or six. Started school. I'll take parental leave, of course, but I'm going to need to get back to work fairly quickly, for my sanity and for the salary. I'd love them to be chatty. A talker. Sociable. That's what I really want: a child I can talk to…about everything, and anything. Oh, and they're going to have to like music, if they're going to be living in my house. How cool would it be if they turned out to be musical?' She looked down at her piece of paper and laughed, loudly, causing the couple-huddles closest to them to look up. Estelle's sketch was an indecipherable scatter of squiggles and lines, all intersecting and arcing across the paper. 'I'd best not show this to Lee. He'll think I'm certifiable.' She smiled at Tom and Grace.

'We want a girl,' they said in unison. Again Kev, Lynne and Estelle laughed, and again the other couples glanced over, put out that fun was being had in the midst of such a serious exercise. Tom leant forward in his chair and squared the paper on his lap, ready to draw, cueing Grace up. She obliged, looking at him as she spoke, silently seeking his agreement with her version of their envisaged child, the wraith-like daughter who, until that moment, had only ever breathed in their dreams and in their whispered conversations in the dark. 'We'd really like a baby. I know everyone says not to hold out for one, but it would be lovely if we could get...' she stumbled, '... adopt a little one. It would just feel, for us...' she added, sensitive to Estelle's feelings, 'better somehow. I think she'd feel more ours, if we could have her from near the beginning. She could grow up with us. She'd be her own person, obviously, but I guess she'd absorb a lot of stuff from us. We're not that bothered about her ethnic background.' Was this true? Grace looked at Tom and was disconcerted when he didn't look up. 'We'd just hope for her to be healthy...and happy. And we'd want her to grow up to be self-confident, for her to know that she was loved enough to be brave.'

'And with Tom's creative skills, hopefully,' Lynne chipped in. He looked up, caught off-guard, having been lulled into reflection by the eloquence of Grace's description. 'Show them,' Lynne prompted. He turned the paper round so that it faced Grace. They all looked.

Tom's sketch was of a young woman, not a child; tall, strong-featured, staring out from the page, defiant. It was Estelle who said what they were all thinking, 'And she's going to look just like Grace.'

This time, when they laughed, Lee decided to call time on the exercise.

They dragged their chairs back into the dreaded circle and prepared *to share*, the pictures clutched in their hands. Steph and Lee looked around the group, waiting. Steph took the lead this time. 'Okay. Thank you for that. It was good to hear you all being so open. There are some quite amazing pictures.' Everyone holding a piece of paper looked down. 'Now, what I'd like you to do...' she paused, checking that she had their attention, 'is to take your picture – and rip it up.' The atmosphere in the room shunted. They all looked at Steph, who stared back at them, unsmiling. 'I'm serious, guys.' The silent response was hostile. 'No?'

'Come on, what's this about?' Lewis was at least ballsy enough to say something.

'I'm not joking,' Steph responded. 'I want you to take your pictures and tear them into tiny pieces.' Still no one moved. Her tone was firm, but it was shot through with understanding. 'Trust me, there is a point to this, and it's important. We need you to look at the images you've drawn, and think about all the things you talked about in your groups – all your dreams and long-cherished fantasies – and you need to take that child and...*let them go*. You have to say goodbye, for ever, to that ideal child.'

The mood in the room softened slightly, losing some of its sharpness, but none of its wariness.

When Steph spoke again, it was with kindness, but also with clarity and force. 'There is no such thing as *the perfect child for your family*. They do not exist.' She stressed every word. 'There are only children who need adopting, and your need to adopt. That's all there is.' Tom's grip on his picture tightened. 'And if you can't accept that, then it's very unlikely you're ever going to make it through to the end of this process.'

The sound of paper tearing filled the room like rain.

And yet, despite the heartache and the frustrations, and the rigorous testing of their faith and commitment, they did make it to the end.

They completed the required training modules and they passed all the background checks. They examined their motivations and they readjusted their unrealistic expectations. They prepared for, and survived the stress of, the final panel interview, and they were, eventually, unequivocally approved to adopt – one child, under five, possibly from a mixed-race background.

They were, officially, *potential parents*.

But after all that work on themselves, and their souls, and their aspirations – there was no child for them. Not in that the first heady month, when they held their breath every time the phone rang, or the second month, when Grace's prayers were still fervent. Or any of the subsequent slow, hope-curdling months that followed. They had, of course, been told that it could take time, they would have to be patient, but the absence of any news was hard to accept, as was the sudden lack of activity. It was as if they'd become addicted to the process of applying to adopt – had, in truth, relied on it to lessen the grief of being childless. Now there was nothing they could do but wait for fate to decide. They had time and space, and deep, swirling reserves of pent-up love, but absolutely no idea what to do with themselves, because the bedroom at the back of the house, which caught the sun in the morning and was quiet in the evenings, was still empty.

Tom and Grace were both drawn to the room at least once, or twice, or five times a day, normally when the other was out or in the bath or at work. They'd push open the door and stand looking at the lined-up toys. Grace would adjust the curtains and Tom would pick up and refold the blanket on the end of the 'cot/bed/sleep space' they'd bought because it was adaptable for almost every eventuality – their acts of solitary observance that were fast becoming rituals. What else could they do, in the absence of an actual child? The room had been empty for eight years. It had been redecorated twice. Once, foolishly optimistically, when Grace first fell pregnant; then again, much more cautiously, towards the end of the adoption process. It was a pastel statement of intent and hope, but it was no guarantee. And the longer they waited, the more unlikely it seemed that the room would ever become a proper bedroom for a real child.

The perpetual breath-holding was hard on both of them; it left very little oxygen for anything else, certainly not enough for 'making the most of their time on their own', which seemed to be the advice that most of their friends, especially the ones *with* children, pressed upon them.

Then on Wednesday 18 February at 2.15 p.m., Grace and Tom received an email from Steph, asking one of them to call. That was it. No detail. Just to call as soon as they got her message. At 2.16 p.m. they rang each other and got an engaged signal, at 2.19 p.m. they simultaneously received a voicemail from each other.

Grace got through to Tom at 2.23 p.m. 'You've seen the email from Steph?'

'Yes.'

'Do you want to ring her?'

'No, it's okay, you call her.'

'I'll ring you straight back afterwards.'

'Okay.'

'Okay.'

Grace disconnected Tom's call and sat with her phone nestled in her hand, the noise of the office drifting around her for a few moments, then she grabbed her bag and hurried out onto the landing, along to the recessed window that looked out across the city. The winter sun was warm through the glass. She tried to calm down, telling herself it could be nothing, but she knew it wasn't.

Steph answered on the second ring. The slight breathlessness in her voice confirmed it. 'Hi, Grace. It's good news. I think we may have found a little girl who could be a good fit for you and Tom. She's just come onto the books. I've put initial feelers out to her social worker and they're open to a possible match. I was wondering if you'd like me to come round and talk you through her profile?'

Grace watched the cars on the overpass whizz by, flashes of silver and blue and white. 'Of course.'

'I was thinking sooner rather than later,' Steph went on. 'How are you fixed for tomorrow teatime? Would you and Tom be able to get off work a little bit earlier? Say, if I came to yours for four p.m.?'

Grace was supposed to be in London; someone else would have to cover it.

'Yes. That's fine.'

'I have a good feeling about this, Grace. Really I do.' Steph sounded genuinely excited.

Just before she rang off, Grace managed to ask, 'How old is she?'

'She's two. Nearly three. Let's talk tomorrow. I promise, Grace, I think you're going love her.' Steph rang off.

For few seconds Grace didn't move. She stood in the shaft of heat, feeling hope bloom and expand inside her. A little girl; not a baby, but a little girl. Could this really be the beginning? No name, no details, but a real child with their names pencilled in beside her. A possible match.

She rang Tom and told him, though there was so little to say.

'So tomorrow then?'

'Yep, at four. She said she'd tell us all about her then.'

'At last.'

'Yeah.'

'Good luck with getting any work done today.'

She smiled. 'You too.'

Grace dropped her phone into her bag. The lift opened and voices filled the landing, but she didn't turn round. She stared out over the city, wondering if their little girl was out there, somewhere.

✳

After Grace ended the call, Tom stood up and walked away from his desk, down the stairs and out into the cold, sun-bleached car park. He kept walking until he reached the path alongside the canal and the bench that looked out over the oil-topped water. He sat down. The same spot. The same view. A blast of emotion hit him, strong and destabilising, bringing with it the echo of past pain. But this time the child was real, living, breathing, fully formed. Not their child – a child that had survived.

Life had been too cruel to Tom and Grace to let his first thoughts be hopeful. Self-preservation dictated that the pessimist within him gained the upper hand. In his head he started drafting a 'Memo to Self'. There was so much that could go wrong: legal barriers, objections from the birth family, a counter-offer from another social worker, never mind possible issues with the child itself – herself. A girl. What they wanted. What Grace so desperately wanted. No, he couldn't think about that, not yet. All he knew was that she was two years ten months old. Young, but not days old, not months old; she was nearly a full three years old. Tom started concocting her probable past from the stew of grim information that was slopping around in his brain from the training sessions. He knew the facts about what alcohol and drugs did to a baby as it developed, and how common abuse was in households that had their children taken away. Cause and effect: a vicious circle. Damage in the womb, chaos outside it. What would Steph be able and willing to tell them about what this child had been born into and survived? How much did he want to know? What mark would those early experiences have left on the child? But survived she had, and she was being offered to them. All those months of theory and preparation, all the months of waiting and praying, hadn't been for nothing; it had led them to this.

A shadow slid over Tom, bringing with it a further drop in temperature and a weird, whooshing noise. From out of nowhere, a swan crash-landed onto the canal in front of him, an inelegant sprawl of white muscle and feathered wing. He watched it skid heavily to a halt as if the flat grey water was asphalt. The ripples spread wide, a sudden disturbance of the stillness. Once it came to a stop, the swan stretched out its regal neck and wings, as if checking for whiplash. It glanced over at Tom, then folded itself, origami-like, back into a perfectly elegant shape, before gliding silently away.

A little girl.

Beneath the weight of worry and caution, and lessons learnt the hard way, Tom felt excitement stir and stretch.

By the time Steph finally rang the doorbell the following day, they were both high on pent-up anticipation. Breathing was difficult, talking normally a lost skill; their future as a family rested on what Steph was about tell them. She sat quite calmly with the file on her knee and smiled at them. 'I'm really hopeful about this. I know you've always said that you wanted as young a child as possible, so this little girl is a bit of a find. Like I said, she's a new referral. She's been with her foster family for three months, but she's only just come up for adoption. She's called Cassidie. I visited her a few days ago. She is, genuinely, a lovely, bright, happy little girl. Something of a find really.'

It struck Tom as a little odd that Steph felt it necessary to do a sales pitch on a child, but he chided himself for being suspicious and concentrated on what she was saying – she was, after all, describing a child who could become their daughter. The look on Grace's face was so hopeful, it was painful.

'Would you like to see a picture?' Steph asked. It was such a bizarre question. Of course they wanted to see her.

'Yes,' they said simultaneously.

Steph opened the file, took out the photograph and passed it to them. They both reached out, but Tom let Grace take it. She sat back beside him, their shoulders touching, the picture held out in front of them. The moment stilled. Steph kept talking.

A little girl. Dark, almost black eyes. A halo of hair. Round checks. A pointy chin. Chubby hands gripping the handles of a toy buggy. A broad, easy smile. She could've been their daughter.

Grace said, 'Oh' softly, and felt something that she'd later describe as love flood through her and wash away her doubts; well, most of them.

Steph beamed. 'I know. It's uncanny, isn't it? It's an out-of-area match. She's in Stockport at the moment.'

Tom couldn't stop looking at the photo. The wanting and waiting, the failure and the despair had become such a way of life that this tangible evidence of a little girl who might become theirs was almost too much.

Steph smiled, seeing how reverentially they were holding Cassidie's picture, and said, 'So can I take it that you're interested?' They both nodded. 'Good. Because I want to talk you through her situation and get your take on the options available to us, before we proceed. It's not straightforward, I'm afraid, but there again, it never is.'

Grace blinked and Tom steeled himself, and they forced themselves to lift their eyes from the image of their perfect match and listen to the reality of Cassidie's wholly imperfect beginning.

Chapter 13

GRACE PRAYED that Tom was right about Cassie being satisfied with what they'd told her about her biological mother, but she had little faith that she would.

Even as a toddler, Cassie had been stubborn, relentless in the pursuit of what she wanted, so very different from Erin. If they were honest with themselves, they'd encouraged Cassie's wilfulness, believing that she was going to need the extra resilience and self-belief as she grew up. They never directly discussed it, but Grace knew they were both trying to ensure that their love, and parenting, were powerful enough to smother any shades of the past that lingered within her. Nature versus nurture? They'd stacked the scales heavily in favour of nurture.

But deep down, in the darker recesses of her heart, Grace had been waiting for Cassie's adoption to have an impact on their family. They'd been *too* lucky. It had all gone *too* smoothly. Cassie had become their daughter and her past hadn't seemed to make an iota of difference. That was too good to be true.

This latest upheaval was some sort of reckoning.

Just how much of one, Grace had no idea.

She sat in front of her laptop in her office, with the door closed, and considered whether they had been right to lie to their daughter, and whether she could bear to keep lying to her. Grace couldn't escape the feeling that their dishonesty was more unforgivable in the face of Cassie's new interest in her roots. Grace knew that Tom didn't see what they'd done, and were still doing, as 'lying' and he would have argued with her if she had used the word, but in her own estimation, omission was as good, or as bad, as deceit. And they had omitted some very significant facts – to protect Cassie, it was true, but also to protect themselves. A parent's first responsibility is to safeguard their child. Tom and Grace had done that all those years ago and they were continuing to do it now, but Grace's beliefs, her basic coding as a human being, also valued honesty, highly, and there was no way round it – they were *not* being honest.

Grace stared at the file, wishing it away and at the same time glad that it existed.

What she felt was ill-prepared, and that worried her. Despite all the courses she and Tom had attended, very little had ever been said about the possible delayed consequences of the decisions they would have to make as adoptive parents. The sessions had primarily focused on how to accept, love and raise a child who was not your own. That they'd done – easily, naturally, or so Grace thought. The challenges of how to explain the realities of adoption to a child had also been covered; well, as it turned out. The mantra had been: *Keep it simple, reassure the child, answer truthfully when asked a question, but in an age-appropriate manner.* And again they had done as instructed… well, very nearly. And it had all gone to plan. But nothing had been said about dealing with that child when he or she became a young adult and started to question the story that you'd so lovingly and carefully told them. No, they had not been warned that the past would be silently accumulating beneath the surface of their lives, and that it would eventually leach up through the layers of love and time and stain their future.

Grace traced her finger across the trackpad, and the cursor hovered over the file. She didn't open it. She didn't need to; she knew what the file contained and what it represented. It was the link to the Cassie's birth family that Grace had never wanted to forge, but which, once started, she had felt compelled to maintain.

At three years old and three feet tall, Cassie was thriving. And that day, like most days, she was full of it, roaming around the house with a glittery-eyed destructive zeal, looking for trouble. Being cooped up inside wasn't helping. Grace had discovered very early on that Cassie hated being confined. It seemed to make her go a little crazy. Unfortunately, it was yet another wet day, in what was turning out to be a washout of a summer. The prospect of going back to work after her parental leave glowed more temptingly with each week that went by. Was that bad of her? Or normal? Surely normal was good, and they had made it to 'normal'. That was a testament to their success. Cassie was their child. They were her parents. The novelty of having a new grandchild, niece, cousin had all but worn off. They were a normal family and she was just another mum with a bored child.

There was no option other than to go into indoor-fun mode. They did some baking, putting green food colouring into the pastry to make the jam tarts look like Play-Doh ones, (God help Tom, when he got home), then they danced to the radio, played Snap! for half an hour and built an obstacle course in the lounge, using all the sofa cushions. All without any noticeable effect on Cassie's fizzing energy levels. It seemed to take for ever to get to 11.45 a.m., the earliest time at which lunch was acceptable, in Grace's mental manual of good parenting. Settled at the kitchen table, Cassie finally quietened down. She ate happily and steadily, concentrating on her food with an intensity that reminded Grace of her Grandma Joyce, a big woman who used to eat with a ferocious commitment and a roving eye for anyone else's leftovers. After lunch, weighed down by hummus, breadsticks, cucumber, cheese and two yogurts, Cassie accepted being put down for a nap, without much of a fight. Again, very much like Grandma Joyce.

As Grace poured herself a proper cup of coffee amidst the carnage in the kitchen, she made a decision to do something she'd been putting off. She took her drink through to the bomb-struck lounge, pushed a couple of cushions back into the gaping maw of the sofa and balanced her laptop on her knee. She opened up a new blank document and stared at the white screen.

A couple of weeks after the final hearing and the issuing of the adoption order, Grace had received a call from Steph. She'd assumed it was a routine follow-up and burbled on about everyday nonsense until Steph politely, and somewhat awkwardly, interjected. 'That's great, Grace, but I was actually calling about something else. I've been asked to approach you with a request, on Leah's behalf.'

Grace's pulse stuttered. The order should have been the end of the process. Finally, a done deal. A closed adoption. All links with the birth family broken.

Steph carried on talking. 'There's been another case review and it's been mooted that some form of update – just something brief – might be useful.' Grace didn't respond, didn't trust herself to. Steph ploughed on. 'There's a system called Letterbox. It's a secure way of passing information back to birth families; quite a few of our adoptive families use it. It's tried and tested, been up and running for years. There's no risk of personal identifying information being released.' Steph paused and cleared her throat, sensing Grace's reluctance. 'You are, of course, under no obligation, but there's still a lot of anger there and her behaviour is causing some concern. Her social worker thought some reassurance that Cassie has settled with you, and is doing well, might help to ease some of her distress.' There was another long pause, which Grace did not fill. Steph was forced to ask, 'Grace, are you still there?'

'Yes,' Grace said. She was too thrown to be more articulate.

Steph persevered. 'Is it something you think you might be able to consider? I appreciate that you'll want to discuss it with Tom, see how he feels about it?'

'Yes. I'll need to talk to Tom,' Grace agreed, though she shrank from the thought of it.

'Okay. Thank you. I really want to stress that you're under no obligation at all, and I do understand you having reservations, but I said I'd pass the request along. Shall I wait to hear back from you then, after you've had a bit of time to think about it?'

'Yes.' Grace felt better sticking to monosyllables.

'Great. Thanks again. Any questions, you know where I am. Give my love to Cassie.' And with that, Steph rang off, having parked her monkey squarely on Grace's back.

Grace stared at her phone. *No obligation* – Steph had said it twice. They had a choice; they were under no compunction to comply with the request, other than a moral one, of course.

When Grace told Tom about the call, his reaction was, as she'd expected, not good. 'So much for that being it. I thought we were through with all this. They've no right to ask.'

'No "right" – no,' Grace agreed, 'but Steph said they thought it might help her to move on, if she knew that Cassie was doing well.'

'They did, did they?'

Grace knew that it was best to retreat. 'Okay. Well, I said I'd mention it, that's all. If you really don't want us to get involved, we won't.' She scooped up a pile of ironing and left it at that.

Except that she didn't. Steph's request clung to her, whispering in her ear every time she looked at Cassie. The call had resuscitated Leah as a living, breathing, hurting human being and, as much as Grace wanted to recommit her to a disregarded corner of her mind, she couldn't. So she raised it again with Tom, appealing to his kindness and his desire to placate her. And, after lot more discussion, he finally agreed to her writing a brief update on how Cassie was doing. She knew Tom had little faith that a letter would make any difference, and perhaps it wouldn't, but deep down Grace believed it was important that they write one; if not for Leah, then for Cassie. It was true that Cassie was theirs now, legally and emotionally, and nothing was ever going to change that, but she wasn't going to be small child for ever. At some point they'd have to tell her about her adoption and explain, and defend, the decisions they'd made on her behalf.

Grace sipped her coffee. Going over everything in her mind was just another form of procrastination. The page was still blank. She straightened her spine, put down her mug and started typing. She was still at it an hour later, when a thud upstairs alerted her to the end of Cassie's nap.

Tom read the letter swiftly, put it down quickly, then spoke slowly. 'Yeah. It's very good.' He picked up the piece of paper again and reread it, his eyes drawn to the descriptions of Cassie. Grace had captured her so well.

Grace waited, feeling defensive. 'There's a "but"?'

Tom stared past her at the dishes spread across the counter tops. 'I'm not sure that it's quite right.'

'Meaning?' Grace sat down, blocking his view.

'It's very well written. It must have taken you ages. I just don't think we should give so much away. I feel really uncomfortable letting Leah know so much about us.' He pushed the paper around on the table top, wishing he could loosen the words from the page.

'I was trying to give her sense of how well she's doing.' To her own ears, Grace sounded prickly.

'And you have. It's very…real, but I think it's too detailed. It's too identifiably…Cassie.'

'Isn't that the whole point of it?'

Tom put the paper down and looked at her properly. 'No, not really. All we have to do is tell her the basics. We're not doing this to encourage her, are we?' Grace took it as a rhetorical question and kept silent. Tom stroked the top of his hand, rubbing his fingers across the veins. 'To be honest, I'd be happy if we never heard from Leah, or about her, ever again. I'm sorry if that's brutal, but I can't see how them having any contact is ever going to be anything other than bad – for Cassie, and for us. It would be too disruptive.' He paused as if waiting for Grace to object. She said nothing. 'So, no; I'm sorry, but I'm not happy for us to send it, not as it is.'

'I see,' Grace said.

Tom was uncertain of her mood. 'Cassie is ours now. Our job is to protect her, and I think keeping her as far away from her past as possible is part of that. It's the best way of ensuring she grows up safe and happy.'

'You really think we have that right?' Grace asked him.

Tom continued to meet her gaze. 'Yes, I do. We're her parents.' The letter lay on the table between them. Eventually Grace drew it towards her and folded it in half, very precisely. Tom watched her walk out of the room, nervous of her silence.

As she stood in front of the bathroom mirror brushing her teeth, Grace reflected on Tom's rejection of her painstakingly composed letter, trying to weigh up their rights against Leah's – their healthy, wholehearted version of love pitted against Leah's damaged, broken variety. It was an unequal equation that, no matter how hard she tried, she couldn't get to balance.

Two days later Grace posted the letter as she and Cassie walked to the shops.

Tom didn't ask to see the new draft, and Grace didn't offer to show it to him.

Grace believed the letters were acts of atonement.

Tom that they were acts of absolution.

They were both wrong.

Grace moved the cursor away from the 'Leah Letters' folder and clicked on the 'Correspondence' file instead. She began searching for a contact number for the Adoption Agency. Steph would, no doubt, be long gone, but there would be someone there who would be able to help. Cassie was asking for the truth, and they were going to have to come up with some answers, whether they wanted to or not.

Chapter 14

IN THE face of all the upheaval in her soul and at home, Cassie turned to Ryan. Only when she was pressed against him did the confusing roar inside her head quieten down.

Ryan was surprised and delighted by Cassie's renewed interest in him, and was simple enough to think it was the car that was making the difference. The rules of engagement seemed to have changed – a lot – since he'd got it. Cassie was more willing to let things go further, and for longer. He was getting handfuls of her now, rather than fingertip touches. He reckoned it couldn't be long before she had sex with him. His penis twitched at the thought of it as he watched her work, swishing in and out of the serving area. She was the best-looking waitress by far; the other girls looked ordinary by comparison. He was definitely batting above his average. Ryan got nothing from Cassie each time she came back round to pick up another order, not even a glance, but that didn't bother him. She'd be his after the shift.

They'd found a tiny car park near some allotments, just round the corner from the hotel, that worked really well. It was so much better than having to schlep all the way to the top of the park, simply to cop a feel. There were no houses nearby and no one ever seemed to be around, especially once it got dark. Ryan glanced at the clock and smiled. He turned his attention back to his station, flipping over his steaks with panache; only an hour or so to go.

When the evening shift finally ended, he drove them straight to the allotments. He parked the car in the space furthest away from the street lamp, unclicked his seatbelt and reached across to stroke Cassie's face. He wasn't a complete trog, he knew that she liked being coaxed and edged towards it. He was a bit put out when she didn't respond, but he chose to ignore her initial frostiness. And when he got out of the car and climbed into the back seat, she joined him without any argument. He moved across and put his arm round her, going in for a kiss.

They started slowly, eyes closed, blocking out anything other than each other. Ryan lost himself in the taste and smell of her. Cassie responded, and it went from there. For how long he couldn't say. He wasn't aware of anything, other than how good she felt and how good she was going to feel, until suddenly she was pushing against his chest. He ignored it for one beat, maybe two at most. It was part of the game – her resisting, then relenting – but this time she kept pushing, hard, the heel of her hand growing more solid and insistent against him. The pressure brought Ryan to his senses. He became aware that she was twisting her face away from him. It took another second or two for him to register that Cassie was crying.

He stopped and climbed awkwardly off her. 'Hey.' She pushed herself upright and pulled her top down, all the while gulping down tears. In the fug of his confusion, Ryan sat limply next to her, like a stupid prick, which was precisely what he was. Cassie kept crying, not prettily, but with big, messy sobs. Ryan zipped up his jeans, in discomfort and dismay. What the fuck was wrong with her? She smeared tears across her face with her hand, wrecking her make-up, still refusing to meet his eye. Finally he was able to say, 'What's wrong? I thought you were okay.' She shook her head. Well, you could have fooled him. He wished she'd stop with the crying. It was beginning to make him feel bad. Had he got it wrong? How the hell was he supposed to know? She sent him so many conflicting bloody signals!

At last she spoke, her voice all cloggy with tears. 'I shouldn't have come tonight. I'm just not in the mood.' She lifted up the hem of her top, revealing a smooth, taut flash of skin, and wiped her face. 'I'm sorry,' she said.

He put his arm round her. 'Hey, it's okay. It is – really, it's okay.' He patted her. 'Are you okay now?'

Given that she'd stopped crying and he'd stopped trying to get into her pants, he expected her to say 'yes'. She didn't. Instead she started gushing words, stuff about her family and her mum, and about being adopted, which was news to Ryan. Not that it bothered him who her parents were. And there was a lot of other stuff, about drugs and being neglected, and how she was having some really weird dreams about being a baby; something about someone cuddling her and singing nursery rhymes to her and, he could have sworn, something about Justin Timberlake?

Ryan kept his opinions to himself, but in his experience, dreams didn't make sense; that was the point of them. His dreams were full of scary shit – falling off cliffs, zombies with worms pouring out of their mouths, turning up to work stark-bollock-naked – more nightmares than dreams really. The sound of Cassie's distress reminded him that he was supposed to be listening to her. So he did, but it didn't help him make sense of what she was saying.

Eventually the words dried up and they sat in silence, with Ryan trying his best to make her feel better. This consisted of him telling Cassie how lovely she was, despite the mascara streaked all over her face and her top. It was true. Even in the dim, stuffy confines of the car, with her features smudgy with sadness, she was still hot. Ryan stroked her shoulder, running his fingers a little further down her bare arm each time, and she leant into him. It felt good to be the one protecting her. He liked that she was relying on him, for a change. She was normally so bloody independent, and bolshie. His fingertips slid further down her arm, feeling her softness. It was so different from his roughness. He could feel the tiny hairs on the surface of her skin under his fingertips. His cock stiffened. The thought of covering her completely with his body, shielding her from everything that might hurt her, made him hard.

'I want to go home.' Her voice filled the car, clear and strong, Cassie-like once again. He jumped, jerking his body away from hers, but it was too late. She stared at him. 'Now! Ryan.'

Busted.

'Wait, Cassie, I didn't mean—' He didn't get to finish his sentence because, in the blink of an eye, she yanked open her door and climbed out. He thought she was joking, making her point, but no, she slammed the door and started walking away – long, quick strides. Still Ryan sat there, expecting her to stop and turn round. But no, she kept going, away into the night. Shit, she was pig-headed. He scrambled out of the car and shouted, 'Don't be stupid, Cassie. Wait. I'll give you a lift home.'

She didn't even break stride. She was now merely a shape fading away into the darkness.

Ryan scrambled back into the driver's seat, fired up the engine and set off after her. He was alongside her in seconds, but she didn't even glance in his direction, just kept walking, forcing him to slow to a crawl. 'Cassie!' Nothing. 'Cassie. Don't be so fucking ridiculous. Get in.' She ignored him. Christ, she was annoying. He must have lost concentration, because there was a sudden horrible scraping noise, his wheel trim grating against the kerb. Fuck her. Let her walk home on her own. It would do her good. He put his foot down. She was such a pain in the arse.

And yet he couldn't just drive away. He checked in his rear-view mirror.

There she was, head held high, walking along the unlit road, not bothered in the slightest that it was dark and late. There wasn't a soul around, and the bushes from the allotments spilled out over the pavement, creating a weird kind of tunnel that shifted and shivered in the wind. It all added nicely to the slasher-movie vibe. It was, actually, the perfect place to jump someone – especially some fucking irritating girl, who hadn't even the presence of mind to get her phone out and put her torch on.

Ryan slowed and watched Cassie, feeling furious and protective in equal measure. Suddenly he became conscious that there *was* another soul around. There was a figure further back up the road, walking a few metres behind Cassie. The figure was too far away to see clearly, too far away to pose any kind of threat, but close enough to make Ryan sit up and concentrate.

At the junction with the main road he stopped the car.

He watched Cassie in his mirror as she walked towards the lit street – back to civilisation and safety. The figure kept coming as well, not gaining on her, but not turning off, either. Still Ryan waited, wanting – despite his all-round pissed-offness – to check that Cassie was okay, before he left her to her own stubborn devices. She came alongside the car, studiously refused to acknowledge his presence and turned right towards the High Street.

Sod her! Ryan indicated left. He had to wait as a couple of cars came past, but even after they'd gone he hesitated, wanting to be absolutely certain Cassie was safe.

His last view was of the figure, crossing over the road and taking a left at the junction, slouching away, hands in pockets, head down, walking in the opposite direction to Cassie.

Not a threat after all.

Just a woman in jeans and a hoodie.

*

So Cassidie was no better than anyone else. That was a surprise and, if Leah was honest, a bit of a disappointment. You'd have thought she'd have turned out better. Surely that was the whole point of adoption: taking bad kids and turning them into good people.

She'd followed them from the hotel after their shift finished. At first she thought she was going lose them, because she was on foot – she hadn't factored in the boyfriend's car – but, as luck would have it, they only drove round the corner into a car park near some allotments. No other cars around. No houses. No people. No risk of being seen. It was almost as if the lad was helping her – though, in truth, he was just helping himself.

She shifted from foot to foot and watched as the windows of the car steamed up.

Giving it out in the back of cars. Not classy, Cassidie. Not classy at all.

And the lad with the Golf wasn't the only one sniffing around Cassidie. There was also the posh-looking twat of a waiter who worked with her at the hotel. The waiter had proved to be another inadvertent little helper. His addiction to selfies and his lack of privacy settings had been very helpful. It was amazing what you could find out about people, without having to leave your bedroom, once you had a name and a face. His feed had been very useful; lots of photos, including a few taken at the hotel, his arm slung round Cassidie. She really was in demand!

Cassidie.

Smiling. Healthy. Beautiful. Tall. Strong. White teeth and glowing skin. A grown-up face with the same halo of hair. A stranger who was unnervingly familiar. The photos of Cassidie had made Leah feel...well, just feel. And that was a rare sensation, rare and strong enough to drag her all this way and make her go to all this trouble.

The car door suddenly opened and the light pinged on.

Leah stepped back into the dark space created by the overhanging trees, making sure she couldn't be seen. But she needn't have worried. Cassidie was in no mood for taking in her surroundings. She slammed the door with a thwack and stormed off.

A ruck. At least it showed that Cassidie had a backbone. And a quite stunning level of stupidity – making herself so vulnerable. It was a quiet, lonely, out-of-the-way spot. Not well lit. Not overlooked. Not the type of place to go waltzing off on your own. Which was precisely what Cassidie was doing: walking away into the darkness with her big, definite, *there's no way I'm coming back and apologising to you, you useless piece of shit* strides.

Leah counted slowly to five, then followed her, at a 'safe' distance.

The lad was persistent. He didn't give up without a fight. He drove slowly alongside Cassidie, trying to coax her back into the car, but she was having none of it. After a few minutes he gave up, obviously pissed off with her. He floored the accelerator and roared off.

Now it was just the two of them, walking down the eerily quiet street, keeping pace. No footsteps. No heavy breathing. Nothing sinister. Simply two figures in the dark.

Cassidie did not look round. She had no reason to. The lights of the main road drew closer and their time together dwindled. Soon they would be back where the real people lived.

At the crossroads Cassidie turned right.

Leah turned left.

Chapter 15

SHE WAS an idiot, thinking Ryan would have any answers, or even any interest in what was going on. She knew full well that he was only interested in one thing. She needed to talk to Erin, her little sister. She was the only one who would listen and understand.

Erin was where she always was, in her room, standing at the big drawing easel that her dad had snaffled from his office for her. She put down her pencil and covered her work with a piece of paper when Cassie knocked at her door.

'Can I come in?'

Erin smiled. 'Course. Work all right?'

'Yeah.'

'Ryan all right?' Cassie shrugged. 'So...what's up?'

'It's this stuff about my adoption.'

Erin moved away from her easel and sat, cross-legged, on her bed.

Cassie came into the room, choosing to perch on the windowsill rather than sit too close. She was too agitated to settle. 'What Mum and Dad said.'

'Yeah?'

'Well, it doesn't square with what I've been...remembering.'

Erin looked up, at that. 'I thought you couldn't remember much from when you were little.'

Cassie rubbed her eyes and Erin noticed how tired her sister looked. 'I didn't, before. Now I am. It's coming back to me in dribs and drabs.'

Erin leant forward. 'So what are you remembering? Bad stuff?'

Cassie took a breath. 'Well, no; some is, some isn't. It's all really jumbled up. It's kinda upsetting, but some of my memories are okay. In them someone is being nice to me. And I don't feel unhappy. Sometimes I almost feel...' she looked down, feeling stupid saying it out loud, 'loved – or at least looked after.'

'Well, that's possible, isn't it? Just cos she had to give you up doesn't mean she didn't love you.' Erin's view of the world sometimes floored Cassie. She seemed so much older than thirteen. 'Mum and Dad said that your birth mum couldn't cope, not that she didn't want you.'

'But you weren't there when they talked about why I was taken off her. It was far worse than they'd let on. It sounds like she was as good as an alcoholic. And there were drugs as well.' Erin didn't flinch. 'Erin, she was in trouble with the police. The place was some sort of dosshouse.'

'So? She could've still loved you.' Erin was trying, as she always did, to make Cassie feel better.

'So? So I'm confused. Why am I having these dreams where someone is taking care of me, if she really neglected me as much as they say she did?'

'Dreams?' Erin asked.

'Dreams, memories...what difference does it make?' Cassie pushed herself away from the sill and started pacing round Erin's room. She knew full well what her sister was getting at, but they felt so real. She waited for her response, genuinely needing her advice, while Erin sat, like a slimline Buddha on her bed, composing her answer. Cassie could see her concentration in the way she was biting her bottom lip, chewing over the problem. Careful, that's what her little sister was; a person full of care.

'Why not just ask Mum and Dad?' Erin said at last. She was still thirteen at heart.

'Because I'm not sure they're telling me the truth,' Cassie replied.

Chapter 16

'SO, WAS she mentally ill or just an addict?' Cassie lobbed this at her mother's back the following morning, as Grace stood waiting for the toast to pop up.

Grace spun round. 'She wasn't an addict!'

'You made her sound like one.' Cassie rested her elbows on the counter and waited for more.

'I'm sorry if that's what you heard, but that's not what we said. What we said was that she was a troubled soul – someone who was struggling to cope. She fell in with a bad crowd, things escalated, got out of control. Whether she was ever diagnosed with an actual medical condition or an addiction problem, I'm not sure,' Grace said.

'How can you *not* know? Surely that's the type of thing you'd want to know before you adopted a child? I can't believe you adopted me, not knowing if my biological mum was clinically depressed, a psycho, a user or just phenomenally weak-willed and self-centred.'

'Oh, Cassie.' Grace took a step towards her daughter, but Cassie swayed away, warding her off. Grace persevered. 'This is exactly why it does no earthly good dwelling on these things. There are questions we simply can't answer – no one can. I'm sorry. I do know how hard this must be for you.' Cassie stared at her mother. Grace tried again.

'If it helps, I don't think she can have had a diagnosed condition; they would have had to disclose it. Is that what's worrying you? That you might have inherited some...' Grace stuttered, searching for a less frightening word, 'sort of problem from her?'

Of course it was, but it wasn't as simple as that. 'Kind of.'

'But, Cassie, there's no sign of anything like that, is there? And there never has been. Up until a fortnight ago none of this mattered. It never has. And it still doesn't now. It's never made the slightest difference to you, or to me or your dad, or the rest of the family. It was a long time ago. It's the past.' Grace so desperately wanted this to be true, for all their sakes. 'I'm concerned that if you keep thinking about this, stressing about it, it's going to really upset you, make you worry about things that you don't have to worry about.'

Cassie seemed to give this some real thought. Grace studied her, watching the battle going on inside her daughter, praying – actually praying – for her to regain her footing.

She didn't. 'I can't let it go. It won't let me let it go.' Cassie pulled her nightshirt down over her knees, distorting the picture on the front. Mickey Mouse morphed into a ghoul. 'I've been dreaming. About her. About my birth mum.'

Grace's heart pinched. 'Go on.'

'Well, just that. I've been having dreams about being little. Really vivid ones. I can see a house, and some of the rooms. And there's someone with me in my dreams. I never see them, but I know they're there – they're always there.'

Grace disguised her concern, poorly. Anxiety made her voice tight. 'And what happens in these dreams?'

'Different things.'

Grace almost couldn't bring herself to ask. 'What sort of things?'

'Nothing bad. Not really. In fact that's what's odd. In most of them I'm okay. In some of them I'm happy, playing or dancing, or doing normal stuff. Nothing weird. And even when I'm not, this person who's with me looks after me. They protect me. She protects me.'

'Oh, Cassie! You think it's your mum?'

'Yes.'

Grace walked around the kitchen island and stood beside Cassie. 'It's not.'

Cassie flared. 'How do you know?'

'It's Jane. It must be Jane you're remembering, your foster mum.'

'Why must it be?' Cassie's voice rose.

'Because Jane was lovely. I'm guessing all this talk about your adoption has stirred up some old memories – memories you didn't realise you had. Jane was a truly kind, generous lady and she looked after you really well. For the short space of time she had you, she loved you.'

'Oh.' Cassie suddenly felt like crying. She let Grace put her arms round her and hug her. It was all so bloody confusing. Her mum smelt of deodorant and toast. Cassie closed her eyes and, in an instant, slipped straight into another embrace, less fragrant, more urgent, more bony. She opened her eyes, freaked out, her heart thumping in her ears. She was still in her kitchen, with her face pressed against her mum's shoulder, and yet a second ago she had been somewhere else entirely. She was scared. It was as if this thing from the past was insisting it must not be forgotten. She wriggled free from Grace's embrace, too overwhelmed to explain, and fled.

Up in her room, Erin was sitting on the edge of her bed, in her uniform, all ready for school, needing her breakfast, forgotten. She could hear her sister and mum talking in the kitchen. She knew exactly what it was about. The drama about Cassie's adoption, it wasn't going away; in fact it seemed to be getting worse. Cassie's voice rose, getting louder, higher and more distraught.

Erin hated it when there was any upset, even when it was about petty stuff, and this wasn't petty stuff. Any disagreement, no matter how small, made her tense. She would feel the ripples of hurt and resentment shivering through the house for days after any row. In the kitchen below, Cassie's voice hitched up another notch. Erin heard her mother speaking slowly and carefully in response, the same low, placating murmur of compromise and understanding that she used whenever there was trouble. After five more minutes of Cassie's indignation and Grace's composed calm, it went quiet. That was somehow worse. Erin waited, hoping for a sign that things had returned to normal – the radio going on or the sound of the fridge being opened – but there was nothing. Another minute and Cassie's footsteps sounded on the stairs. As she crossed the landing she glanced in at Erin. She looked upset. She shook her head as she passed, indicating that whatever had been said hadn't helped.

With the quiver of her sister's distress still resonating inside her, Erin went downstairs. As she entered the kitchen, Grace looked up from her uneaten breakfast and smiled, brightly. 'Do you want me to put a couple of slices in for you?' Just a normal everyday morning then, that's how they were going to play it.

'Yeah. Thanks.' Erin poured herself a juice and sat at the counter, in the seat that her sister had vacated.

Grace picked up a dishcloth and wiped the surfaces. 'All sorted for school?'

'Yes,' she mumbled. She relented when she saw the sag in her mum's determinedly sunny smile. 'I've got an extra art session tonight, so I'll be a bit late home.'

'That's fine.' Grace busied herself taking Erin's toast out of the toaster and passing her the spread and the Marmite. Neither of them turned round at the sound of Cassie crashing down the stairs, across the hall and out of the house on her way to college. There was no 'goodbye' for either of them. The reverberation of her departure took a few seconds to settle.

'Is everything all right?' Erin asked.

'Yes. Of course,' Grace lied. Erin looked at mother, questioning her with the slightest lift of her eyebrows. Grace smiled even more concertedly. 'You mean Cassie and this business about her adoption?' Of course Erin meant that; what else would she be talking about? 'It's fine. She's just a bit unsettled at the moment. It really isn't anything for you to worry about. Honestly it isn't. You know how Cassie gets sometimes – all worked up over things. And before you start worrying about us, we're fine with her asking, we really are. It's natural.' To Erin it felt like a prepared speech. Not a very good one. Grace glanced at her phone. 'I'm sorry, love. I'd best get off. I'll see you later. Have a good day.' As she went out she kissed Erin's cheek clumsily.

Erin climbed off her stool and walked across the kitchen. She tilted her plate and watched her toast slide into the bin on top of her mother's discarded breakfast. No one seemed in the mood for eating. The kitchen clock showed 8.10 a.m.

The front door banged shut for the second time that morning.

She stepped back, far enough away from the window not to be seen, but still close enough to see out. She watched her mum toss her briefcase and jacket into the front of the car, climb in and pull the seatbelt across herself. Grace sat for a couple of seconds, doing nothing, staring at the house as if it had the answer. Then her lips starting moving. For a second Erin thought her mum was praying. She did sometimes, when she thought no one was looking, little whispers under her breath of thankfulness at mealtimes and family get-togethers, or muttered invocations for patience when Cassie, or her dad, was being irritating. But through the open window Erin heard the dial tone reverberating on the hands-free. She took another step backwards, wanting to hear, but not be seen.

Grace's voice was distorted, but amplified. 'Hi, sorry, I know you're driving, but have you got a minute. It's Cassie.' She was calling Tom, not God.

It was impossible to make out her dad's response.

Grace went on. 'We've had another conversation. She's getting herself very worked up.' She paused, listening. 'But what I'm saying is that this isn't going to go away on its own. All the talking in the world isn't going to satisfy her; if anything, I think it's just making things worse. She can sense that we're not being straight with her, I can hear it in her voice. We're going to have to do more than talk.'

Again her dad's reaction was unintelligible.

Her mum's next comment was a hesitant one. 'I was going to tell you before, but I didn't get the chance... I've been in touch with the Adoption Service. I think the more we know, the better. They've not come back to me yet.' There was a pause. 'Tom?'

Whatever her dad said, it was short and to the point.

Grace sounded defeated when she replied, 'Okay. We'll talk about it later, when we've both got more time.' She disconnected the call. She sat for a moment, as if gathering her strength. After a few moments of absolute stillness she started the car, reversed off the run-up and drove away, leaving Erin fearful of what came next.

Chapter 17

THE SQUARE in front of the college was busy with students and parents, but Leah still felt self-conscious. She slid her hands into the pockets of her hoodie, creating an ineffective but reassuring barrier in front of her thin body. She didn't fit in. Her clothes, her hair, her face, that taint of otherness that she carried in her skin, all marked her out. She knew they could detect it, like dog shit on the soles of their shoes. A number of the smartly dressed mothers glanced at her, their eyes revealing their surprise that someone *like her* should be present at a college open day. Leah stared back into their judgement, flatly, defiantly, and most of them looked away, embarrassed to be caught out. They would assume that she was staff – a cleaner or a cook – let them, it was as good an alibi as any. She had her reasons for being there, more personal than theirs and darker, to be sure, but no less valid.

She was family.

Blood was blood.

She had as much right as any of them.

Leah moved through the crowd, heading towards the benches under the trees on the far side of the square. She chose the one with the two nervy-looking teenage girls sitting on it. They stopped chatting, got up and moved away the second she approached – just as she'd intended. She sat, alone and largely ignored, which was what she wanted, watching the swirl of activity with disgust. Most of the kids were loud, greeting their mates like long-lost relatives, shouting out, hugging, pretending to be *super*-interested in each other's news. The girls shimmered and flicked their hair with a kind of weird excitement and the boys strolled and sauntered. They were arrogant shits, all of them. There were a few quieter kids, nerds with hunched shoulders and pained expressions, but they were of no interest to her. She knew exactly who she was looking for – a confident girl, with a halo of hair.

It was probably a waste of time. She knew the odds of spotting Cassidie were close to zero. It would be down to luck, and Leah knew that she wasn't lucky, but she'd wanted to come. It was another piece in the jigsaw of Cassidie's new life.

The square was quietening down as the students disappeared inside, ready to take the next steps on their smooth, straight paths to success. There was still no sign of Cassidie, but she was prepared to wait. She was good at waiting. She was getting plenty of practice. It made her smile, briefly and sourly, to think that she was only there courtesy of the interfering social worker. It was a safe bet this wasn't quite what he'd had in mind when he'd contacted her.

It had started with a voicemail, which, of course, she ignored. Nothing good ever came from a call from Social Services, especially one out of the blue. But they kept on at her: more messages, the same old shit, but this time with a persistent bastard running the show. She finally picked up, out of sheer irritation. That and the faint but familiar anxiety about their power to screw with her life.

It had been a short conversation.

The social worker had been thrown by her sudden, barked 'What?', but he regrouped and stumbled on, coming out with the same insincere spiel they all peddled. He asked her how she was getting on or, to use his word, 'coping' – she said fine. He wondered aloud how things were going 'on the housing front', trying to find out where she was living – she didn't tell him. He fished for clues as to what she was doing with herself – again, none of his sodding business. She waited for him to ask about her health, meaning her compulsions and her anger issues, but he didn't dare. Eventually he ran out of questions, only then did he divulge his real reason for hassling her.

Cassidie.

Cassidie had starting asking about her birth family.

She could hear the bloke's breathing in the dark space that her lack of response had created. She had no intention of helping him out. He could choke on his request, for all she cared. 'We were wondering if you might be willing to help us update the information we have on file.'

It was always 'we', never 'I'. Never them, always someone else.

'No.'

'It's just – she wants to know more about her background and we—'

Leah cut him off. 'I said "No"! Not interested. Don't contact me again.'

She'd ended the call and stood with the phone in her hand, stalled by his request. A kid carved past her on a skateboard, missing her by a sliver. She watched him fly along the pavement, slam to a stop outside the shop and jump off.

After all this time.

She'd started walking again, eyes down, skirting round the abandoned skateboard and the smears of dog shit that patterned the pavement, her pulse rapid and uncomfortable. She walked slowly at first, then more quickly, picking up speed.

So Cassidie was finally asking about her past.

About fucking time.

*

Back in the flat, she'd stared at her phone screen.

The social worker hadn't been lying. The Facebook page was proof of that. There it was, in black and white, and colour, a shout out for information that had been shared, and shared, and shared again. As Leah read the appeal, the words punched small, deep holes into her heart, but her expression didn't change. She was good at maintaining a blank expression, it was her default setting: say nothing, reveal nothing, feel nothing. It was better that way. But these words weren't nothing, they were the past coming back to attack her. As she'd read Cassidie's oh-so-polite appeal for information, an old, but still-fertile rage had germinated inside her.

So Cassidie was ready now, was she?

After all this time, she'd finally started asking questions.

It had taken her fucking long enough.

There were photos alongside the words. Not many, but enough. Leah studied them. Cassidie all grown-up. Seventeen, but looking older. A young woman, not a child. Tall and strong. Smooth, flawless skin, a face dominated by clear eyes and an easy smile. Even then, based on only a handful of small images, Leah had been able to tell that Cassidie was a confident girl, one who walked with her head held high and looked people full in the face. A girl who was shame-free.

Cassidie had made it to the other side.

She'd turned into a healthy, happy, normal person.

She'd turned into a complete stranger.

Leah had dropped her phone onto the sofa and walked over to the window.

The sun was out, the view clear and brutal. Below – the concrete pathways and the patches of brown grass that littered the estate; beyond – the grey flats, red-brick houses and a mess of roads; and in the far distance – the half-built glass-and-steel towers of central Manchester. She leant her head against the window and closed her eyes, imagining the drop on the other side. It gave her a welcome rush of adrenaline. She pressed, hard, bone against glass, both unyielding. The pain radiated across her forehead into her skull. It felt good. She pressed harder. It hurt more. She knew she should stop doing it. She made herself move back a fraction, losing contact with the glass. With her eyes shut, the dizziness was disorientating. The temptation was strong, but she resisted it. This is what happened when she started thinking. It did no good. She turned, picked up her phone, rammed it into her back pocket, grabbed her jacket and made it as far as the hall. Then she turned and ran the eight, short strides back to the window.

One sharp, hard bang.

Forehead to glass.

The pain vented the pressure.

That had been the beginning.

Of course the social worker's intention had been to get information *from* her, not give it *to* her. But once the interfering bastard had called, it was out of his hands and into hers, for a change. Social media had provided the rest. The hotel had come courtesy of Cassidie's waiter friend Freddie; Cassidie's college Leah had identified from the badge on her prissy blazer on a Facebook photo; the date of the Open Day had been plastered all over the college website.

It was all useful information – from which Leah was slowly but surely creating a picture of the new world that Cassidie now inhabited. There were still a lot of gaps, but she had hopes that today's visit would provide a few more of the missing pieces.

In contrast to Cassie's low-rent waitressing job and grubbing around on the back seat of cars, the evidence from the college pointed to a world of tree-lined streets and double-parked 4x4s. She should have known that Cassidie was only slumming it at the hotel. This was her real existence: a polite, middle-class universe where seventeen-year-olds were treated like little kids, ferried around by their 'mummies' and kept in school. Where they were protected and pampered and provided with the latest phones and bags and shoes – and anything else they asked for. A world of the 'haves' and 'want mores'.

The bitter little creature that had being growing inside Leah ever since she'd spoken to the social worker stretched and pushed its sharp fingers up between her ribs. She sat on the bench and studied the scene in front of her, silently feeding the creature titbits of information that fuelled rather than sated its growing hunger.

'Cass, wait! Can I get that book off you?'

Leah hadn't realised the buildings behind her were part of the college as well. She dipped her head.

'Yeah, sure.' Cassidie's voice was close. The accent born of a different upbringing. Leah didn't turn round. There was a pause – the book exchange? – then footsteps. Cassidie passed along the path in front of the bench, within touching distance.

Leah kept her eyes down, letting her hair fall down to mask her face. She glimpsed black skinny jeans and good trainers. Then Cassidie was past. Leah raised her head and watched her cross the square and head towards the college entrance. Just another student. But not. The hair was the clincher. The halo. It was definitely Cassidie.

Leah waited for her to be swallowed up by the building, where she couldn't follow, but Cassidie didn't head inside. She veered to the left and went to sit on the low wall that ran in a curve around the front of the college. Cassidie was facing Leah, looking straight at her, looking straight through her.

The observer and the observed.

A fourteen-year gap separated them. It felt like a hundred. Enough time to blank it all out, but never forget. Plenty of time to imagine, but to never know. And yet there she was, thirty feet away, flesh and blood. Real. Reachable. Not that Leah had any intention of reaching out to her. None whatsoever. This was a reconnaissance exercise, not a reunion. That would come later, when she'd made up her mind about what she was going to do and, more importantly, how she was going do it.

For five, maybe ten minutes Leah watched Cassidie as she messed with her hair and rooted around in her bag. She watched Cassidie check her phone repeatedly, and say 'Hi' to a couple of lads, and not once during that time did Cassidie seem to register her presence. She was invisible. Irrelevant. For now.

A group of Cassidie's friends finally emerged from the main building and they set off together, walking away from college, laughing and chatting.

Leah waited a few seconds, then got to her feet.

Then she followed Cassidie – at a 'safe' distance – all the way home.

Chapter 18

LEAH WASN'T surprised by how nice Cassidie's house was – how big, how pretty, how much space and greenery and light there was. It exactly suited this reborn, alien creature who used to be Cassidie.

She was beautiful.

Her house was beautiful

Her life was probably fucking beautiful.

It all added up.

Cassidie let herself in and banged the front door shut. Cassidie on the inside, Leah on the outside. Leah counted the blips of the alarm. You never knew what might be useful.

Then nothing. No signs of activity at all. The house stared back at her blankly, challenging her to state her business or piss off out of there. She had no excuse, after all, for hanging around the leafy suburbs. It looked suspicious – like she was up to no good. But hang around she did, hidden in the passageway between the two massive houses that faced Cassidie's lovely detached home. It helped that it was so quiet. Apart from the distant sound of someone cutting a hedge, it was like a ghost town. There was nothing to see, no one else around, but that was good. It meant there was less chance of her being spotted and questioned. When her phone suddenly beeped, it sounded way too loud. She read Naz's message, but didn't respond. She switched it to silent after that, just to be on the safe side.

Leah leant back against the wall. She was prepared to wait for as long as it took. In her notes they always described her as impulsive, impatient, someone who was easily distracted, who gave up easily – but they were wrong. She'd just never had anything to concentrate on or care about before. Now she had. She shifted her position, scratched at the scars on her left hand and carried on watching.

And her patience eventually paid off, with the arrival back home of not one parent, but two.

'The mother' got back first.

A five-second glimpse was all Leah got, but it was enough. The shocking black skin against the smudged colours of the garden. The strong profile. The pronounced lift of her chin. The stature. The presence. The long, striding walk. It was less an image than a deep, indelible impression of grace and confidence. She was obviously a total bitch. The physical reality of 'the mother' brought up bile. It filled Leah's mouth with sourness.

Ten minutes later 'the father' arrived.

She watched his car turn into the driveway and park. Him she saw more of. He got out, stretched his back and turned away from the house towards the road for second or two. It was as if he was preening, just for her. He was one of those trendy business types in a smart suit with a stupid, splashy tie. His hair was too long for his age, touching his collar – an attempt to hang on to his youth, which failed. She guessed he was in his forties; dark-framed specs, a fucking man-bag to complete the image. He was obviously a total wanker.

The 'parents' and their 'daughter' – all home safe and sound together. Such a happy family.

The creature in Leah's gut shifted. She slumped back against the wall, feeling tired out. Stick or twist. Something deep inside her told her to stick it out. The evening wasn't anywhere near over yet.

So much for her having no stamina.

The council of peace took place in the lounge. Grace gathered them together as soon as Tom got in from work. He didn't even have time to change out of his suit, though he eased off his shoes and pulled off his tie in a bid to feel more comfortable and look more dad-like. He chose the big chair in the corner and sat, wrapping and unwrapping his tie round his hand like a silk knuckle-duster, a repetitive, nervous gesture. Erin offered to step out again, but Grace shook her head. 'No, darling, this affects you as well – we want you to stay. As long as that's okay with your sister.' Cassie nodded.

Tom stilled his hands and cleared his throat. 'Your mum and I have been talking about the questions you have about your adoption. We know how much it's been on your mind recently.' He took a breath. 'What we told you was the truth, as far as we know it. We're sorry; we should've shared more of it with you – with both of you – before now. I suppose we didn't because we wanted to protect you. And, in all honesty, we didn't realise you really wanted to know the details.'

Cassie shifted in her seat, as if she was about to say something, so Tom picked up the pace.

'But now, obviously, you do. And that's completely understandable. So we were wondering if it would help if we told you more about Jane, your foster mum, and about what happened in those early few weeks when we first met you. Mum says you've been having dreams about her?'

Cassie made a noise, which Tom took as assent. Erin wasn't so sure.

'She was a very experienced foster carer. She looked after a lot of kids, over a lot of years. She was a motherly sort of person. Well suited

118

to her job. She really helped us get to know you at the start, kind of introduced us to you. Made it all less stressful, for everyone. They lived over in Stockport. She, her husband and their daughter. She must have packed it in by now, given her age, but if you think it would help, we could try to contact her. We don't have her an up-to-date phone number or address for her any more, but we could try getting back in touch with Social Services and see if they can arrange something. They might be able to track her down. Do you think you might want that?' Tom seemed to lose momentum as he spoke. 'You know...to have the chance to talk to someone else about your adoption? And about what you were like, before we came on the scene?'

Grace and Tom looked expectantly at Cassie. She nodded. 'Yeah, I suppose that might be useful.' There was a beat. 'And while you're talking to them about Jane you can ask them about my biological mother.'

Tom blinked and looked at Grace. 'Is that what you *really* want?'

'Yes.' Cassie sat up straighter on the sofa, to underline her seriousness. 'It isn't anything to do with not feeling part of this family.' At this, she glanced at Erin. 'I do. I love you all. You know that. But I want to know more about her. Can you understand that?' She did want them to understand. She really wasn't doing this to hurt them.

Tom pulled the tie free from his fist, then started slowly rewinding it around his knuckles again. Erin focused on the way the pattern changed as he worried away at it. 'But, Cassie, what are you hoping to discover?'

Cassie was already leaning forward, ready to argue her point. 'I just want to know what happened to her.'

'And if she's still around, what then?' Grace asked. 'Would you want to contact her, write to her? Meet her?' The dark red flush on her neck belied the calm tone of her voice.

'Maybe? I don't know.' The thought of it made Cassie feel vaguely sick.

'That's what's worrying us,' Tom said. Cassie arched even further forward, but he held up his hand. 'Cassie, listen for a minute. We're not saying "No", we're saying let's take this a step at a time. It's not sensible to start on something like this, not knowing what you want out of it and where it might end.'

Grace joined in. 'And there will be processes that need to be followed. A closed adoption is an absolute thing – legally binding. I honestly don't know what the situation is, in terms of contact. It's such a long time since we've had any dealings with the Adoption Service. Why not let me speak to them, explain the situation? They'll know, from experience, what to do and what the outcomes are likely to be. Isn't that sensible? To tread carefully, at least to start with?'

They all looked at Cassie. At last she muttered, 'All right.'

Tom leant over and patted her hand. 'Good girl.' He was too busy meeting Grace's eye to spot that he'd tipped the scales too far.

'I'm not six!' Cassie growled.

Tom began back-pedalling, but it was too late. 'No one said—'

'You can't fob me off with a trip to see some old lady who looked after me for a few months when I was tiny. I want to find *my mum*. It can't be that difficult to understand.' They really didn't get it. It was all just words to put her off.

'Cass!' Tom met her aggression with a hint of his own. He tossed the tie aside in frustration.

Cassie burned brighter. 'No. You don't get to decide this for me. I do.' She stood up and looked down at all three of them. 'It's my life. I've a right to find out about it.' She didn't wait for Grace to reach out to comfort her, or for Tom to argue with her; she simply turned and stalked out of the room. Followed, a few seconds later, by Erin.

Cassie's bedroom door was shut, so Erin had to knock.

'Leave me alone!' Cassie shouted.

'It's me,' Erin answered.

There was a long pause. 'All right. You can come in.'

Erin pushed opened the door. Cassie was rifling through her clothes drawers, bad-temperedly trying on tops. 'Going out?' Erin asked. Ryan! Erin hated Cassie having a boyfriend who took up so much of her time and her attention in general, but what she hated even more was that when the going got tough, she turned to him.

'There's no point staying here, is there?' She yanked off a shirt, without undoing the buttons, and threw it on top of the growing pile on her chair. She pulled a T-shirt over her bra, glanced at the fit, approved of what she saw and flumped down onto the floor, in front of the big mirror that was propped against the wall. She started 'putting on her face'.

Erin stood by the door, uncertain. She desperately wanted to prove to Cassie that she was the only one who understood, the only one who truly cared what she was going through – certainly more than Ryan – but it was hard to break through to her sister when she was in one of her fierce moods, so Erin stayed on the threshold. In the mirror she watched her sister transforming herself from someone familiar into someone barely recognisable; someone harder, more polished and more alien.

'What?' Cassie paused, pencil in hand, one eye heavily rimmed with kohl, the other smaller and naked-looking. Erin was struck by the image and wished for a split second that she had her phone with her, to take a picture. 'Erin! What do you want?' Cassie looked back at her own reflection and continued to submerge herself beneath a palette of well-applied cosmetics.

'I want to help.'

'I don't need your help.'

Erin shrank back from her fierceness, and Cassie noticed. Her hand dropped into her lap. 'Sorry. I shouldn't take it out on you, but they drive me insane.'

'They did say they'd contact Social Services.'

'Yeah, but they don't really want to. You heard them.' Erin made a non-committal noise and Cassie went back to making up her face. 'They want to control everything. Just like always.' She paused and reviewed her handiwork: two slashes of lip-tint and she was done. Then she said something that sent a shiver through Erin. 'Anyway, it might not be up to them.' Cassie picked up her phone, scrolled through it, then held it out to Erin.

Erin came into the room and took it from her sister. She looked at the screen and found herself staring at an old photo. It took her a second to realise what she was seeing. It was an appeal for information about Cassie's birth mum. 'But what are the chances...'

'Well, crap, obviously,' Cassie said dismissively. 'I've had nothing back yet – well, nothing useful – but you never know.'

Erin passed the phone back. The thought of the appeal pinging around cyberspace freaked her out. It seemed such a risky thing to do, so revealing and vulnerable. There was no telling who might reply to it. She was shocked that Cassie had taken things into her own hands so directly, but on reflection, she wasn't really surprised. It was classic Cassie, jumping in, feet first.

Cassie slung on a jacket and grabbed her bag. 'Don't look so worried, Sis. It's a long shot, but she must be out there, somewhere.'

Chapter 19

LEAH WAS tired and needed to piss, but she stuck at her post. It was tedious, but also curiously compulsive to stand in the shadows, watching someone else's life. It was if she was absorbing information through her skin, committing tiny details to memory. The layout of the house and the gardens, the path at the side that perhaps led to a back door, the absence of a dog, the big windows in the roof that must look straight up to the sky: that might be Cassidie's room. And from her vantage point she could just about make out who was who, through the big lounge window. They seemed to be sitting there – doing nothing.

Six days ago she'd known nothing about Cassidie's new life, or at least nothing useful. Now she knew where her college was, what her friends looked like; she had her home address, knew who her parents were, which cars they drove; she knew where Cassidie worked – even who she was screwing, and where.

But it still wasn't enough.

It would never be enough.

There was still a huge gap: the years and years of denied access and ignorance. The thought of it was messing with her head, stirring up emotions that she thought had died long ago, due to wilful neglect.

Thinking again, feeling again, reflecting on the past – it was bad. It never led anywhere good. And yet ever since that first phone call, she'd been unable to stop thinking – and feeling – and hurting. She put her hand to her forehead and pressed.

The door slamming brought her back to the matter in hand.

Cassidie burst out of the house and strode away, her bag bouncing against her hip. Leah could tell by her pace and the set of her shoulders that she was pissed off. For a second she was tempted to let her go, let it all go, leave the past alone, but the creature inside was demanding more, so she pushed herself off from the wall and set off in pursuit.

Cassidie was easy to track, a distinctive rush of colour powering along the morgue-like streets, but she was less easy to keep up with. Leah was breathless by the end of the first road. Cassidie looked dressed up – out to meet her friends? – spending Mummy and Daddy's money, no doubt. Leah could still taste the sourness in her mouth at the thought of 'the mother'. The stuck-up black bitch who had taken Cassidie away from her.

She was so churned up that she momentarily lost sight of Cassidie. She panicked, scanned the street, then saw her on the other side of the main road, heading towards the hotel. She must be off to work? But Cassidie didn't walk up the driveway; instead she went to stand near one of the entrance pillars. Leah spotted a bus stop, the first she'd seen in ages, and went and positioned herself on the stupid little metal ledge that served as a bench.

It was a short wait.

The lad from the Golf appeared in the driveway. In broad daylight he was nothing to look at: scrawny, cropped hair, tattoos, jeans and a plain tee; totally, utterly ignorable, until Leah saw his face when he caught sight of Cassidie. It changed completely. He cracked a full-beam smile, even broke into a jog to get to her and, when he did, put his hands gently on either side of Cassidie's face and cradled her head as he kissed her, his eyes closed. He held Cassidie like she was something precious.

Leah had seen enough.

Cassidie really did have everything.

She set off walking, tired to the marrow of her bones, but ready to start getting back what was rightfully hers.

Chapter 20

IT TOOK Leah nearly two hours to get home, or nearly home. Naz intercepted her outside the shops. He'd been waiting; for how long he didn't say, but it was obvious that he was *not* happy. 'Where the fuck 'ave you been?' She should have replied to his message. She knew better than to ignore him – she had been schooled – but she hadn't wanted to deal with him, not with everything else that was screaming through her brain.

'I'm sorry.' She thought about lying and saying that her phone had died, but she daren't risk it. He always knew. It wasn't worth it. He looked at her, his face dark with frustration, then without another word he stormed off. She didn't know what to do. Follow him, wait, walk away? There was no clear instruction, so she hesitated, standing in the middle of the pavement like an abandoned dog. He got ten paces before he shouted, 'What ya fucking waiting for? Come on!' It was all the invitation she was going to get.

They headed back to her flat. The thought of letting him in filled her with fatigue. In the lift they were silent. She stood one side, he stood the other. There was no tender welcome for her.

They never went to his place. Leah didn't actually know where he lived, or with who, and she'd never asked. Naz liked to have secrets.

He paraded them in front of her, teasing her, trying to provoke her by offering up little snippets of his life: his cash – he always had a fold of notes down his sock or in his back pocket, not that it stopped him taking the odd tenner off her; the deals he was doing, or was going to do; his 'contacts' – names never volunteered; his crew – nicknames only; and his other girls – itemised by their attributes, all more luscious than her own. She never got the whole picture. She suspected there was a family somewhere, maybe even a wife. Kids? It was possible. Ludicrous as it sounded, Leah sometimes wondered if he might still be living at home with his parents. Either way, there was definitely a doting woman somewhere in his life; no guy kept their clothes *that* clean, and she couldn't imagine any of his 'girls' doing his laundry. She'd seen their pictures, the pouting, the lashes, the big tits – they didn't look the type. The meticulous personal hygiene was one of the things that Leah liked about Naz. He kept himself spotless and he always smelt great, despite the places he hung out. He had pride in himself and she liked that. It reflected well on her, even as it overpowered her.

He was still in a mood when they got back to the flat. He crashed around in the small kitchen, flipping open cupboards and drawers, searching for something to eat. She stayed in the front room and listened. He emerged with a packet of biscuits and a can of Coke. Her treats for Friday night. She let it go. He cracked the can open, crashed down on the sofa and started unlacing his trainers, all the while ignoring her. Leah didn't sit down. She was waiting to see which way it would go.

'Quit staring at me.'

'Sorry.' Where else was she supposed to look?

'For fuck's sake!' He started rubbing at the toe of one of his shoes, trying to obliterate some tiny spot; he was obsessive about his trainers. As he rubbed at the offending mark his gestures became more and more exasperated.

'Do you want me to...' she offered. Without warning, he hurled the shoe. It caught her full in the face. It went quiet.

'Stop looking so sodding tragic.'

She blinked and touched her mouth. Her fingers came away sticky. Her lips buzzed with the pain, but she didn't move. She didn't look at him or say anything; she simply stood in the middle of her flat and waited to see what Naz would do next as she surreptitiously wiped the blood off her fingers onto the back of her jeans. She heard him stand up and braced herself, but he walked away, not towards her.

A couple of minutes later he was back. 'Here. You're bleeding.' His voice still carried the crackle of irritation rather than apology, as if the injury was somehow Leah's fault, but there was less anger in it. Still, when he reached out to touch her, she had to concentrate hard on not flinching. 'Head up.' She obeyed him. Gently he dabbed at her split lip with a wad of loo roll. The mood shifted, but she was still wary. 'Babe. I'm sorry, but you know it drives me fucking crazy.' He didn't elaborate on whether it was the blemish on his shoe or Leah herself that had infuriated him.

She let him tend to her, loving and hating every minute of it. When he'd had enough, he kissed her like a child on her cheek and returned to the sofa, clicking on the TV as a signal that it was all over and done with, and that everything was forgiven. He scrolled through the channels and found some sport, leant back, grabbed a biscuit, took a bite and washed it down with a slug of Coke, completely at home.

Leah crossed the room, retrieved the shoe and carried it through to the kitchen; there, she filled the sink with warm water, added washing-up liquid and, with a clean cloth, slowly and very carefully buffed the small mark off the pristine surface of his trainer.

Chapter 21

TOM WAS absent-mindedly scratching his weekend stubble and looking out at the lawn, debating whether he could leave it another week before he had to mow it, when it occurred to him that he had no idea where Elmo was. Stupid name for a dog, but that was creative types for you. Elmo was some sort of expensive cross-breed: a quarter poodle, a quarter spaniel, probably half dachshund, for all he knew. He never listened to the canine conversations at work; there was too much gushing for his taste. He shouldn't be so sniffy. Lettie, one of the young designers, had generously loaned him the love of her life for a couple of days, and for that he was grateful. And it was nice having a dog around. It had lifted the atmosphere in the house – just as Tom had hoped.

Erin was loving it, taking the hound for walks and sitting with him draped across her knee like a fluffy scarf. Cassie had merely scowled and very forcefully expressed her concern that the dog would chew stuff, and that it had better not be her stuff. Tom felt slightly aggrieved at the thought of having to put down his coffee and go looking for Elmo, but he knew he'd better. If the dog was somewhere in the house, that was fine, but if he'd got out in the garden, that wasn't; there were plenty of gaps in the fence that a little scrappy, expensive, much-loved pooch could wriggle through.

He went outside to check. 'Elmo! Elmo?' There was no sign or sound of the animal as he walked around his plot.

They were no further forward with the whole adoption-reboot nightmare. Tom was quite happy that the adoption people's progress had been negligible; the more time it took, surely the more likely it was that Cassie would lose interest and it would all go away. Grace said that when she finally got hold of the right department, it had been like stepping back in time. Gail, their contact, had been courteous and understanding, and helpful in terms of general information, but very unforthcoming about her capacity to actually *do* anything. She'd promised to look into it and, in the meantime, to send them some leaflets. Cassie's response to the news that there was *no news* had been stony silence and an increase in nights out with Ryan, or in with Erin; in fact she seemed keen to be anywhere other than with them. They were peeling apart as a family.

Hence Elmo.

Tom lifted the branches of a few of the bushes, checking for signs of tunnelling, but there was no evidence of any great escape. Where was the stupid mutt? As he straightened up, he could have sworn he heard whimpering. He headed back towards the house to investigate.

Cassie was achy with tiredness. For the past few days she'd felt like she was getting a cold that never came. It was because nothing was happening. Her parents were the main problem. They were doing nothing. No, it was worse than that; they were doing the opposite – they were blocking her, telling her that Social Services *might* be able to help, but it was going to take ages, and she mustn't hold her breath. Apparently the most she could expect was a leaflet. A fucking leaflet! What she wanted was facts; something concrete and true about her past. And the appeal had made no difference at all. All she'd had were a series of sympathising likes and, even weirder, a load of slightly creepy messages from complete strangers who were in *the same position*. And all the while that absolutely nothing was happening, her old life was continuing to bleed into her current life, leading to restless days and broken nights.

The dreams were still stalking her, stepping out of the shadows when she least expected them. They were as vivid and disturbing as ever, and as evocative. She'd tried to make herself believe they were snatches of her time with this Jane woman, like they'd told her to, but that hadn't worked. She'd been so desperate to prove she wasn't losing her marbles that she'd even dug Jane's photo out of the drawer and slept with it under her pillow. It had triggered nothing. The person in her dreams was *not* her foster mum. She didn't know how she could be so certain, but she was.

Cassie closed her eyes against the glare coming through the skylights and felt sleep tug at her. She'd been late back the previous night after a tedious shift at the restaurant and an equally draining session with the ever-horny Ryan. Then this morning the bloody dog that her dad had inexplicably brought home for the weekend had woken her up at 6.30 a.m. with its 'I need a pee' barking.

She lay on her back and let the wooziness win.

She tastes sugar on her lips, scratchy and sweet. Her mouth is full of dough. It's heaven, sticky, stomach-filling heaven. The bag lies on the mattress between them, the cellophane window reassuringly full of small, brown, squishy circles. Plenty to share. And she has to share. That's the rule. There's to be no snatching. She can't take a handful. She can only have one at a time. When it's her turn, she creeps her fingers into the bag very slowly, trying hard to keep the sugar crystals inside, so as not to waste them. If she's good she'll get to lick the bag out at the end, sucking the wrapper to get every last trace of sweetness onto her tongue.

They don't talk. They're too busy eating, chewing in blissful silence. Well, not silence, it's never quiet in their house; through the closed door and down the stairs the phones are, as always, ringing and beeping and singing. She knows to ignore their chorus. They are nothing to do with her.

Her mouth is empty, but she must wait her turn. This is a lesson in anticipation as much as sharing. The nod finally tells her that she can take another one, but as her fingers close round her next lovely, soft, munchable treat, the door crashes open and there's the frightening swish of doggy muscle and meaty breath. He rushes straight at them. Fearing that he's going to get the doughnuts, she grabs the bag, meaning to keep it safe, for both of them. The dog leaps at her face, barking his demands. She is shoved backwards by the weight of him. His nicotine-coloured claws scramble for purchase, scoring red lines into her bare legs and chest. She's too shocked to cry as he snaps at her hands, at her face, in a mad frenzy to get at the bag. But the doughnuts are theirs, not his. She grips the bag in her fist and tries to shield it with her body, determined that he won't have it. She pays the price.

'Get off! You stupid...bastard...dog!' There's a flurry; hands, jaws, barking, snapping, pulling, scrabbling. 'Get down!' It seems to go on for ever. Then the weight is gone. The dog's wet gums and sharp teeth are no longer in her face, but she can feel the cold trails of his slobber on her skin and the sting of the scratches from his razor-sharp nails. She feels shivery. But it's all been in vain. The doughnuts are ruined. The bag is crushed and sodden with dog-slaver. She curls up, clutching it in her fist, trying to block out the sounds of the fight that is taking place right beside her: the snap and snarl of frustration, the cursing, his claws gouging and skittering across the floorboards. A tussle of strength. It stops, finally, with the slam of the door, the scrape of a chair and the heaving, panting breaths of relief. The barking drops from ear-splitting to loud. He batters himself against the door, but it holds. The dog has lost, this time.

It takes her a few seconds to realise that the crying is not coming from her.

*

Tom couldn't find any evidence of the dog, injured or otherwise, downstairs. Where the hell was it? He headed upstairs to check there. No sign. The little beast had to be on the top floor. He hoped to God it hadn't actually damaged anything of Cassie's – that really wouldn't help.

It was as he put his foot on the bottom step that he heard the whimpering again. A pathetic, sad, shaky sound, more like a human baby than a dog. Tom quickened his pace. Cassie's bedroom door was ajar. He walked in, scanning the room for a distressed ball of fur – instead he saw his eldest daughter, curled on her side, crying.

He stopped in the doorway, transfixed by this momentary glimpse of Cassie without her guard up. Her eyes were closed and she seemed to be asleep, but she was definitely not peaceful. She was rubbing her head back and forth against the pillow and her hands were twitching and fluttering as if trying to ward something off. The noise she was making was breathy and snatched. A nightmare.

He stepped forward, intending to go and wake her, gently, but he only got halfway across the room. There was a scrabble of nails and a rush of muscle and fur. He was too slow to react. Elmo shot past him and jumped up onto the bed – right on top of Cassie.

Chapter 22

THE FRIEND request from someone identifying themselves as 'LW' popped up out of the blue. Cassie was chilling in Erin's room at the time, mooching around aimlessly, trying to distract Erin from her homework. 'Look at this.' She passed her phone to her sister. Erin looked at the request silently, the glow of the screen illuminating her face. The bio stated that 'LW' lived in Manchester. The tiny circular profile photo wasn't very informative. The woman in the picture was white – probably. Hair – brown? Age – it was difficult to tell; anything between twenty and forty. The quality of the photo was very poor. They both stared at the request, aware of its potential significance.

'Are you going to accept her?' Erin asked.

'I guess so.'

'It could be a coincidence.' Erin said, though she didn't believe that for one second.

'Could be, but it's not very likely, is it?' Cassie replied. 'Only one way to find out.' She took the phone back from her sister's clammy hand and clicked 'Confirm', then slipped the phone back into her jeans pocket. 'At least it's something.' Cassie's ambivalence was fake. They both knew it. This could be huge. This could be the door into her past. But she downplayed it, changing the subject to her righteous indignation with her parents. 'Did you read that leaflet that came from the Adoption Service? All that crap about "moderated truths". It was a load of—' Cassie's phone pinged.

The girls looked at each other. Surely not?

It was a message from the woman: If u want to know about yr mum contact me.

It was as if she'd been just sitting there, miles away, waiting for Cassie to let her in.

Cassie's stomach contracted. She let the pretence of indifference slip. 'Game on!'

Cassie had looked at the woman's Facebook account a hundred times since that first contact. She wasn't stupid, she knew that the Internet was full of fifty shades of weird: dirty old men who pretended to be teenage girls, and fat sweaty nerds who, with the aid of Photoshop, became hench models. The account was plainly very dodgy. For a start, it was brand-new – the woman's timeline empty. It was obviously just a means to an end, namely a way of contacting her.

But you can't argue with an old-fashioned photograph of a baby and a child and an ugly old mirror. And it *was* the same photograph, there was no doubt about that. Cassie sat and stared at the image for a long time after LW had offered it up as proof. Why would this person have the self-same photo of Cassie and her birth mother in her possession, if she wasn't somehow involved? When Cassie had messaged her and asked how she'd come to have the picture, the woman had ignored the question and instead suggested that they meet up in Oldham to talk. That she'd refused to speak to Cassie on the phone, insisting that all their contact be done via Facebook, and that she wouldn't give her real name was all really suspicious, but there was nothing Cassie could do about that. Was this LW woman cautious, or simply lying through her teeth? There was no way of telling, without meeting her.

Cassie had read and reread her semi-literate messages and wondered. And she'd stared at the profile image and held it next to the old photo over and over again. Was it the same person? Could this woman be her mother? Or was it someone just cruelly messing with her? But if so, why? And how had they got their hands on the photo?

Erin was, of course, completely wigged out by it all. She was absolutely against Cassie going to Oldham, seeing all sorts of dangers in meeting up with a complete stranger whose motives were unclear, and who was being very cagey about who she was and what she knew. And course Erin was right, but that wasn't going to stop Cassie. She had to give it a try. This woman knew things. Cassie had to meet her at least and find out what. And she was taking precautions. They'd agreed to meet in a public place, Ryan was driving her there and she would have her phone with her all the time. Add to that the fact that her defences were well and truly up. What could go wrong? She'd be fine. Or at least she hoped she would. But Erin wasn't in any mood to be placated. Much to Cassie's shock, and surprise, her reticent, nervy little sister had played her blackmail hand coolly and without blinking. She threatened to tell Tom and Grace about everything, unless Cassie let her go with her. Cassie had been secretly impressed.

Now, as they bombed across the M62, Cassie was reassured to have Erin's slight but determined presence in the back of the car. If Ryan was pissed off, having been demoted to chauffeur, that was his problem.

'How much longer?' she asked.

Ryan stared out through the windscreen, scanning the roadside for a junction number. 'Dunno. Half an hour?' He sped up.

Cassie sighed and sat back in her seat. Another hour and she'd get to find out if she was being played or not.

Once on the high street in Oldham, they headed into Subway, as agreed. Cassie was reassured by the familiar sounds and smells. 'You go grab a table and I'll get us a drink,' she commanded Erin. 'I'll message you when we're through.' This to Ryan, who scowled and stumped off.

From her position at the back of the queue, Cassie watched Erin walk self-consciously across to the furthest unoccupied table and slide into a seat. Cassie felt a rush of affection and gratitude for her little sister. She was bricking it, but trying very hard to cover that up. They exchanged a look that said: *Okay, that's stage one completed without any major disasters.* Cassie eventually got served by a woman who looked too old to still be working, but who called her 'duck' and smiled as she passed over her change. Armed with two boiling hot cardboard cups of coffee and two six-inch subs – which she knew they wouldn't eat – she went and sat next to Erin. It was a good vantage point. She could see the door; in fact she could see through the whole wall of glass that fronted the cafe, out onto the street beyond. Now all they had to do was wait.

Their coffee was too hot to drink. The heat radiated through the ridged cardboard of the cup into Cassie's fingers. Erin peeled the lid off her drink and blew on it, like their mum used to do with their hot chocolate when they were little. The girls took it in turns stroking their phone screens back to life, checking the time and looking out for any messages. There were none. Time slowed to a dribble of unfeasibly long minutes.

The counter was busy, a steady stream of people arriving, then departing clutching their bandaged rolls of greasy comfort-food. The queue built and shrank, then grew again, but never disappeared entirely. Cassie felt a mixture of panic and dislocation. She wasn't stupid. She knew it wasn't going to be some happy-clappy reunion like on the TV. She was ninety-nine per cent certain this woman wasn't going to turn out be her real mum. And even if she was, that she wasn't going to walk in, open her arms and beg forgiveness. And what if she did? What difference would it make? She hadn't been forced into giving up her baby by society; she'd been declared unfit. But – and the 'but' was important – that couldn't be the whole truth, could it? Because if her birth mum had been a terrible mother, why did Cassie remember being cared for? Where had her memories of love and affection come from? Her mum and dad were still adamant that it was her foster mum, but they were wrong. Cassie could only vaguely remember being with Jane; all she could conjure up was a fug of food smells and furniture polish. The snatches that had been flooding back in the past few weeks were different, very different. The smells, the images, the feelings, the texture of those memories seemed to be from another place altogether. Knowing that she might, in the next few minutes, either meet her mother or at least find something out about her – or be left sitting there like some pathetic loser – was making her heart race.

People wandered past outside, going about their everyday lives. Cassie watched them, looking out for potentials. On a midweek morning there were plenty of candidates, though very few that she wanted to stop, turn into the cafe and walk towards her. She wondered, when LW finally did arrive, if she would come over to the table first; surely she wouldn't go and join the queue? That'd be awkward. Cassie started stressing about whether she should offer to buy her a drink, but that wouldn't work, because it would leave her having to talk to Erin. And Erin wouldn't cope with that.

Cassie decided that the best thing would be to send Erin up to fetch her a drink. Yeah, that would be a better plan. All of which fussing would be irrelevant, if she didn't show up. But she wasn't *that* late. Cassie wasn't even certain that she'd recognise her when she did, not from the tiny thumbnail picture. And besides, that picture could be – probably was – a fake. It could all be fake. This could be just some cruel hoax. Cassie turned her attention to the people inside the cafe again. Any one of them could be the person playing her, laughing at her for sitting there like a gullible idiot. The corkscrew of her emotions twisted again, replacing hope with anger.

The other girl was a shock.

A nasty one.

It threw Leah off her game.

She'd been building up to this showdown with Cassie for weeks. It had taken huge amounts of time and effort and ingenuity on her part to get this far; time and effort that she couldn't really afford. The stalking, the scheming, the preparing, the imagining – there was a cost to all that investment and emotion, a cost that would have to be repaid.

This meeting was supposed to be Leah's first taste of retribution.

But it looked like her moment, alone at last, with Cassidie was going to be denied her – by *this girl*.

Whoever she was, she was an interfering bitch.

She was like a bad photocopy of Cassidie, paler, less defined, weaker, but oddly like her. She looked too young to be a friend and yet they seemed very close. The bitch-girl was attentive and very anxious, but not for herself, for Cassidie.

The sudden insight into what Leah was looking at struck her hard.

The girl was Cassidie's sister.

That was the only logical explanation.

A sister was not part of the plan. A sister had no right to be there, sitting fussily alongside Cassidie, whispering in her ear, patting her arm. This was nothing to do with her. Why the fuck had Cassidie brought her along? Safety in numbers, moral support, someone to hold her bag and pass the tissues? Cassidie ought to be ashamed of herself. It was pathetic...and it was disrespectful. This was between her and Cassidie. It had nothing to do with this girl. She wasn't family.

Leah watched the pair of them and, with each passing minute, grew more and more incensed. The cafe was small enough that she could hear snippets of their conversation – not that Cassidie was saying much; it was the girl who had verbal diarrhoea. And what she kept saying – kept suggesting – with increasing insistence, in her posh, childish, fucking irritating voice, was that Cassidie should leave, that it wasn't worth it, that *she* wasn't worth it.

The snotty, interfering little skank. How dare she?

Leah's only comfort was that Cassidie seemed to be ignoring her.

She blanked out the girl – she would be dealt with later, when the right opportunity arose – and instead she focused on Cassidie.

Close up, Cassidie was beautiful. Leah wasn't the only one to be struck by it. As people queued for their food she saw how they glanced at her, looked away, then looked back again. It was the type of beauty that made Leah want to scream and rip something to shreds. It was so fucking unfair. Waves of resentment, jealousy and anger rippled through her. For a split second she very nearly gave in to the impulse to leap across the cafe and slap Cassidie's perfect, flawless face. That would get her to wise up.

But of course she didn't.

Leah knew that getting worked up was not good for clear thinking – that if she let her emotions get the better of her, she would lose more than she might gain. So she focused hard and managed to bring herself down one notch, then another and another. It was a struggle, but she managed it. Shallow, regular, slow breaths; that was what worked whenever she was in pain. And this – seeing Cassidie and finding out that there was a bitch-sister in the picture – this was as painful as any kicking she'd ever had. In and out, in and out, through tense lips. They said that she had no self-discipline, but they were wrong. She was stronger than anyone ever gave her credit for. With every minute that passed she felt more stable, more in control.

In contrast, as the time ticked by, Cassidie's composure crumbled. Leah watched and started to see more than just perfection in her face. Beneath the fake calm, messier emotions were bubbling away:

frustration and anger and irritation and, near the end, what looked a lot like disappointment. It was satisfying to watch.

The knowledge that she could have put Cassidie out of her misery easily enough made the experience even sweeter. It felt good to sit and observe and know that she was the cause of all that agitation.

The reappearance of the scrawny boyfriend put an end to it. Surprisingly, he seemed to have more influence than the sister. There was a short debate about what they were going to do, then they all stood up and started getting ready to leave. And that was when – just because she could, and because it had been a very long time since she'd been the one able to toy with someone else's feelings – Leah delayed their departure.

She reached into her pocket and pressed the Call button.

There was a tiny delay, then Cassidie's phone began to ring.

Leah watched her scramble to retrieve her phone, hope blooming on her face. When there was no one there, that hope shrivelled and died.

They left with an awful scraping of chairs and Leah sat alone, content, after all, with the ways things had worked out.

Chapter 23

CASSIE AND Erin got home just after 3 p.m. They both made more noise than was strictly necessary, chucking their shoes into the hall cupboard and opening and closing doors. Cassie couldn't stand the way Erin kept looking at her. It made her want to slap her.

All the way home Cassie's phone had burnt in her hand. She felt such a powerful mix of anger, frustration and profound disappointment that she didn't know what to do with herself. Ryan had dropped them off outside the house, with a look of relief on his face. She'd endured his kiss. Now Erin's pinched, distressed little face seemed to be tracking her from room to room. She couldn't bear it. 'Stop, will ya! I'm fine.' Erin flinched, and Cassie's desire to slap her increased. 'Erin. I mean it, stop trailing around after me like a bloody puppy.'

'Okay.' Erin sat down on the couch, but did nothing other than look more upset than she had any right to.

Cassie snapped, 'I mean it. Just be normal, can't you?' Erin nodded, but Cassie drove her message home. 'Seriously. You have to act normal when Mum and Dad get home. I don't want them knowing anything about today.'

'Okay,' Erin said, but she still looked wobbly.

'I'm not joking, Erin. If you say a word to anyone about today – anyone – I swear I'll never speak to you again. Understand?'

'I said, "Okay".'

'Well, that's okay, isn't it?'

'Yes.'

'Yeah, well, good!' Like little kids all over again. With that agreed, Cassie escaped upstairs to get away from her sister, who she knew would never betray her anyway. In the privacy of her bedroom she sat on her bed, staring at the abandoned call. It had to have been her, so there was a sliver of hope, but Cassie didn't know what to do with it. Why set up a meeting and not show? Why call and not say anything? What was stopping her? Embarrassment? Shame? Cruelty?

Her room was stuffy. She climbed up on her chair, pushed open one of the skylights and poked her head up through the gap. It was as warm outside as in. Not a breath of wind. The roof tiles creaked in the heat. The view hadn't changed since the last time she'd sought sanctuary up there. Whichever direction you looked, there were looping skeins of houses, road after road of different-sized boxes, interspersed with swathes of green and bright patches of colour. Cassie wondered, not for the first time, whether she could somehow lever herself up through the window and onto the roof, but even as she grasped the frame and tried to hoist herself up, she knew it was pointless; she was too heavy. She was stuck, with her head poking through the gap. She very nearly didn't hear her phone ringing. She scrambled clumsily down off the chair to answer it, scraping her arm badly on the window frame in the process. 'Hello,' she stammered.

Silence. It had to be her. Then, 'Sorry.' A female voice, so quiet that Cassie had to strain to hear her.

'Why didn't you come?' Her arm was stinging, the skin raw around her wrist. More silence.

'I couldn't get there.' It wasn't much of an apology.

Cassie wanted to hear contrition, guilt, something that indicated a beating heart at least. 'I sat there for an hour.' More silence or, more accurately, more muffled background noise. She persisted. 'I gave up, came back home when it was obvious that you were gonna be a no-show.'

'Like I said. I'm sorry.' There was a spark there now, a flash of energy and defiance. She didn't sound sorry at all. Cassie held her ground, forcing the woman to say the next words. The silence was fraught. Then, 'Do ya still wanna meet?'

Did she? No. Not if this woman couldn't be arsed to even apologise properly and explain herself. But of course that wasn't what Cassie said. What she said was, 'Yes. I need to talk to you.'

The woman said ''Kay.' Nothing more.

'When?'

'Whenever.' Whoever she was, she was good at pretending to not give a damn.

Cassie ploughed on, feeling like she was begging, and hating it. 'I might be able to come this weekend, but I'll need to sort out a lift. Are you going to turn up this time?'

'Yeah.' It didn't exactly inspire confidence.

'I'll text you then? If I can come. With a time. On this number?' Cassie said.

''Kay.' One syllable. That's all she was prepared to offer.

'You'll text back?'

'Yeah.'

Cassie was just about to end the call when the woman said, quietly, but very clearly, 'This time – come on your own.'

Chapter 24

GAIL FROM the Adoption Service rang Grace at work. She apologised for the delay in getting back to them. 'But I've finally been able to find out a little bit, with regards to your enquiries. Is now a good time to talk?'

'Yes, of course,' Grace said. It wasn't, but she was hardly going to say that.

'Well, I've had some success with the foster family, in terms of information, rather than direct contact,' she added hastily. 'Less so with the birth family.' Grace waited. 'Jane Marshall is, I'm afraid, deceased.' It was such oddly formal phrasing. 'She died five years ago. Heart problems, I believe. She carried on fostering for quite a number of years after Cassie. She was a stalwart of the service actually.' Grace heard the click of a keyboard as Gail checked her facts. Some things *were* obviously saved accurately on their databases. 'She fostered, let me see, forty-eight children over the years that she worked for us.'

They both honoured this feat with a few seconds of silence. In the pause, Grace readily conjured up Jane's brisk kindness and her tired face.

Gail carried on. 'When Jane retired, her local office wanted to put on a bit of a do, celebrate her years of service, get in contact with some of the children she'd helped, invite them back to say "hello". That sort of thing can also act as good publicity. You would, no doubt, have been sent an invitation. But it never happened. Her family – her daughter especially – weren't keen. She died within nine months of saying "goodbye" to the last young person in her care. Not much of a retirement, sadly. In the circumstances, I'm not sure that approaching the family is such a good idea. I'm sorry. I know you were hoping that a meeting might be possible.'

Grace was shaken by how upset she suddenly felt. Poor Jane, all those years of sticking children back together and handing them on to the next stage of their lives, only to retire and die so quickly. She roused herself. 'Well, thank you for at least finding that out for us. Are we okay to tell Cassie that she's passed, if she asks?'

'I don't see why not,' Gail said.

'And have you been able to discover anything about Cassie's biological mother?' Grace felt a red flush of anxiety creep up her neck.

'Well, there, I'm afraid, I'm coming up with a blank. It isn't being helped by the fact that it was an out-of-area adoption.'

Greater Manchester to Yorkshire – hardly a giant leap. 'What have you been able to find out?' Grace asked.

'The honest answer is nothing concrete, I'm afraid. That doesn't mean we won't be able to. I've sent emails to all the bodies involved, but as I explained the last time we spoke, it can take a little while for enquiries to get passed to the correct person, in the right department. People move on.' This sage observation rankled with Grace. They thought that they'd moved on, too. 'I'm waiting for a couple of people to come back to me. Adult services are very separate from children's services – different processes and protocols, and suchlike. I will keep trying.'

'Thank you.' What else could Grace say?

'I'm sure you're handling it, but you do know how important it is to that you make Cassie aware there is the issue of consent, don't you?' Gail paused. 'Given there has been no contact post-adoption or, if I've got this right, any indication of any desire for such contact, Cassie may have to prepare herself for disappointment. We don't want her building up her expectations.'

Grace forced herself to ask, 'And the letters? Isn't that a possible route?'

Gail sounded like she was double-checking on her computer again. 'The file just confirms what you told me – that you've submitted them *every* year.'

Grace confirmed that she had. She was relieved Gail didn't question such commitment in the face of such indifference; she wasn't sure she'd have been able to give a truthful answer.

'I'm obviously pursuing that, but this is where we get into per-missions and mutual consent. You've never had a reply?'

Grace's response was quiet. 'No. We've never received anything back.'

'Well, I'm sorry to say that's not unusual. They move on with their lives. They want to forget, not remember. Or even if some of them do want to know, they often don't want actual contact. I know it can feel very unsatisfactory, given your current circumstances, but it's quite common with a closed adoption.' Gail shifted into a brisker tone after this slightly mournful observation. 'How is Cassie doing at the moment?'

Grace was taken aback by such a direct question from this virtual stranger. 'Okay. I suppose. We're keeping talking, making sure that she knows she can come to us, about anything, but it's hard, given that we have nothing new to tell her.'

The implied rebuke was ignored. 'Well, I'll keep plugging away. I know it may be of little comfort to you, Grace, but you'd be amazed how often this flares up with adopted children; in their mid- to late teens. It's natural curiosity. Quite often it runs its natural course, especially if the birth family aren't interested, as seems to be the case here. But, as I said, I'll keep going and see what we can uncover. I'll be in touch.' Grace didn't get a chance to say 'Goodbye' before Gail put the phone down.

Grace sat for a while after the call ended, stalled yet again by events and emotions that she'd thought she'd processed and filed away, long ago. They'd been fools to think it was going to be so simple. She'd *so* wanted to believe Jane when she'd said that Cassie was untainted by her early experiences, that she was different from the other kids, that she was special. Grace had cherished their early morning conversation that first week of the match – in truth, she'd relied on it as a guarantee that everything would be fine.

The morning after the bedtime visit, Grace's taxi had dropped her off at Jane's house before dawn. The plan was for her to be there when Cassidie woke up and for her to learn the morning routine, having mastered the night-time one. The rest of the street was in darkness. She knocked gently, not wanting to disturb anyone.

Jane opened the door without switching on the hall light. 'Tea?' Her voice was croaky with sleep. In her dressing gown and slippers, bare-faced, at 6.30 a.m. on a cold winter's morning, she looked much older – or maybe just her age. Her movements around the kitchen were slow, deliberate, the chirpiness of the preceding visits absent. They sat together at the kitchen table, listening out for sounds from upstairs. They both knew that when they heard anything, it would be Grace who would go up to Cassidie.

'Thank you,' Grace said.

Jane looked up from her brew.

'I mean it. For helping us. It must be so hard letting them go.'

Jane pulled her robe a little tighter. 'We've done it before. Thirty-six times, all told. No, I'm wrong, it's thirty-seven.'

'But still...'

Jane put her mug down. 'I'd be lying if I said it wasn't difficult. It is. You grow attached to them; there's no way you can do the job and not – well, at least that's the way it is with most of them. I'm going to miss her, of course I am. But I know that in a month or so, it'll be okay. It always is. You adapt to life with them, then you adapt to life without them. And anyway, before you know it, they'll have talked me and Doug into taking on another one. We keep saying we're going to retire, but we never seem to manage it. There's always just one more child that they're struggling to place.'

'Well, I want you to know how much Tom and I appreciate it. What you've done for her, and for us.' It sounded patronising, even to Grace's own ears.

Jane got up and rinsed her mug, allowing her to turn her back. 'That's what we're here for.' She put the mug on the rack, paused, then turned round abruptly. 'Cassidie's one of the best we've ever had, you know. She's amazing – considering.' Grace's face must have given something away that Jane misinterpreted. 'I mean it. We've seen enough of them over the years to know that she's special.'

'How?' Grace prompted, wanting the reassurance.

Jane seemed to give it some real thought before answering. 'She's not got that hole in her that most of them have. Whatever you do, that gap, it doesn't ever really heal up, not completely; too much damage has been done. When they're not loved as babies, they never totally recover. I think it's a trust thing, they learn that it's not wise to trust anybody. A child needs to know that it's loved, to grow up well. Well, that's what I think.' She shrugged her shoulders, deprecating her own experience, but Grace was convinced by every word. Jane went on, 'Cassidie is different... She does trust people – once she feels safe with them. She knows that she's lovable – that she's worth loving. She's not broken. You're very lucky to get her.'

Grace said nothing. She didn't want to have to think about the others; all she wanted to think about – all she could think about – was Cassidie, and how impatient she was to take her home and make her properly theirs.

As if on cue, there was a shout from upstairs. For a split second they both hesitated, then Jane said, 'It's okay. You go.'

Grace didn't need to be asked twice.

Three short weeks later, Jane bent down, dropped a swift kiss on the top of Cassidie's head and hurried out of Tom and Grace's house. Cassidie didn't even look up from the toy bus she was pushing along the carpet.

She played and ate a good tea, she splashed in the bath, her hair tucked away inside a bright-pink shower cap that she thought was hilarious, then Tom read her *The Snail and the Whale* and she rolled over and went to sleep.

And, just like that, the bedroom at the top of the stairs was no longer empty, and Cassidie was theirs for ever.

Or so they had thought.

Chapter 25

RYAN WASN'T happy about it. Not at all. 'Why can't I?'

Cassie watched the leaves ripple in the bright afternoon sunshine. 'Because I don't need you there. I'll be fine on my own. I just need you to drop me off.'

He frowned and his lower lip actually drooped, like a toddler's. 'I think I should be there. She could be a complete nut-job.'

'Cheers, thanks for that.' She looked at him, marvelling at his capacity to be completely insensitive at exactly the same time as trying, in his own cack-handed way, to do something thoughtful, like drive her all the way over to Oldham – again.

'You know what I mean.' How often did he say that?

'Yep. You meant...that my mum's going to turn out to be some sort of Jeremy Kyle reject.' Her fury was, in part, that Ryan could be right. The woman's accent, her badly spelt text messages, the lack of even basic articulacy and politeness on the phone, it was all pointing to someone...well, rough.

'I'm only trying to look out for you.' He pulled his baseball cap off and slapped it against the palm of his hand in frustration.

She relented, slightly. 'I know, but it's something that I have to do on my own.'

He looked at her and half-nodded. 'I get that.' They both watched a young lad on a bike trying to do wheelies along the bottom path, in front of a group of girls who were sitting on the climbing frame picking at their nails. They didn't seem overly impressed with his performance. 'I could just hang around at the start. Check that you're okay when you first meet her. Besides... I'll need to stay around to bring you home.'

God, he was persistent. 'It might scare her off.' The tense phone conversation nagged at Cassie, making her fearful of two conflicting things. Firstly, that Ryan being there might very well scare the woman away, and secondly that *not* having him there might be quite scary as well. Why had she insisted that Cassie come on her own? And, more unnerving, how had she known Erin had been with her in Subway? The woman had given so little away on the phone. The only thing Cassie was certain of was that when, and if, they met, it was going to be truly uncomfortable. In truth, a growing part of her wished she'd never bothered trying to find her birth mother. All it had done so far was make her feel rattled.

The lad on the bike misjudged one of his wheelie attempts and his front wheel skewed awkwardly. He tipped forward and for a second it looked like he was going to fly, head first, over his handlebars. Ryan laughed. 'What a doughnut!' But Cassie felt a moment of panic – for the boy, and for herself. After another five minutes of arguing, she accepted what she knew, in her heart, she'd wanted all along: namely, that Ryan would take her to Oldham and would wait and watch to make sure she was okay. Only when she gave him the signal would he take himself off and leave her alone to talk to the woman, whoever she was.

'It'll be like summat in a film.' Ryan grinned and stretched, making his shadow grow taller and wider against the scorched grass.

'Yeah,' Cassie said, though she didn't for a second think that it would be.

And it wasn't.

For starters, Ryan was late.

Cassie sat on the wall at the T-junction, on her own this time –
as instructed – and waited, the pressure building inside her like gas
in a can of Coke. Twenty-five long, tedious minutes she waited. The
argument kicked off the minute she clicked her seatbelt into place.

'Where the hell have you been? I've been calling you.'

Ryan grunted something unintelligible in response and proceeded
to stall the car as he pulled away from the kerb. The snort of disgust
that Cassie let out was the perfect opening salvo to the tense and
bad-tempered start of their journey.

Ryan stared ahead, concentrating on where he was going, as she
bitched and moaned. He had half a mind to simply pull over and tell
her to shift her lovely arse out of his car and do one – but he didn't.
At last they made it to the motorway. Ryan accelerated down the
sliproad and straight across two lanes of traffic. She wanted fast, she
could have fast. He'd said he'd get her there on time and he would, but
still she didn't let up. As they sped along, he heard Cassie nagging,
but tuned out the words. It wasn't just the turning up late that she
seemed mad about; it had morphed into something else, something
about his 'not quite good enoughness' in general. This was *not* how
he wanted to be spending his first Saturday off work in weeks.

He didn't understand how he'd gone from simply fancying the
pants off Cassie to being snared by her. She bossed him around like
a f---ing teacher. And she was *so* pig-headed. He wondered, not for
the first time – while flashing his headlights at an old bloke who was
pottering along at sixty-five in the middle lane – if she was worth
it. His other girlfriends had been so much easier. They'd seemed
grateful for any attention. With them he'd been the one in charge,
the one deciding the when, the where, the what, even 'if he could be
arsed'. Not with Cassie. She had him by the balls.

He pulled into the outside lane and glanced at her, silent at last, looking away from him out of the window. Even when she was pissed off he still fancied her, wanted to get to her, touch her, squeeze her. Just having her sitting so close to him in the car was screwing with him. He looked back at the road and had to brake suddenly as the traffic slowed. He put his hand out and stroked her thigh through her skinny jeans. His reward – not even a glance. And so it went on; foot on the accelerator for five miles, foot on the brake for the next ten. The M62 was a ball-ache – much like Cassie herself.

Cassie wasn't thinking about Ryan. She was thinking about what she was going to say to the woman. It seemed too big a conversation to have, using normal words. She couldn't imagine how it would play out. She wasn't even sure she knew what she wanted from the meeting. Clarity as to who the woman was, that would be good for starters, but after that, what? She wasn't sure. That's what made it all so scary. Until this point in her life Cassie had always known what she wanted; she hadn't always got it – that was not Tom and Grace's style of parenting – but at least she'd known. It was the way she was. She'd inherited her single-mindedness from Grace, or so everyone said. But that was just it, wasn't it? Who knew why she was the way she was? Until she found out more about her biological mum, she'd never really know what was inherited from her family and what was in her DNA; and until she knew that, how could she go on and become whatever she was supposed to be?

Ryan touched her leg with his free hand, but Cassie was so wrapped up in the swirl of her own conflicting emotions that she didn't even feel it.

They parked in a side street and Ryan set off for the bus station, as agreed. He kissed her on the mouth before he left, as much to leave his mark on her as anything. She waited, leaning against the car for support. She counted down the minutes by studying the litter in the gutters and avoiding eye contact. After the agreed five-minute delay, she set off, her pulse beating as fast as if she'd been running. She willed herself to calm down. When she arrived at the bus terminus she spotted Ryan straight away. He was sitting, with his earbuds in, phone in hand, his cap pulled low over his face. He was probably loving every minute of it, the drama making a nice change from peeling spuds and frying chips. As she walked past him, he glanced up and swiftly down again, faking disinterest.

Cassie picked a seat on the end of the row, settled in it and looked at the departures board. Ten minutes to go. Ryan had been as good as his word and had got her there in time. She tried to swallow, but her mouth was dry. A series of buses arrived and deposited a ragbag of people onto the concourse, a steady flow of humanity. There were a lot of women. The old ones huffed and puffed and clutched their shopping bags to their bodies, as if expecting to be mugged at any minute, while the young ones juggled buggies, small kids and packets of crisps, talking non-stop into their phones. Cassie didn't know where to look, at the passengers or at the passers-by. She had no idea where this LW person was coming from. Every woman under fifty was a candidate, but most walked past Cassie without so much as registering her existence.

The minutes edged by. Her eyes kept returning to Ryan. If he was getting impatient, she couldn't tell; he looked like he always did – just Ryan, just another lad in a cap and expensive jeans. He blended in fine. They were separated by only a few metres of concrete, but she felt much further away from him than that. Two more buses arrived and departed, but there was still no sign of her. The cruelty of being stood up twice was too much for Cassie to contemplate and yet, with every minute that crawled by, it seemed that was exactly what was happening.

Cassie checked her phone. Nothing. As she was looking at it she became aware of a presence, someone standing to the left of her, not moving. Her pulse thumped. But no, it was a woman in her twenties.

Thin, wearing jeans, cheap trainers, a hoodie, dyed hair – the type of hard-faced girl Cassie would normally have avoided. The woman/girl just stood there. Waiting for someone? Cassie ignored her. LW obviously wasn't coming. She felt so strung out she could have cried.

The hard-faced young woman came and sat down, one seat away from Cassie. Ryan leant forward. Cassie shook her head at him. Another five minutes, that was all she would give her and that would be it; she wasn't going to be taken for a mug twice.

'Are you Cassidie?' The voice Cassie had heard on the phone was coming from the woman. Cassidie was too shocked to say anything. 'I said – are you Cassidie?'

Cassie saw Ryan get to his feet, but she shook her head again, more clearly. He sat back down, but on the edge of his seat.

'Don't then.' The woman stood up.

'No. Sorry. Yes. I'm Cassie.'

'Cassidie,' she insisted. Three flat, assertive syllables.

'Okay. Yes. I'm Cassidie. Who are you?'

'Not here.' She stood up and started walking away. Cassie was forced to follow her, dodging in between the shuffling bus passengers, her heart rate rocketing. The woman didn't look back, and so didn't see Ryan get to his feet and join their bizarre little procession across the road and along the high street. Cassie stayed a few paces behind the woman, who didn't glance behind her once, but walked quickly with her head down and her hands rammed into the pockets of her top. It felt ridiculous, and not very bright, to be following a complete stranger down unfamiliar streets, but she'd known Cassie's name or, more tellingly, she'd known her birth name, so she had to take a chance.

Their trek didn't last long because, without warning, the woman suddenly veered left into a pub. Cassie checked that Ryan had seen, then stepped through the doors after her.

The sudden shift from bright sunlight to interior gloom was disorientating, the smell of beer strong. Cassie looked around. The woman was at the bar, ordering. She turned and indicated a table in an alcove. As Cassie moved towards it, Ryan came in. They passed so close that Cassie could have reached out and touched him, but she didn't. He continued to play his part well. He strolled up to the bar, where he waited. Cassie was impressed that he was controlled enough to glance at her only briefly.

The woman paid for two Cokes and brought them over to Cassie.

'Thanks.' She accepted the offered glass. The woman put her drink down on the table. She stared at it. Cassie sat, feeling uncomfortable and very, very out of place. For the want of anything better to do, she concentrated on the woman's hands. Painted stubby nails, neon-blue varnish, chipped at the edges. A lot of rings, a band of fake gold running across her fingers. Dry, flaky skin. A scatter of small white scars across the back of her left hand.

'You don't know who I am, do ya?'

Cassie was startled. She looked up. Their eyes met properly for the first time. 'Well, I'm not sure. I came because...well, you know why I came. I'm trying to find out anything I can about my birth mother.' The woman didn't say anything, she merely picked up her drink and took a long, loud swallow. Cassie pushed on, risking humiliation. 'I thought it was maybe her that I was coming to meet.'

'Did ya now?' Her tone was mocking.

Cassie set her chin. She was determined not to be intimidated. 'You know that. The texts, they were from you, weren't they? It was you who called me.'

The woman seemed to think about whether to deny it, but didn't. 'Yeah, it was me.'

'Why did you pretend to be my mother?'

'I didn't.'

'Yes, you did.' Cassie suddenly wasn't so sure. Had she just assumed – hoped – that it was her mother? Had this woman actually said anything to claim that she was her birth mum?

'No I fucking didn't.'

Cassie felt a lot less brave. She checked Ryan was still there. He was: leaning against the bar, watching them closely. 'I never said who I was. If you got the wrong end of the stick, that's on you.'

'But you sent me the picture?'

There was a long pause. Truth or denial. The woman chose truth, this time. 'Yeah.'

'How come you've got a picture of my mother and me?' Cassie asked.

'I've as much right to that picture as you 'ave. More.' The defiance was hard and sharp.

Cassie felt confused, and frustrated. 'Look, if you've got something to say to me, say it. If not, why did you come today?'

The woman held her gaze. 'Becoz.'

'Because what?'

'Nothing. Just becoz.'

Cassie crossed her arms and waited, determined to tough it out.

The woman shuffled in her seat, then said, 'I saw your post asking for info. It kinda shocked me. Seeing the picture. And seeing you. And it was like a weird coincidence. The timing. Cos they'd been in touch with me – about you.'

'Who got in touch with you?' Cassie asked.

'Social Services.' She said it in a weary, sour tone.

'Oh.' Cassie didn't know what she was talking about.

'It seemed...like now was maybe the time to...ya know.'

Cassie didn't know. 'I don't understand what you mean. I don't even know *who* you are.'

The woman pushed her drink across the table top. 'You really don't know?' Her face was unreadable, blank. Cassie shook her head. The woman took a shallow breath and said, 'I'm Leah. Your sister.'

Chapter 26

LEAH SAW the flinch and the recoil when she said 'sister'. That stung, but she didn't show it. She held her ground, and her silence, as the shock on Cassidie's face was replaced, in rapid succession, by dismay, distress, confusion and disbelief. It was like watching waves running into each other on an incoming tide. It looked like an honest reaction, but Leah knew, all too well, that faces could lie. She pressed on the bruise that her announcement had inflicted, seeing if she could squeeze any more emotion out of Cassidie – true or false. 'Ya really didn't know?' Cassidie shook her head. Leah pressed down harder, curious to discover how much damage she could inflict, and how quickly. She was pleased to see that it was a lot. 'Are you saying they never told ya that you had a big sister?'

Cassidie shook her head again. Then suddenly her eyes widened and she shouted, 'No!'

Leah jumped, twisted round in her seat and saw the boyfriend freeze, mid-stride, halfway across the pub. Cassidie flicked her hand at him, shooing him away. He made a 'what the fuck' gesture, but retreated back to the bar, as instructed. Leah was glad that Cassidie had dismissed him; she even admired her for a split second. Cassidie's control over him was impressive. It also relieved Leah of the need to get rid of him. She'd recognised the boyfriend at the bus station, posing in his stupid cap and sunglasses, sticking out like a sore thumb. It was a complication, having him trail around after them like some sort of cut-rate PI, but not an insurmountable one. That Cassidie didn't want him close to the action was interesting.

'You all right?' Leah asked, not caring really.

'Yeah, sorry.'

Leah watched the ripples of Cassidie's confusion and felt an unfamiliar, but very welcome sense of calm. Her moment in the spotlight had finally arrived. She sat with her drink, waiting, perfectly content. There was no rush. There was no bitch-sister around to steal her limelight this time. Only when she felt the time was right – and that Cassidie was ready to concentrate – did she reach for her evidence. She pulled her bag onto her lap, rummaged through it and found the grubby, dog-eared envelope. She lifted the flap, took out the photo and placed it on the table.

Ta-dah!

Cassidie blinked and blinked again, then slowly reached for her bag, took out *her* copy of the photo and slid it across the table. Lined up, side-by-side, the two were identical.

'It was in your family pack as well,' Leah said. Cassidie nodded and stared in disbelief. 'I'm guessing they didn't show you this one, though, did they?' Leah reached inside the envelope and pulled out her *coup de grâce*. She held it to her chest for a second, savouring the moment, before laying it down on the table. The photo was of the same woman with the same baby on her knee, the same ugly mirror was behind their heads, but in this shot there was another child – a thin little girl with a pale face and straight brown hair, leaning in against her mother's side.

'You?' Cassidie whispered.

'Yeah. And you. And our mum.' Leah's voice was bleached of emotion.

160

'I don't understand.' Cassidie looked at the photo, then back up at Leah.

Leah shrugged, as if it was neither here nor there. 'What? What don't you understand?'

'How I can have a sister that no one told me about?'

Again Leah sniffed for bullshit, but couldn't detect any. 'Because they lie...when it suits 'em.'

'Not my mum and dad.' She was too wrapped up in her own emotions to see Leah stiffen. 'Why would they lie about something as huge as this?'

'Cos they wanted to keep us apart. They still do.'

'But why?'

Leah watched Cassidie grasping for the truth...and deciding – despite the evidence Leah was putting in front of her – that she still believed her lying, bastard parents. Doubt clouded Cassidie's eyes and she drew herself back from the table, putting physical distance between the two of them. The stuck-up bitch. Leah's sense of calm evaporated. A cold, deep rage flooded through her and she reacted honestly, without control. 'Cos they wanted you, but not me.'

Chapter 27

TOM HADN'T meant to spy on them, he just happened to be on the upstairs landing, changing a light bulb, when he heard Ryan's car pull up outside. It was the unnecessary tyre squeal that alerted him. The cars were nose-to-tail along their street, as Alyson and Dan, their next-door neighbours, were hosting her mum's sixtieth birthday party. They had warned everyone – well in advance. There was only one fairly tight space free. Pettiness made Tom hope that when Ryan tried to reverse into it, he did it badly. He didn't, of course. He swung the Golf in backwards deftly, at a crazily acute angle, and parked perfectly, first time. Cocky little bastard. Tom climbed down from the stepladder and, with naked curiosity, watched to see what would happen next. It was a bright, sunny Saturday afternoon and people were out and about. Chris, from across the street, was washing his car on his drive, not ten feet away from them. Surely they wouldn't… but evidently they would.

As the minutes ticked by, Tom was sorely tempted to rush outside on some fabricated errand and catch them at it. He didn't, of course, but only because he couldn't bring himself to face the embarrassment of having to haul his seventeen-year-old daughter out of some boy-racer's car in broad daylight. Five, ten minutes passed. It was a long time to spend imagining his daughter being pawed by a greasy ferret of a lad.

Eventually there was some movement. The driver's door opened and Ryan climbed out. What happened next shocked Tom.

Ryan walked round the car and opened the passenger door. Then, in an act of chivalry that was quaintly old-fashioned, he bent down and extended his hand into the vehicle to help Cassie out. She emerged, slowly, like a princess from a fairy-tale carriage. But that wasn't the end of their courtly dance. They stood toe-to-toe, on the pavement, their faces only a few centimetres apart, seemingly oblivious to the slow hum of suburbia surrounding them. Tom watched, horribly fascinated, as Ryan lifted his hand and gently stroked Cassie's cheek. For what felt like an eternity she leant into his touch, covering his fingers with her own. The tenderness of the gesture was evident. In that moment Tom felt, not anger, but surprise and an uneasy jealousy.

Ryan's protectiveness seemed to contrast starkly with his own recent failure to approach Cassie with anything other than ineffective words and conflicting emotions. When he'd discovered her asleep and distressed in her room the previous weekend, Tom had felt powerless, no longer certain of his rights or his role in physically comforting his own daughter. It was like a dark echo of the early days of her adoption. He'd remained silent in the doorway of her bedroom for a few moments, bizarrely worried that he was going to wake her, which would surely have been a good thing, given that she was obviously having a bad dream. He'd listened to her snuffly whimpering, horrified but also transfixed. He so rarely saw his ebullient, confident daughter vulnerable these days. Then the bloody dog had appeared from nowhere and launched itself across the room and onto the bed; so much for waking Cassie calmly and gently.

Though it was obviously a bit of a shock, Cassie's reaction had been extreme. It was as if she'd been attacked. She started awake and sat bolt upright, scrambling away from the dog – and from him – shouting hysterically. He'd tried to reassure her as he'd dragged Elmo away and shut him out of the room. Tom then went over to her and knelt beside the bed, his arms outstretched. 'Whoa! Sorry. It's okay, love. It was only Elmo getting over-excited. You were dreaming. A bad one, by the sound of it. It's over now. Cassie. Honey. It's okay.'

But she wasn't listening. She edged further away and looked at him with real fear in her eyes. It was awful, and horribly familiar. After a few truly frightening minutes of panic, she glanced beyond him at the room with all its familiar things; this seemed to root her back in the present, because her distress finally ebbed away. It was replaced by something much calmer, but still very guarded. She rubbed her hand across her mouth and cheeks, as if wiping away cobwebs. 'What time is it?' Her voice was raspy and unsteady.

'I'm not sure. About half-four, I think.' Cassie reached for her phone and checked, leaving Tom kneeling awkwardly beside the bed, wanting to comfort her but not knowing how. 'Are you okay? You sounded upset, even before the bloody dog.'

Cassie moved so that she could swing her legs off the bed, making him shift out of her way. 'Yeah. Just a weird dream.' She stood up. 'Do you mind, Dad? I need to go and have a shower.' And with that, she dismissed him.

Tom got awkwardly to his feet and walked out of her room, carrying with him the uncomfortable sensation that their relationship had slipped back to its shaky beginnings.

The first time it happened was the day that Tom repaired the fence.

Grace and – a *two weeks with us, settled amazingly well, can't believe she's ours* – Cassie were in the house, playing. Tom had reluctantly left them to it. A panel had blown out in the back garden, and Jean, their nice-enough but fussy next-door neighbour, was stressing about the wind damage to her plants and the increased likelihood of intruders.

It was the last thing Tom wanted to do on the final weekend of his parental leave, but he knew, from past experience, that Jean's softly spoken but persistent comments wouldn't stop until the fence was sorted. It turned into a real pain of a job. To add insult to injury, it started to rain heavily as Tom was trying to wrestle the new panel into place between the warped posts. He pulled the hood of his sweatshirt up and carried on working, wishing that his DIY skills and the weather were better. After a half-hour of hammering, bashing and cursing, the fence was finally fixed, at least until the next blustery day. Tom packed up his tools and headed back to his natural milieu, a warm house with a coffee, where there was little or no risk of digit loss.

The girls had decamped into the kitchen. He could see Cassie sitting on the floor, playing. Grace was talking to her as she moved around, getting things out of the cupboards ready for lunch. Tom eased off his muddy trainers, pushed open the door and stepped inside. Grace smiled at him. Cassie didn't move. She continued with her 'project', chattering away to herself, her back to him, head bowed, enthralled. She was making dough shapes with a random assortment of kitchen items: eggcups, pastry cutters, plastic beakers. The air was filled with the smell of Play-Doh. Tom crept up behind her, meaning only to see what she was making, nothing else.

He didn't get far.

Cassie must have heard or sensed him, because she suddenly dropped the beaker she was holding and twisted round, but instead of delight at seeing her daddy, her face wavered for a second, then spilt open. She screamed. Once, then again and again. Screeching, high-pitched yelps, mouth stretched wide, teeth bared. Tom rushed forward to reassure her, but that only made things worse. She scrabbled backwards away from him, sending her playthings skittering across the kitchen floor, her eyes huge and dark. She was screaming with fear.

Tom backed off and Grace put out her arms. Cassie looked from Grace to Tom, then launched herself at her mother. Grace encircled her and hugged her close. The screaming stopped, abruptly, and a weird, brittle silence descended on the room. Tom eased himself down onto the floor. He pushed his hood back, but otherwise kept very still, scared of making another wrong move. Grace met his eyes with a look of pure bewilderment. 'Cassie, honey, it's only Daddy. He didn't mean to frighten you.' The child wriggled, burying herself further into Grace's embrace. Grace gave it another long minute, then tried again. 'Cassie. Please look up, sweetheart. It's just Daddy. He needs to see that you're okay. You gave him a fright.' Cautiously Cassie raised her head and peeped at Tom. He smiled, equally cautiously, back at her. Her face seemed to balance, momentarily, on the cusp of two emotions, as if she were seeing two versions of him. Then her eyes cleared and she smiled and held out her hands, after a nod of encouragement from Grace, Tom went to take her.

A few minutes later it was as if nothing had happened. Cassie was calm and seemed perfectly happy, insisting that Tom and Grace admire her play-food, chatting away, a stream of new words and observations. When they nervously asked what had frightened her, she shook her head and simply passed them another Play-Doh cake to 'eat', refusing to be drawn on the subject. Tom raised the lump of bright-red and yellow dough to his lips and pretended it tasted lovely.

The second time came equally out of the blue, and it was worse, because this time they were in public.

It happened a month to the day after Cassie came to live with them – long enough for Tom to be feeling sufficiently confident to go out with his daughter on his own, and long enough for Grace to agree, hesitantly, to meet a friend for coffee, just for an hour. They were shopping when it happened, the most mundane of household chores, but one Cassie seemed to find fascinating. She loved shops, big or small, toy store or grocery; she adored anywhere with shelves full of stuff. Tom and Cassie had driven to the supermarket, spotting buses on the way and exchanging views about the best type of sandwich. Cassie favoured jam. Tom proclaimed worm-and-brown-sauce to be the best. In her cardigan pocket Cassie had her very own shopping list: Pom-Bears, a 'nice' banana and (if she was good) a Freddo Frog – Grace had added the caveat.

At the store, Tom let Cassie walk rather than suggesting that she ride in a trolley. She hated being cooped up when they went out; she preferred 'helping', which, in reality, meant ambling up and down the aisles, stopping at anything and everything that caught her eye. It slowed the process down immeasurably, but for Tom and Grace it was still a novelty. And it was nice to catch the indulgent smiles of other customers, who often stopped to chat and ask Cassie's age and compliment them on her manners.

The trip that Saturday was going fine until Tom saw Cassie take a packet of chocolate biscuits from a shelf, without asking. Before he could stop her, she ripped it open and crammed one into her mouth. Jane had warned them about her slightly compulsive eating patterns, rooted, she believed, in the hunger that had been an everyday reality of her life with her birth mother. Even now, the regularity and availability of food in their house seemed to surprise Cassie, but the speed-eating and squirrelling food away in odd places were definitely on the decline. Grace still checked Cassie's drawers and under her bed every day, just to be sure, but they hadn't found a stash recently. So there was no excuse, not for blatant stealing.

'Cassie!' She looked at Tom, her cheeks still moving as she tried to swallow the crumbly evidence. 'What *are* you doing? Give me that packet, this instant.' He held out his hand. An old chap shopping nearby paused, obviously intrigued to see who was going to win the stand-off. Cassie swallowed what was in her mouth, looked defiantly at Tom and took another biscuit. 'Oh no, you don't, young lady!' Even at this point Tom was still secretly amused by her stubbornness – the kid had some front! She bit into the second biscuit. 'Cassie Haines, come here!'

But instead of heeding Tom's instructions, Cassie turned and started walking – then trotting – away. Tom stood his ground. She carried on, running now: to the end of the aisle, then around it. That's when Tom moved; in a battle of wills, being in the right was no substitute for having her in plain sight. He raced after her. She was already by the store entrance by the time he rounded the end of the aisle. He shouted, panic forcing his voice higher than normal. Cassie glanced at him and bolted outside. The entrance opened straight onto a busy car park. Tom chased after her, shocked at how quickly something so innocuous had turned into something potentially so dangerous. He lunged, grabbed and managed to catch hold of her arm just as a white van cruised past within centimetres of her. He pulled Cassie's resistant little body to him, his heart pounding. Relief flooded through him. Then a sudden, razor-like pain flashed across the fingers of his left hand. It took him a second to register that she'd bitten him. In shock, his grip on her arm slipped and she shot away from him. 'Cassie, stop!'

She ran straight across the car park, full tilt into a middle-aged woman who, thankfully, had the presence of mind to bend down and circle her arms around the squirming, red-faced Cassie – trapping her safely. 'Where are you off to in such a hurry?' The woman's voice registered amusement as well as surprise. Tom arrived on the scene and stood, pulse thumping in his temples, as the woman focused on Cassie. 'Whoa, whoa! It's okay, but you can't go running around a car park, sweetheart, not with all these cars about.'

Cassie twisted within her firm embrace, caught sight of her dad, opened her mouth – and yelled.

Tom froze. His stomach dropped. Not again!

The woman looked from Cassie to Tom and her expression shifted from concern to suspicion. Cassie continued to wail and thrash. The woman held onto her; if anything, she pulled her even closer.

Tom tried to sound calm above the noise. 'She ran off. From the store. A disagreement about biscuits, would you believe?' The woman's expression didn't soften; she obviously didn't believe him – about biscuits or anything else. 'Cassie?' Tom bent down. 'You need to calm down, honey. Daddy isn't cross with you. I was worried that you were going get knocked down. It's all right.' He risked reaching out to her.

Cassie drew breath and screamed. People stopped and stared.

It took a frantic call to Grace, a move back into the shop, up into the office – Cassie still clinging, limpet-like, to a complete stranger – and Grace arriving in a state of panic to persuade the store manager not to call the police, and to convince the woman that Tom really was Cassie's father and that he meant her no harm. It was only after Cassie had transferred from the stranger's lap onto Grace's, calmed down and been allowed another biscuit that they seemed willing to believe them. Tom found himself on his knees in front of Cassie, apologising for frightening her. She listened, nodded and the fear in her eyes slowly faded. When she offered Tom one of the remaining, broken biscuits, the atmosphere in the office finally relaxed and they were free to take their child home.

It wasn't until later that same day – when Tom and Cassie were building a den in the front room – that he realised *why* the woman had been so reluctant to believe that he was Cassie's father. It wasn't only the way she'd behaved. It was the way he looked. Tom was white. Cassie was not. Cassie did not look like his daughter.

The thought rocked Tom back on his heels.

He stopped playing and sat, looking at the broken skin on his hand, trying to make the woman's and the manager's suspicions not matter. Their prejudice and narrow-mindedness weren't his problem; there would be a lifetime of this, people querying their relationship because of their skin colour. He would have to get used to it. Rise above it. Let it not matter. But Cassie's behaviour did matter. That *was* his problem. Why had she wanted to get away from him so badly that she'd sunk her teeth into his flesh? Why had she acted as if he were a total stranger rather than her father?

Unbidden, Tom's anxieties about Cassie's genetic 'inheritance' slithered free. Were these flashes of anger and fear her past coming out? Was there another thin, fierce, feral child packed away inside the happy, joyous little girl that he and Grace had fallen in love with? And if there was, would all their love and attention and effort be enough to smother that dark, troubled soul? Would she ever truly be their child, or would there always be a tiny part of her that belonged to someone else?

Tom suddenly became aware that the room had gone quiet.

He looked up. Cassie was sitting cross-legged opposite him, her face solemn, her chin tucked down on her chest, a mirror image of his posture. He forced himself to smile. She smiled back and his heart ached. Then she got to her feet up, grabbed the edge of the sheet and started pulling at it, her face a picture of determination. Slowly, awkwardly, Cassie tugged the sheet over their heads, hiding them both, safe and sound, inside their makeshift shelter.

Outside on the pavement, Ryan said something to Cassie, then he kissed her, briefly, almost chastely. They broke apart and Cassie turned and walked up the drive. Tom hurried across the landing and contrived to be coming down the stairs as she opened the front door. He wanted, he told himself, to check that she was all right. Though why shouldn't she be? They'd only been out for the day, shopping, though there was no sign she'd bought anything, which was unusual. Really he just felt the need to say something kind to her, something bridge-building and conciliatory, something that would convince her that he really wasn't the enemy. But all he managed was a falsely cheerful 'Hi'.

She looked up at him, surprised by his sudden appearance on the stairs, and in an instant her face shifted from open to closed. Her unnervingly blank expression robbed Tom of all the things he had intended to say and, as a result, all the love that was beating through his heart stayed trapped inside. When she brushed past him on the stairs, with a flat, mumbled 'Hi' his only acknowledgement, Tom's failure was complete.

He had no other choice than to let her go.

Chapter 28

CASSIE PROMISED Ryan, faithfully, that she wouldn't go anywhere near Leah again, not without telling him.

He'd listened patiently to her confused ramblings in the car on the journey back from Oldham and made lots of sympathetic noises, some of them in the right places, but as they'd parked up outside her house, he'd made his real opinion clear. He firmly believed that nothing good would come out of chasing after the ghosts from her past. 'Cass. It's not worth it. You have a nice family, a nice life.' His eyes flicked to their obviously very nice house with their nice garden and the two nice cars on the drive. 'You don't need to get involved with this skank. You've no idea who she really is or why she's contacted you. Leave it alone. Please.'

And that's when Cassie had lied to his face, not because she'd wanted to, but because this new, improved version of Ryan – though something of a revelation, and one that her shaken soul badly needed – sounded just like her parents!

But Leah wasn't a ghost. She was real and she was claiming to be her sister. Cassie couldn't ignore that. No sane person would. And even if she was lying, Leah was some sort of link to Cassie's birth mum – the photo proved it. Cassie had to follow that up. If that meant lying to Ryan, so be it. So she'd held his cool fingers against her cheek for a few moments, loving his concern, relaxing into this softer, gentler brand of his affection, and she'd let him kiss her goodbye; then she'd turned and walked away without a twinge of guilt.

She'd let herself into the house and been immediately confronted by her dad, looming above her on the stairs. Tom had said 'Hi' and Cassie had sensed, to her horror, that he was wanting to talk. She wasn't ready. She hadn't yet had time to come up with the disguise that she was going to have to wear until she had some answers, or at least the right questions. So she did what she'd been doing more and more lately – she blocked him, hurried past with her head down, escaping to her lair at the top of the house, where she closed her door and examined, in private, the wounds inflicted by Leah.

Chapter 29

THREE DAYS later Cassie found herself sitting at the back of a long purple bus as it lumbered through the red-brick splendour of Manchester. Her makeshift disguise had held, but only just. Lying to her parents had been difficult; avoiding Erin's careful questions even harder; reassuring Ryan fairly easy.

No one knew where she was.

No one knew what she was doing.

None of them would approve if they did. It was a slightly unnerving thought.

To all intents and purposes, Cassie had dropped out of her life.

The bus swung round a corner and, for a split second, it looked as if it was about to smash into the sharp corner of a glass office block that seemed to rear up suddenly in the middle of the road. But there was no shatter of glass, simply a wheeze of brakes and a hanging, suspended sensation as they cleared the corner, then a muffled rumbling noise as the bus bumped over the tram lines across the square. They pulled into a stop. People got off and more people got on.

Cassie had no idea where she was. A journey on a website was nothing like one in reality, especially not one in a place that was so unfamiliar. The other passengers looked and sounded very different from her. The texture and the grain of their skin, their clothes, their accents, even their smell – it all seemed so alien. She tried to avoid meeting anyone's eye by gazing out of the window, but it didn't make her feel any less awkward. The bus pulled free of the congested roads of central Manchester and they drove on through the scruffy anonymity of the no-man's-land between the heart of a city and where the real people lived – where Leah lived. As she sat holding onto the rail, Cassie tried to work out in which direction the truth actually lay: at home with her parents, the people she had trusted all her life, or ahead of her in the unknown streets of Oldham, with a girl who was claiming to be her sister.

It was a frosty welcome. 'So what do ya remember?' Leah's question put Cassie under pressure from the outset.

'Not much.' Cassie had spent a lot of time since they'd met searching through her past for any recollection of Leah, but it had been impossible – like forcing yourself to laugh or cry. What memories she did have couldn't be anchored to any one person or place, not with any certainty. Nothing was certain any more, least of all this girl's role in any of it. But Leah was waiting for her to say something to justify this second meeting. 'I think my earliest memories are of Jane, the foster carer. At least I can remember a house that was always too hot. And a big toy box. I was frightened of falling into it and getting trapped.' Cassie saw that this was not what Leah was asking. She stalled.

'So ya don't remember me at all?'

Cassie found Leah's abruptness unsettling. She was used to the truth being framed and hung up neatly for her to take her time looking at, not being dumped, unceremoniously, in her lap. She swallowed down her discomfort. She had tried, she really had, but she had no memories of Leah. She couldn't – she wouldn't – lie about it. 'No. I don't remember you.'

Leah blinked and flicked her fingernail three times. 'Well, I *was* there.'

The distance between them was huge.

Cassie was the first to break eye contact. She looked around for a distraction from the spiky awkwardness of the situation and found it outside, on the street, just in front of the cafe. A man in a grubby hi-vis jacket was emptying the litter bin. He was struggling. The black bin bag he was holding kept twisting in the wind as he tried to fill it. Cassie watched as a couple of burger boxes caught on the breeze and escaped his grasp. They lifted, opened and floated away like polystyrene butterflies. He didn't bother chasing after them.

Leah watched Cassidie. She studied her face, saw her distress and sensed her desperation. It was time to start building a bridge: slowly, piece by piece, truth by half-truth, white lie by black – only then would she be able to get to her. It was time for Leah the storyteller.

She tossed out the first scrap. 'We were sent to Jane's together... to start with.' That got Cassidie's attention. Leah drained the last of her drink and set it down on the table. 'But they split us up.' She fell silent.

The yawning blanks in Cassie's early life needed filling. 'So what happened?' she prompted.

Leah stared flatly at her. 'Well, that depends on who you talk to.'

'Meaning?'

'What I said. There's what I'm guessing they *said* happened, and there's what really happened. They ain't the same thing.'

'So tell me your version.'

'After I get another drink.' Leah understood delayed gratification.

Leah added two sachets of sugar to her insipid, froth-covered cappuccino and stirred it with the little plastic stick. When she spoke again, she did so with her head down, watching the coffee swirl and slow to a stop. 'After they took us away from our mum, they put us

176

with that Jane woman. She was an emergency placement. She was supposed to be experienced. Must've been, I suppose, or they'd not have given her us two. But she was a cow. A vicious old cow!'

The two older women at the next table stiffened, and Cassie saw their eyes flick on and off Leah, disapproval hardening their expressions. Leah didn't notice or, more accurately, she didn't care.

'She'd had loads of kids. Did it for the money. Her and her creepy husband...always wanting you to sit on his knee – he needed sorting out. They were supposed to look after us until they found a family that would take us both.'

'How can you even remember any of this? You'd have only been, what – seven or eight?'

'I can remember enough. It's not the sort of stuff you forget. They hated me. They loved you. You were cute. I wasn't. They said I was trouble.' Leah paused, then dealt the blow. 'They split us up. Sent me away. Kept you, until you got adopted.'

'But aren't they supposed to keep siblings together?' Cassie asked. Leah shrugged. She ripped open one of the spare sugar sachets, spilling the contents all over the table. The old women at the next table exchanged another look. 'I mean, brothers and sisters.'

Leah sent Cassidie a sharp look. 'I know what *siblings* means!'

'Sorry.' Chastised, Cassie shut up.

'They're supposed to, yeah.'

'So why not us?'

'I just said. First Jane, then your "parents", Leah used air quotes and her expression plainly expressed her dislike, 'they only wanted *you*.'

'So what happened to you?'

Leah split open another sachet and poured more sugar across the table. 'That's a long story...for another day. I don't want to talk about that today.' She zipped up her jacket and Cassie expected her to bolt off again, but she leant back in her seat. They sat in silence, each inside their heads, Cassie picking at the scab of her parents' deceit, Leah debating exactly what Cassidie should be told, and when.

Cassie spoke first. 'I still don't understand. Even if they had their reasons for not taking both of us…' she saw Leah's eyes darken, but ploughed on, 'why have they never told me about you? All these years – they've acted like you never existed.'

'Why would they say anything? They got what they wanted. You.'

Cassie felt horribly trapped. Tom and Grace were her life, her stability, her family. They had loved her and raised her. She loved them. But they'd never uttered a single word about her having a sister. Even in the past month, with all the talk about whether she should be looking for her biological mum or not. Nothing. Not a single mention of a sister. Again the creeping ill-ease returned. Leah knew things – things that only someone closely involved with Cassie's early life could know – yet did that mean what she said was true?

'It doesn't make sense. Why did they split us up, really?' Cassie persevered.

'Cos they could,' Leah said.

'No. It can't be as simple as that. There has to have been another reason. If Mum and Dad had known about you, they would have taken us both, especially my mum.' Cassie's voice sounded childish, even to herself.

'Would they now? Are you sure?' Leah really was asking. Cassie hesitated for too long. 'Don't fucking believe me then!'

The old women hastily gathered their bags and left.

Cassie stumbled on, in the face of Leah's anger. 'I do. I believe you. I'm sorry. But I'm struggling to get my head round it.'

Leah suddenly leant forward. 'It's not complicated, Cassidie. You were what they wanted. What they all want: little, sweet, nice, no trouble. And I wasn't.'

'But you were just a little girl. You needed looking after as much as me.'

Leah blinked, and for a second Cassie caught a glimpse of something buried deep inside her that didn't match the brittle 'fuck you' attitude that she projected. 'Yeah, well...'

'I'm going to ask my parents,' Cassie said.

'No!' It was so loud that everyone turned and looked at them. 'No. Don't!' Leah repeated. 'If you breathe a word about me to them, you'll not hear from me agen. Ever.'

'But why?'

Leah's face was impenetrable again. A trap snapped shut. 'Cos they've no right knowing anything about me.'

Cassie felt like crying, but she knew Leah would despise her if she did. She wanted the truth, but she was no longer sure who could give it to her; and yet she knew, in her bones, that Leah was somehow the key to the past. She had to give her the benefit of the doubt. 'Okay. I won't say anything. I want us to keep in touch, to keep talking, now we've found each other. It's important.'

Leah picked up her phone. 'Good. Our little secret, then. No one else's. And I mean *no one!*'

Cassie nodded, but she felt anxious rather than excited by the thought. Then, to her dismay, Leah stood up and started gathering her stuff together.

'I gotta go.' The tone was mocking again. Combative. 'I can't spend all day sitting around here, drinking coffee, even if you can.'

'What? Now? But we haven't talked about our mum at all. What you remember about her. Please, Leah, stay. I've come all this way to see you. I need you to tell me about her. You're the only person who can!'

Leah looked down at her. 'Not now. Like I said, I gotta go. Places to go, people to see. I'll text ya.' And with that, she slid out of her seat and out of the cafe, and it was as if she'd never been there.

Chapter 30

TOM PULLED in as soon as he saw a space. There was no point driving into Flo's cul-de-sac as he knew, from experience, that it would be blocked by cars, most of them looking like they'd been abandoned rather than parked.

They climbed out in silence. Of the four door slams, Cassie's was the loudest. Tom and Grace had insisted that she come with them. It had not gone down well. It was as if Cassie was allergic to them at present. Tom carried the beer, Grace a big Tupperware box full of cakes, and Erin the gift. Cassie bore nothing, other than an air of studied martyrdom. Tom took a deep breath and promised himself that he would not rise to her silent provocation. They fell into step, Erin beside him, Cassie up ahead with her mum. Even from behind, it was obvious that they were mother and daughter. The sway of the hips, the lift of their feet, the deceptive speed: little traits that were identical. The irony of Cassie's physical fit within their family seemed more of a taunt than a reassurance to Tom than ever before. Their daughter, but not. The past month had brought that home to Tom and Grace in no uncertain way.

Within a minute, Grace and Cassie were a good fifty metres ahead. Tom let them go – the more distance, the better. His renewed attempts to communicate with his eldest daughter had been met with stony resistance. He had tried, he really had, but Cassie had blocked him with a wall of monosyllabic answers and minuscule shoulder shrugs. He watched them turn the corner and disappear from sight, with something akin to relief. Feeling the need for kinder contact, he linked his arm through Erin's. Her silence was companionable, free of sharp splinters. He squeezed her arm. 'Byron's going to be there,' he teased her. Byron, Sharee's youngest son, was back from university on a visit. Erin had always had a soft spot for her cousin.

'Don't you dare, Dad!' Erin warned.

'You could show him some of your drawings,' Tom teased, aware of his own cheesiness. His reward was a thump on the arm.

The party was well under way by the time they arrived. It was Flo and Ray's twenty-eighth wedding anniversary. Any excuse for a party was a good excuse for Flo. 'Why wait,' she'd laughed when she rang to invite them, 'we'll only be two years older and two stone fatter, if we leave it.' There was already a landslide of food and booze on offer, but Tom and Grace added their contributions to the pile. Relieved of his beer barricade, Tom submitted to the obligatory round of welcoming hugs and kisses. Grace's family were very tactile, their physical boundaries non-existent – and that was before they'd had a drink.

Flo appeared, resplendent in a red-and-purple dress that was just a little bit too tight and quite a lot too loud. 'Hi. Come on through! Erin, your grandpa's out in the back garden. Would you be a love and take him this?' She passed Erin a can of Guinness. 'Help yourselves to a drink. There are cold ones in the fridge. I'll be back in a minute. I just need to dig out some more loo rolls.'

Erin took the beer and went off to find Pete. The way that Grace's family had absorbed Pete into their midst so thoroughly, since the death of Tom's mum, was one of life's surprises and blessings. It had been a process of slow osmosis. It had started with the occasional impromptu visit, and developed into Sharee picking Pete up for Sunday lunch once a month. Now he had a standing invitation to every family event and gathering. They never took 'No' for an answer. And by such open-hearted, concerted stealth they had loudly and unapologetically saved Pete from himself, and from his stoic but suffocating grief.

Tom looked out through the open conservatory doors and spotted his dad, sitting listening to one of Ray's friends: Ty, or was it Eddie? Whoever it was, they were obviously telling some tall tale, judging by the flamboyant hand-gestures. Pete looked bemused, but quite content. At the sight of his granddaughter picking her way towards him through the scatter of people and folding chairs, Pete's face broke into a full-on smile. Pleased to see his dad so thoroughly ensconced in the heart of Grace's family, Tom turned to consider the vast collection of soft drinks on the counter top, then went and fetched a cold beer from the fridge. One wouldn't hurt. He hadn't even closed the fridge door before Grace took it from him and flipped off the cap with a 'Why, thank you! How thoughtful.'

Grace sipped her beer and let herself be sucked into the currents, and undercurrents, of the party. She half-listened to Sharee sniping, none too subtly, about how much Ray had spent on the party, by which she really meant Flo; and she feigned interest in Jade's niece's elaborate wedding plans. Next she found herself stooping down to listen, with genuine sympathy, as Auntie Rita whispered her way through the lowlights of her recent bout of radiotherapy. Byron wandered into their orbit, to kiss them both and say 'Hi', but drifted away quickly when he caught the topic of conversation. Rita had bowel cancer. She never named the disease out loud, none of the family did; they all seemed to share a deep-seated superstition that, in naming the malignance that was eating away at Rita, they would somehow increase its power. Grace admired Auntie Rita's fortitude in the face of her illness and with the obtuseness of the family. She took hold of Rita's arthritis-gnarled hand and promised to pray for her. After she'd left her aunt in the safe care of Faye, Grace somehow got dragged into a discussion about school discipline or, more accurately, the appalling lack of it, with her ebullient cousin Leon and his silent wife.

Twenty minutes later Grace was still only a halfway across the room. Her target destination – an empty chair, in the sun, in the garden – seemed a very long way off. She was still nodding non-committally along to Leon's strong views on grammar schools when she felt a hand brush across her bottom. She looked around, expecting Tom at best, or at worst Dennis, an old neighbour who always invited himself over whenever Flo had an open house, but there was no one there. She'd been mistaken. But a second later she felt it again. This time when she twisted round, she realised it wasn't a hand that was touching her, it was the pressure of a little head. Lexie, Ty's granddaughter, was standing behind her, trapped in the sea of legs, her thumb wedged in her mouth.

Grace crouched down so that she was face-to-face with the little girl. 'Hi, Lexie. Are you all right, honey?' The little girl nodded, but continued to suck her thumb as if her life depended on it. 'Do you know where your mummy is?' Lexie shook her head. 'Do you want to come with me and we'll go and find her?'

Lexie took a moment to consider this offer, then she unplugged her thumb and let Grace take her hand. Despite the sticky dampness of her fingers, Grace smiled.

Cassie had parked herself in the doorway between the kitchen and the back room. She stood fiddling with her necklace, wishing herself anywhere other then where she was. Family parties – she felt like she'd been to hundreds of the bloody things. They always went on for ever and, no matter what her mum said, they never *only stayed for an hour or so*. It was always the same people, having the same tedious conversations, about the same things. It was always the same food, and there was always too much of it. And the parties always started out loud, and got louder and louder as the beer and the wine flowed. She really wasn't in the mood.

A parade of relatives trooped past her. They all said 'hello' and asked her how sixth form was going. She cut off any further conversation by keeping her responses very short, and not very sweet. Cassie could see her mother working her way round the room, spending time with everyone, smiling and chatting and listening patiently – even to the old ones who did nothing but moan on about their ailments. Her mother was so patient, so kind, so bloody nice! Or so everyone thought. She was talking to Leon now. He was awful, always banging on about something. Even with him Grace was being polite. What a hypocrite!

Suddenly, mid-conversation, her mum disappeared from view. Cassie watched as the kaleidoscope of people in the room shifted, a blur of noise and colour, then a gap opened up, revealing her mother. She was crouched down, talking to a little girl in a painfully pink dress. The little girl had her back to Cassie. She was tiny. The biggest thing about her was her hair, which was caught up in two huge bunches on either side of her head. Amidst the sea of people, Grace and the little girl were having a private moment, suspended in a bubble of light and quiet. When Grace straightened up and took the little girl's hand, Cassie looked away, too confused by the emotions raging through her to watch any more.

The kitchen was as jam-packed as the rest of the house. Cassie edged around the bodies of her many relatives carefully, making sure she didn't come into contact with any of them, heading towards the drinks. There was a whole counter top of booze. Name your poison and there was probably a bottle of it open. She searched around until she found a clean glass on the draining board. She poured herself half a glass of

Coke, then she picked up the vodka and clumsily splashed some in. She screwed the lid back on the bottle, picked up her drink and took a big gulp. As she did so, her eyes met those of her mother. Cassie took a second swallow of fizzy alcohol, without breaking eye contact.

Ten minutes later her glass was empty. She reached for the Coke again.

'Go steady, love.' Grace appeared at her side.

Cassie could already feel the fuzziness in her head and the loosening in her spine. She reached for the vodka bottle again. The cool metal lid felt lovely under her fingertips. She slowly unscrewed the cap and placed it very carefully on the worktop. She didn't want to lose it – that would be irresponsible. The vodka made a nice, heavy glugging noise. Her mother watched as she filled the glass to the top, her face pleading. Cassie ignored her and took another sweet mouthful.

'Cassie, please.'

She raised her glass to her mother, a mocking toast, and Grace turned and walked away. But then she was back, in what seemed like a flash, this time with her dad in tow. Cassie was curious to see how this little stand-off was going to play out.

'That's enough, Cassie.' Her dad actually went to snatch the glass out of her hand. How rude was that? Cassie jerked her drink away and a spray of brown liquid leapt out of the glass and splashed across her mother's top. The sight of it made her laugh. While she was momentarily distracted by their stupidly shocked faces, Tom succeeded in grabbing the glass and pulling it forcefully away from her. Cassie was infuriated. How dare he? She swung her hand into the air and connected with his arm. Then he shocked her by grabbing her forearm, hard. 'Cass, stop this, right now!' They were actually wrestling with each other. Cassie, in a haze of indignation, was determined not to give in. Tom was equally adamant. 'We're leaving! Grace, go and find Erin. I'll get her out to the car.'

'Her.' They were talking about her as if she was a naughty child.

'I don't want to go home!' Cassie hissed. She was too steamed up to notice the embarrassed shuffle of relatives as they looked anywhere but at Tom and his daughter. Quite a few of them suddenly decided it was time they sought out some relative they'd only just spotted, for a chat.

Tom started tugging at Cassie. She pulled back. It was an ungainly, almost comical tug-of-war that widened the circle of space and bad feeling that surrounded them.

'Cassie, that's enough. You're not going to spoil the party for everyone else. Come on. You need to come home, now.' Tom yanked at her again.

'You're hurting me!' Even she could hear that she was yelling.

'Cassie!' Tom tugged vainly at his daughter, fearful of actually hurting her, but determined to get her out of the kitchen, out of the house and away from the prying eyes of the other party-goers. Cassie's body jerked and he suddenly lost his grasp. She cannoned backwards and crashed into the sink. There was a clatter of glasses and a weird ringing sound as the bottles of booze rattled against each other.

'Ow!' She clutched at her side, possibly in real pain, but possibly not. She looked down and saw her necklace on the sticky floor amongst the crud. Her favourite necklace. Her nicest necklace. The one Ryan had given her. Her dad had broken it deliberately – that's how spiteful he was. She picked it up, at the second attempt, and glared at him. Neither of them backed down, they were too wrapped up in the intensity of the moment. More relatives fled the scene.

Unnoticed, a stern-faced Grace reappeared, followed by Erin.

When Erin stepped into the kitchen, it seemed to go silent. She looked at her dad and saw his clenched fists. She looked at Cassie and saw that she was staring intently at something in her hand. Her sister's face was a mish-mash of distress and anger; her dad's the same. 'What's going on?'

At the sight of Erin, both Tom and Cassie came to their senses. Cassie straightened up and Tom relaxed his hands. The clamour of blood rushing through their veins was still fast and loud, but it was diluted by an injection of shame.

It was enough to stop the fight.

They left in single file, Grace leading the way, with Tom and Cassie following and Erin bringing up the rear, a gap between each of them.

Chapter 31

NAZ HAD called round to see Leah after some *meet* he'd been at, with some *big shot* that he knew, about *some business* he was doing. He was buzzing, hyperactive, bouncing around the flat with an excess of adrenaline. And it was just adrenaline. Naz didn't touch booze or drugs. He wasn't a sucker! What Naz got off on was reputation, pecking orders, dog-eat-dog, getting one over on someone else, moving up through the ranks, getting respect…that, and the money, of course. Leah tried to follow what he was banging on about, but she was finding it hard to concentrate. She nodded – hopefully in the right places – and kept her responses to a minimum.

He didn't like her drinking, said he hated the smell of it on her, but fuck him – if he left her home alone, what did he expect? Drinking smudged time, dulled the edges, drowned out the voices. What else was a girl supposed to do on her own, in a shitty flat, on a sunny weekend? This afternoon's little treat had been vodka and Coke, until the Coke ran out; then it had been just vodka, until the vodka ran out. She really needed to focus on what he was saying, but he kept circling the room. It was making her dizzy. Leah knew she was getting it wrong; she could tell by the way Naz kept looking at her that she was not supplying the required level of enthusiastic adoration. The booze had blunted her brain, and that was dangerous. Thankfully, her self-preservation instincts were still intact. He needed distracting, and fast. It took a heroic effort to get up off the sofa and slide over to him.

Twenty minutes later she lay on her front, waiting for him to finish. She couldn't breathe properly, but there was comfort to be had in burying her head in the pillow, muffling the sound of him, letting his weight push down on top of her. It helped her to peel her thoughts away from her body. She imagined herself being pressed through the sheet into the dense wadding of the mattress – her body sieving between the sharp springs – dropping through the cheap bed slats onto the thin carpet, and from there on through the floorboards – her bones splitting and splintering against the thick, resistant wood – on into the thin layers of plaster and paint and the spider's web of wires, on through the ceiling…until she fell, free, into the flat below.

He finished.

There was a long pause. The weight of him was intolerable. It was squeezing the air out of her lungs. Thankfully, he rolled off. She breathed again. They lay still for a few minutes.

Slowly Leah lifted her head off the pillow and turned her face towards him. He was staring into space, absent-mindedly stroking his belly. His eyelids drooped. Three minutes later he was asleep.

She waited another ten before she slid out of bed.

Her skin was a livid pink – at least the parts in the water were. It was a small bath, impossible to submerge yourself completely in it. Leah had tried, more than once, but she'd only succeeded in cascading water all over the floor. She stretched and reached for the tap, adding more hot: boiling away another layer.

Naz walked in without knocking. He was dressed, ready to leave, though his hair was not quite as pristine as usual. 'You should've woken me up. I'm gonna be late.' For what, he didn't say. He always had somewhere else that he needed to be. She didn't respond. He lifted the toilet lid and peed, a long, heavy, pungent stream, which, if he'd shifted his stance even a fraction to the left, would have been straight into her face. When he'd finished, he flushed and zipped himself back up. Then he bent down and plunged his hands into the water, into the space between her legs. Even in her 'heat and vodka'-dowsed state, it gave her a tiny thrill to see him wince at the temperature. Naz feigned indifference, but pulled his hands out, quickly – not, however, before splashing a handful of scaldingly hot water into her eyes. Leah flinched.

Playtime over, she thought he would leave, but instead he put the toilet lid down and sat on it, drying his hands. 'So when am I gonna get to meet her?'

Leah was fairly certain she hadn't mentioned Cassidie's latest visit to him, but she couldn't be sure. Booze did that, loosened words and thoughts that should be kept screwed down. It was a rookie error. She knew that Naz was a hoarder of information. It was one of his skills, keeping tabs on people and things that might be of use to him; and Cassidie was, potentially, very useful. Leah had known, the moment she'd mentioned Cassidie, that he was interested – unhealthily interested. She sat up and gestured for a towel, buying time. He ignored the request.

'Soon,' she conceded. Something in her wanted to keep Cassidie to herself, at least for a little while longer.

He relented and passed her the towel. 'I wanna meet her. See what she's like. Different to you, I'm guessing.' He meant better. He stood up, glanced down. 'Text me, when it's set up.' It was an instruction, not a request. Leah dried her face, smothering her response. 'I'm looking forward to it,' he grinned. 'It's about time we had some fun.

Chapter 32

GRACE HAD fabricated a reason to work from home: a presentation that needed her full attention, but the fact that she'd been sitting pointlessly in front of the same half-finished chart for the past ten minutes was testament to the truth that there was no peace to be found at home, either.

Cassie had thrown up on the way home from the party, all over the back seat of the car and all over Erin. They'd pulled over and tried their best to clean the girls up, but Grace's handy pack of tissues had been wholly inadequate for the job. Erin kept saying, 'It's fine. It'll wash out. It doesn't matter' as she flicked lumps of half-digested food off her jeans. Cassie had vomited again, into the gutter, retching noisily once, twice, three times. It was Erin who had comforted her, patting her back and moving strands of sticky hair away from her face, indifferent to the mess and any embarrassment. Getting back into the car had been an ordeal, the smell nauseating, even with the windows wound down. It had felt like a very long drive home.

Back at the house, Grace had forced Cassie to drink two glasses of water before supervising the collection of the soiled clothes, while Tom was left to tackle the carnage in the back of the car. Erin absented herself as soon as they stepped through the door.

An hour later, with the car scrubbed and airing, the washing machine swishing away and everyone showered, Grace was nominated to go up and speak to Cassie. Tom was still too angry. Cassie was sitting on her bed, swathed in her dressing gown, doing nothing when Grace went into her room – having knocked first.

'Are you all right to talk now?' Grace she asked. Cassie nodded. She still looked ill. Grace sat on the bed. 'What's going on, Cassie? What on earth was that all about?' Cassie sniffed and looked down. Grace steeled herself. 'Cass! Come on.'

She finally looked up. 'I'm sorry.'

Grace held firm. 'As you should be. You need to apologise to Dad, and to Erin.' At the mention of Erin, Cassie blinked. 'And tomorrow I want you to ring Ray and Flo and apologise to both of them for your behaviour.' Cassie nodded. 'Flo has just rung to check that you're okay. She was worried about you.' No response.

They sat in silence, Cassie staring at her duvet, Grace staring at her daughter. Grace's dominant emotion was sadness, but there was anger and impotence mixed in with it as well. It was a queasy, uncomfortable combination. Cassie did not behave like this. She had been brought up to know better. It was inexcusable. Grace tried one last time to crack her daughter's silence. 'Please, Cassie. This isn't you. Talk to me.'

Slowly, but very definitely, Cassie shook her head.

They were failing as parents. Everything about Cassie's behaviour was screaming 'Help me' and yet they weren't; they were standing back and watching her drown. Grace couldn't bear it. Work would have to wait. She shut down the presentation and instead looked up the contact number for Gail. When she finally got through, Gail wasn't available. Grace insisted on speaking to her as soon as possible. When the voice on the other end of the line enquired if it was an emergency, Grace said 'Yes'.

She still had to wait a couple of hours before her phone rang. Gail apologised. 'Sorry. We're under the cosh a bit this month – we've a number of colleagues off sick. What's happened?' Grace related the changes in Cassie's personality and described, briefly but honestly, the debacle at the party. She lost confidence and momentum as she spoke. Cassie's behaviour was hardly intolerable, and Gail was presumably used to much worse. But to Grace's surprise, her response was sympathetic. 'I can see why you're worrying. Look, I've had a little more information come back about Cassie's birth family, but I'm afraid I've another meeting I need to go into now.' Grace heard the rustling of papers and the clunk of something connecting with the receiver. 'I've an hour tomorrow morning. How about we meet up? If you could come here, that would be a great help. I'm in court at ten a.m., but I'm free before that.'

Grace agreed immediately.

They arrived at 8 a.m. They were buzzed straight through to the office. Gail wasn't the only one at her desk; at least half of the poky workstations were already occupied. The phones rang intermittently, persistently, as if whoever was on the end of the line was used to having to wait to have their needs met.

Gail waved at them, a cheap notepad clutched in her hand. She showed them into one of the conference rooms. They shook hands across the table. Gail Mason was a small woman of indeterminate age, brisk, friendly. 'Thank you for coming in to see me. I would've liked to come to see you at home, but I'm afraid – with workloads as they are – home visits are a *luxury* we have to reserve for our more challenging families.' As an ice-breaker, it wasn't wholly appropriate, but Grace smiled, indicating their gratitude that Gail had managed to fit them in at all at such short notice.

They took a seat. Gail put her notepad on the table. On the wall facing them was a pinboard. Neatly displayed on the board were a number of posters promoting adoption and fostering. The sunlit, happy children looked exactly the same as the ones in the leaflets they'd been given all those years ago – the same images of promise and perfection. Not the truth, but a well-intentioned deceit.

Gail smiled at them kindly. 'I gather, from talking to Grace, that Cassie is still quite unsettled at present. That she's frustrated by the lack of progress regarding her birth family.' They nodded. 'Well, I'll start with what we haven't had any success with – her biological mother. We've searched as thoroughly as we've been able to, but I'm afraid we've drawn a blank. She certainly isn't in our system in any way that I can determine. That could mean any number of things: that she's moved out of the area, though I did try a national search and still got nothing; or that she hasn't had any further recourse to our services. Once an adoption is complete, as you know, that can be the end of it. So I'm afraid it's a dead-end. That isn't to say that other voluntary or private agencies might not be able to help you – and Cassie – but I'm afraid I've exhausted our resources.'

'Might she be dead?'

The brutality of Tom's question didn't seem to bother Gail in the slightest. 'She might be. I couldn't say. You'd have to pursue that information yourselves.' She glanced down at the notebook on the table, but didn't open it. 'In terms of her sibling, however, there have been some developments. Adult services have been very helpful actually. She obviously left the care system at eighteen, but a colleague followed up her Letterbox details and found a contact number and an address for her on file.' Grace felt Tom stiffen in his seat. 'We got in touch—'

Tom blurted out, 'What!'

Gail paused. 'You did ask us to pursue Cassie's remaining connections. The only way to do that is to seek their permission. Without it, any release of information or any contact is a non-starter.' Grace forced out another smile. Gail continued. 'My colleague called her.

In this day and age, and with that age group, letters and emails tend to fall on deaf ears, the direct approach often works better. After a number of attempts he managed to have a conversation with her.'

'And?' Tom asked.

'I'm afraid she was uncooperative. In fact, I gather she was quite hostile.' Tom breathed out. 'My colleague explained the situation, with regard to there being an expression of interest from her birth sibling. We of course didn't tell her anything specific about yourselves, or Cassie's situation, location, et cetera...but she was very clear that she was unwilling to have any contact, of any kind.'

'So that's it,' Tom said with studied neutrality.

'For now, I'm afraid so,' Gail said.

'Did she say anything about the letters? Had she received them? Read them?' Grace ignored Tom's sharp glance.

'I'm not sure they were even discussed. I gather she was very unwilling to engage in any meaningful conversation.' Gail looked sympathetic. Tom's hand on hers told Grace to 'leave it!' Gail continued, 'People do sometimes change their minds, of course, but it didn't sound as if that was likely with Cassie's sister. And there's nothing we can do to compel contact. That wouldn't work anyway. It has to be mutual, for anything good to come out of it.'

'So what do we say to Cassie?' Grace asked.

Gail reflected, but only for a second or two. 'I suggest you're honest with her. It's normally the best policy. Tell her the truth.' Tom and Grace didn't look at each other and Gail misinterpreted their hesitation. 'We do have specialist counselling services. I'd be happy to refer Cassie to one of our schemes, if you'd like me to, but there's a waiting list and,' she fiddled with the spirals on the pad, 'my personal advice is to try to work through it as a family. In my experience, some of our sessions – they're group sessions, with peers, young people in the same situation – well...' she hesitated, 'what I'm trying to say is that as good as they are – and they *are* good – there is a tendency for the group dynamic to encourage rather than dampen their fascination with their pasts. We can control the meetings themselves to an extent, but with social media,' she shrugged, 'it can all take on a life of its own. Given how close you obviously are as a family, I'd stick to what you seem to be doing: loving her and letting Cassie know that you love her. I'm sure it will calm down with time.' Gail stood up and shook their hands. 'Ring me, any time, if you feel that I can be of any further assistance.' And she guided them out of the room and out of the office.

Tom and Grace walked out onto the street and stopped. Their cars were parked in different car parks and they needed to go their separate ways, but they both paused, unwilling to pick up their normal, everyday responsibilities. A coffee shop across the road resolved the problem. It wasn't busy at this early hour, but they still instinctively chose a table at the back, away from the counter and the slow footfall of customers.

'I assumed that she'd been found a family,' Grace said.

Tom took a second to catch up. 'Leah?'

'Of course Leah! Did you hear Gail let slip that she was in care all her life, until she was eighteen?' Grace felt an awkward, sharp pain at the thought of Cassie's sister, in the system, on her own. She recognised that pain as guilt.

'Yes. I heard her.' Tom had put a lid on any reaction to the news of Leah's fate. It was, if he was honest, what he'd expected. 'At least we know for certain that Leah has no interest in Cassie. "Hostile", that was the description Gail used, that she was "hostile to contact".'

'I can imagine that she was.' Grace shifted in her seat, but the pain tucked in between her ribs wouldn't shift.

'So what *do* we tell Cassie?' Tom asked.

'As Gail said: *the truth*.' Grace knew the answer wasn't as simple as that.

'Meaning?' Tom asked.

'I don't know.' Grace admitted. She felt suffocated.

Tom slid his drink aside and took hold of her hands. 'How about this? We tell her that they tried – they searched their databases – but they couldn't find any information relating to her mum. And, as hard as that is, she's going to have to accept the fact that it's a non-starter. We need to get her to see that she may never be able to find out what happened to her biological mother. I think we have to be very clear about that. Otherwise, this could hang over us for years. It's already screwing things up. We need to put an end to it.' Seeing Grace recoil slightly from such certainty, Tom softened his tone. 'We'll help her, make her see that it doesn't matter. We just have to get past this, and what Gail has said today has got to help.'

'But is that enough? What about Leah?'

'Grace, it *is* enough. It's more than enough for her to have to cope with. Imagine us breaking the news that her birth mother is, in all likelihood, never going to be found, then hitting her with an elder sister she never knew about – who exists, but who won't have anything to do with her.'

They both sat in silence for a moment, contemplating how such a revelation might go down, and the damage it would do to their relationship with their daughter. It made them both feel ill.

Tom went on. 'If – and it's a big "if" – she decides to pursue it any further when she's older, maybe then we'll have to handle it, but not now. I think if we tell her now, it will totally mess with her head. Besides, Gail said nothing to suggest that Leah's behavioural problems have gone away. If anything, they're probably worse now, after all those years in care. We don't want to let anything like that near Cassie.'

Tom's arguments carried weight, but Grace still felt trapped by their wilful denial of Leah, Cassie's only known flesh-and-blood relative. But it wasn't only their deceit that was bothering Grace; it was the thought of all the years Leah had spent in care. She had written the updates to Leah, imagining, if not an idyllic life, then at least a decent foster family. It was awful to think that as she'd been detailing their happy, cosy existence, Leah had been adrift; without parents, without stability, without protection. If only she'd known, if only she'd bothered to find out – but she hadn't.

And, in truth, what would she have done if she had known?

Nothing.

Grace was honest enough with herself to know that they would have done absolutely nothing if they'd found out about Leah's fate all those years ago, because by then they loved Cassie as their own, and they'd been blessed with Erin and they were complete. Finally, a proper family. The pain beneath her ribcage pulsed.

Tom was still talking. 'Think about it. What good will it do, telling Cassie? None. It's too late now. It would be cruel to tell her just to salve our consciences.'

Grace couldn't disagree with his logic, but she still hated the weight of the deceit. She took a few breaths and nodded, glad of Tom's firm grip around her fingers. They sat holding hands, shoring up each other's resolve, until the ringing of Grace's work phone became too insistent to ignore.

Chapter 33

MANCHESTER PICCADILLY Station was very different from Oldham. Buzzing, busy, much slicker, more anonymous. Cassie stood waiting underneath the departure boards, as agreed. Leah was late, as expected. She'd called the day before and sounded as if she was going to pull out of meeting up again. It had been a staccato conversation. At first, all Cassie could hear was background noise.

'Leah?' Something clattered on the other end of the line. 'Leah? Is that you?'

'Yeah.' Her voice sounded flat and lifeless, as if all the air had been punched out of her.

'Are you still on for meeting up on Friday afternoon?'

'I can't.' Leah's voice was distant, as if she wasn't actually speaking into her phone.

'Why?' Cassie asked.

'What?' Leah sounded distracted.

'Are we meeting or not?'

'I was just talking to someone else.' Leah's voice drifted away again.

'Look, if you're too busy.'

'It's not that. It's…wait, can't ya?' This seemed to be aimed at someone with her. There was a pause, then she said, 'I'm 'aving some grief off the council. They're being twats about my rent.' Cassie had no idea what to say. There was more talking in the background. 'Yeah, in a minute.' Again, this wasn't aimed at Cassie. Then Leah was back. 'I can meet, but it'll have to be tomorrow, and in town. I'll text ya.'

Hence Piccadilly, and another day of skipped college and more lies to her parents.

Cassie suddenly stumbled forward, bashing into a couple who were passing by. They harrumphed and hurried away. Someone had thumped into her, hard.

'Soz.' Leah smiled, thinly.

Cassie hadn't expected such a sudden, physical – playful? – greeting. It seemed out of character, but then what did she really know about Leah's personality? It all felt so awkward and false. 'Where'd you come from?' she asked.

'Naz dropped me off in town.'

'Oh.' Cassie had no idea who Naz was. She thought it best not to ask. 'Where do you want to go?'

Leah scanned the concourse. 'There's a Maccie D's.'

Standing in line, Cassie wondered what people made of them. A posh mixed-race girl and a not-posh-at-all white girl – a world of difference in the way they looked, sounded, even in the way they stood. Not natural friends, not obviously related, so what, then? At the counter Cassie panicked, not knowing what she wanted. The server asked for her order again, like a robot. Leah cut across her and ordered a burger meal – large – with a doughnut. Cassie, just to get away from the counter, asked for an ice-cream sundae. As their order was dumped on to the tray, Cassie realised that her choice made her look like an eight-year-old.

She paid and was relieved to follow Leah up the stairs to the big seating area. It was rammed, not the best place for a private conversation, but Leah seemed unfazed. She weaved through the crowds, aiming for a free table near the back wall. Leah ate quickly.

Cassie toyed with her sticky ice-cream-and-caramel mess. Neither of them seemed able, or inclined, to be the first to start talking.

Burger finished, Leah wiped her fingers and tossed her serviette onto the table. 'You didn't say owt to your parents, did ya?'

'No,' Cassie said.

'Good.' Leah picked at the remnants of her fries. 'What're they like?' She wanted to stoke the embers.

Jesus, how was Cassie supposed to answer that? 'They're okay. Grace, my mum, works at an insurance company, and my dad, Tom, at a design agency.' Head of department and partner respectively, but Cassie had enough awareness not to crow. Leah didn't react. Cassie couldn't tell whether she was bored or angry.

'And?' Leah was beyond angry, but she gave no sign of it.

'Well, they're just normal.' 'Cassie-normal', which was not, she suspected, the same as 'Leah-normal'.

'Do they treat you different?'

'Sorry, what?'

Leah flicked a burnt chip on the floor. 'Do they treat you different to their real daughter?'

Cassie was taken aback. Again a rush of uncertainty and suspicion swept through her. How did Leah know about Erin? Had she been there, at Subway, all along?

'No.'

Leah shoved her fries box away and, in the process, knocked over Cassie's ice-cream. The girls watched the slow ooze of unnaturally white ice-cream, caramel and nut bits spread across the table top. Cassie righted the cup and tried to mop up the worst of it with a handful of serviettes. Leah didn't apologise.

Cassie risked a direct request of her own. 'Leah, I want you to tell me about our mum.'

'What do you wanna know?' So finally they were getting round to it.

'What was she like?'

Leah screwed up her face, a parody of thinking. 'Like?' She was in no rush to supply details.

'Yes, what was she like?'

Leah shrugged. 'She was a piss-head.' She took pleasure in seeing Cassidie flinch.

But Cassie was stronger than Leah was giving her credit for. 'I know that. But I want to know what living with her was like. What sort of mum was she?'

'A crap one.' Leah leant back against the rigid moulded seat and stared Cassidie down, or at least tried to.

Cassie wasn't going to give up without a fight. 'Leah, please. You're the only person who can tell me anything about her. All I've ever heard is how useless she was, how she couldn't cope, about her drinking and her mental-health problems, but nothing about her as a person. You remember her. You're the only one who can help me. I want to know.'

'Oh, I remember her all right.' Leah said.

'So, please, tell me. Tell me anything, even if it's something really small.'

Leah bit the skin at the edge of her fingernail. It bled. ''Kay.' There was a long pause and Cassie waited, frightened about what Leah would choose to share. The insight she got was not what she was expecting. Even Leah surprised herself by starting with a truth. 'She liked dogs. She was forever coming home from the shops or the pub with 'em, puppies especially. She just *loved* puppies! Let 'em chew everything, piss on everything. She'd be all over 'em – at first; buying 'em sparkly collars, letting 'em kiss her face, coochy-cooing at 'em all the time. Then she'd get bored. Let 'em run off, or she'd give 'em away. Too much hassle. Everything was too much hassle for her, in the end.' Cassie didn't know what to do with this glimpse of her mother, other than feel bad: for herself, and for Leah. It was like wading into dark water, uncertain of her footing, with the current tugging and pushing at her.

But Leah was on a roll. 'Oh, and she liked a party. Before it got bad, it was any old excuse – anything to get her out of the shit-heap we lived in. She'd find money for a new dress easy enough, if she was off out. Get her nails done. It was always a sign that she was about to piss off: a full set of fake nails.'

Cassie could feel her past starting to stick to her. She lowered her head and tried to breathe slowly. She hadn't ever really thought of her birth mother as an actual person before all this started; she'd been just a blank outline drawn for her by other people. Cassie couldn't remember her face or her voice, nothing specific about her at all, except...except there were the glimpses from her dreams, the messy fragments of affection and kindness, mixed in with the sense of isolation and threat. It was all so confusing. She didn't know what to do with Leah's version of their mother. There had to be more to their childhood than the sorry image of selfishness and neglect that both her parents and Leah were depicting. Hadn't there? And Leah seemed to be deriving a cruel kind of pleasure from rubbing Cassie's nose in the bad bits. Was that because of what had happened afterwards, because of how differently their lives had turned out? Cassie could understand it, but she didn't want to accept what Leah was saying as gospel. The challenge was how to get beyond her bitterness and jealousy.

Cassie looked up and fought back. 'I remember music and someone dancing with me.'

'Well, it weren't her!' Leah snapped. 'She did her dancing in clubs and pubs, she wasn't fussy – anywhere there were blokes with money in their crotch pockets. What else explains us two!' That again was true, but she would have to watch herself; it was a fast becoming a habit, this telling-the-truth lark. She looked at Cassidie and felt a flush of irritation at the sight of her hopeful, naïve expression. 'What did you expect?

Some crap about how she loved us really. That if only things had been different, we'd 'ave been a happy little family. She was a terrible mum. She was pissed or high most of the time. There was never any food in the house. She'd disappear when it suited her, for days on end sometimes. She was nicer to the fucking dogs than to her own kids. And that was before she started letting every scumbag from a ten-mile radius doss in the house. I hope she is dead. She fucking deserves to be!'

It was too much. The waters were too deep and Cassie was drowning. She sat, surrounded by slack-faced strangers eating chips, and cried, quietly, steadily. She wanted Leah to stop, to just shut up. Leah watched her, her face impassive.

Out of nowhere someone intervened. 'Are you all right, love? Is this lass bothering you?' It was the table cleaner, a white-haired old man with a cloth in his hand.

Leah glared at him and Cassie was tempted to say 'Yes' and put an end to it there and then, but there were still so many questions, so much that was unresolved. 'No. It's fine. Sorry. We're fine. Honestly. Thank you.' She wiped her eyes and forced a smile.

Leah settled back in her uncomfortable seat, challenging him to take it any further. The old guy glanced between them and shrugged, as if to say *Who knows what goes on between folk*, then struggled down on one knee and wiped up the puddle of melted ice-cream. They waited in awkward silence until he'd finished and moved away.

When he'd finally gone, Cassie said the first thing that came into her mind. 'I'm sorry.'

Leah blinked. 'Wot?'

'I said, I'm sorry. I'm sorry that you remember it, and that it still hurts so much.'

In response Leah made odd movement, a mixture of puffing out her chest and crossing her arms across her body, hugging herself – defiance and vulnerability in one contradictory move. 'I've done okay, considering.'

Cassie nodded and dived deeper. 'Do you remember us being taken off her?' Leah nodded, but didn't elaborate. 'Please, Leah, I need you to tell me.'

'Why, what difference will it make?' Leah honestly didn't know.

Both girls were silent for a while. They sat amidst the random assortment of people chewing and slurping their way through their meals. At a table nearby, a baby boy sitting in a high chair was sucking a chip. He paused when he caught Leah's eye and beamed. To Cassie's surprise, Leah smiled back. The smile transformed her face and gave Cassie heart.

'Leah, please. I want to try and understand how it was for you.'

'Okay,' Leah relented. Sympathy-gathering time. She spooled out a little more of the tale, and watched as Cassidie lapped it up. 'I vaguely remember some woman coming. Our mum must've known in advance, cos before she arrived, they cleared off. The house was quiet for the first time in ages.'

'They' – the dark shapes in the room on the left? Cassie didn't dare interrupt the flow of Leah's retelling by asking.

'The woman wasn't a copper. She didn't wear a uniform, didn't have a radio, but she asked a lot of questions. You could tell she weren't happy with what she was seeing.' Leah's voice was monotone. 'She said she'd come back. But she never did. It went back to being shit again.' Her voice started to lift and colour, revealing shades of anger and something else, something much rawer and sadder. 'If anything, it got worse. It weren't safe. I never knew who was downstairs. Keeping you quiet was a fucking nightmare. We were hungry a lot of the time. Who lets their kids go hungry, when there's money for gear?' Leah took a deep breath and got herself back on track; she was supposed to be convincing Cassidie, not seeking counselling. 'Then the police raided – in the middle of the night. They came in mob-handed. There was a lot of shouting and torches. I remember the noise they made, it sounded like thunder coming up the stairs. You were petrified, crying and carrying on. *She* kicked off, of course, started screaming and shouting, saying how much she loved us – that they couldn't just take us away from her. But they did. In a cop-car. We never saw her agen. There was a night or two somewhere – I don't remember where – then we got sent to Jane's. We had nowt with us. Just each other.' It was a good place to stop.

Cassie felt a shiver inside her chest. The thought of those two little girls, clinging onto each other, stripped of all the certainties of safety and love, was awful. Instinctively she felt the urge to reach out and touch Leah, but almost as if she'd anticipated it, Leah shoved her hands deep into her pockets. She took out her phone and checked the time. The screen was smashed, a spider's web of cracks. 'Shit! I'm gonna have to get going.'

Cassie wanted her to stay, but didn't know how to make her.

They stood up and walked out together.

Hitting the busy station concourse was a shock. The restless tide of people and activity was disorientating. Leah turned towards the exits. 'I'm this way.'

Cassie was still holding onto the image of Leah as a small child, abandoned first by their birth mother, then by her own parents. She wanted – needed – to say 'sorry' somehow. The problem with the council: she hadn't even asked. 'Leah, did you get it sorted? Your rent, the deposit thing?'

Leah paused. Bingo! 'Nah. They're claiming I owe them some bond, or summat. Said it was in the contract.' She kept her face turned away. 'They're just gonna have to wait. I ain't got that kind of cash.'

'Can I help?'

Leah stopped walking and turned round.

'How much is it?' Cassie asked.

'Nah.'

'I'd like to,' Cassie insisted.

Leah looked her in the eye. 'Two hundred pounds.'

Cassie didn't blink. She looked round, spotted a cash machine at the far side of the station and set off towards it. Leah followed in her wake. Within a few minutes Cassie was pulling a wodge of twenties out of the machine. She folded them in half and passed them to Leah. 'Take it. Please. I want to help.'

Leah mumbled, 'Thanks' and shoved the money away inside her jacket.

'I'll see you soon, then?' Cassie asked.

'Yeah. Soon.' Leah turned and walked away a few steps, then she stopped. 'I've gotta pick something up for Naz, in town. You can come with me – if you want to?'

Cassie was surprised and touched to be asked. 'Yeah. That'd be good.' She fell into step with Leah as they weaved their way out of the busy concourse.

Chapter 34

SINCE THEIR expedition through the packed streets of Manchester, Cassie had heard nothing from Leah, which was strange because, against the odds, they'd had a good time.

After Leah had eventually found the right shop – some sort of mobile repair place – and collected the package for Naz – something small and insignificant-looking – they'd gone for a wander, shopping without buying. The assistants looking at them with wary suspicion had been new, for Cassie, but it had added an interesting edge of hysteria to the experience. Leah had revealed a cruel but accurate eye. She'd mercilessly mocked their very different tastes, deliberately picking out clothes that she knew full well wouldn't suit Cassie; and they'd had a good time poring over the bargain baskets at the make-up counters. It had been kind of fun, despite the ever-present element of ridicule. But since they'd said goodbye at Piccadilly, there'd been nothing. Cassie found herself checking her phone incessantly.

'Will you *please* put that away?' Her dad's voice was tight with forced politeness. She pushed her phone away from her plate, all of three centimetres. 'I said "away".'

His pissy tone made her seethe. Her mum was no better, her face a picture of concerned disapproval. Even Erin, with her tense shoulders and watchful eyes, was irritating. In that moment Cassie hated it all: the home-cooked meal, the jug of iced water, even the stupid, expensive pepper mill that her dad had an embarrassing habit of grinding with an affected flourish, like waiter in an Italian restaurant. It was all so civilised. Who ate like this any more? She hated them for their pretensions and their fake niceness. They had no idea, any of them. None at all. They were so sealed off from real life, so bloody comfortable and smug.

And it was a sham.

Because they were liars. Flat-out liars. Cassie knew that now. All this time with not so much as a hint that she had a sister. The level of deception was unbelievable. They'd written Leah out of Cassie's history so completely, and so effectively, that she had no memory of her. How could they do such a monstrous thing? Cassie couldn't conceive of a justifiable reason. None. She was itching to call them out on it, shame them, here and now, in front of Erin, as they sat around the dining table pretending to be nice, civilised, loving parents. But Leah's warning stopped her. Leah didn't strike Cassie as the kind of person to make empty threats. If she broke her promise, Leah would disappear. Cassie couldn't bear the thought of that.

Tom scraped his knife across his plate in pursuit of a piece of chicken, and Cassie wanted to snatch it off him and fling it across the room. The knowledge of their bare-faced dishonesty burnt inside her. They'd been prepared to let her think she was alone in the world, because it suited them. She couldn't stand being in the same room as them. 'I've had enough.' She put her cutlery down haphazardly, deliberately.

They all looked at her. Her mum questioning, her dad annoyed, her sister pained. Tom cracked first. 'You've barely touched your dinner. And besides, we haven't finished.'

Cassie turned towards him and announced, 'Well, I have.' As she picked up her phone, it buzzed. In defiance of her father, she checked to see who the message was from, then opened it and read it.

'Cassie!' Tom warned. He held his voice steady. 'I'd like you to do as asked, please. Your mum has cooked a nice meal for us all, so the least you can do is have the common courtesy to eat some of it.'

'I'm not hungry.'

'Fine,' Tom said through gritted teeth, 'but I'd appreciate it if you could stay at the table until we finish ours.'

Cassie caught a look pass between Grace and Tom, but her mother did not argue with her dad's sudden swerve into Victorian parenting. There followed another five minutes of excruciating chewing and scraping. Cassie didn't eat another bite. She sat with her arms folded, watching them. The second Tom put down his knife and fork, Cassie made a move – Erin still had half her dinner left, Grace likewise.

'Sit down.' Tom's patience stretched and pinged. Grace's hands fluttered to her throat.

Erin quickly pushed her plate aside. 'It's okay. I've had enough.'

'I said, "Sit down!"' Tom repeated.

'Please, Tom. Let her go.' Grace's voice wavered slightly. Cassie was up, out of her seat and across the room in a flash.

'She has no respect for anything any more.' Tom's accusation hung in the air as she slammed out of the front door.

After Cassie's abrupt departure, the energy in the room plummeted, but not the tension. Erin looked at her mum, who nodded, thereby releasing her from her obligation to stay and try and make things better. Grace was worried that Erin's efforts to hold them all together were becoming too much for her; their youngest daughter was looking increasingly tight-wound and unhappy. It was heartbreaking that in failing to *deal* with Cassie, they were also failing to protect Erin.

It was the rapidity with which their family was disintegrating that shocked Grace. Only a few weeks ago they'd been okay, more than okay – they'd been happy, normal, settled. Now nothing felt right. And Cassie was blocking them, refusing to talk to them about the impasse they'd reached. Grace and Tom had both tried, but Cassie simply refused to discuss it. Their relationship seemed to have fallen apart. Yet Grace could feel the roar of emotions surging and pulsing through her daughter. There would be no peace for anyone until all that anger and grief either subsided or exploded.

Tom slumped in his seat. 'Sorry. I know we're supposed to be cutting her some slack at the moment, but it drives me nuts when she's that rude.' His voice sounded tired.

Grace felt relieved that at least Tom was back on an even keel. 'I know.'

'It's like she's deliberately provoking us...provoking *me*,' he corrected himself.

'I don't think it's aimed specifically at you. I think she's angry because she's frustrated.' Grace knew she was stating the obvious.

'I know, but how long is it going to go on for? And it's getting worse. *She's* getting worse.' Tom was right, but Grace didn't want to agree with him. 'It's like she's a different kid.' The one they thought they had banished, all those years ago.

'She's not a kid any more,' Grace observed.

'No,' Tom sighed, sadly.

They sat at the abandoned table, cast adrift, unable to negotiate the huge gulf between the daughter of their memories and the furious young woman that Cassie had become.

Chapter 35

NAZ WAS furious. Leah knew it the moment he came into the bedroom. She shrank against the wall, pulling the duvet up for protection. He sat down on the bed, on her side, very close, his hands hanging down, both fists clenched.

'Is there something you wanna tell me, Leah?'

No. There was nothing she *wanted* to tell him, but she knew what he was getting at. Cassidie! It had to be Cassidie. She was the only secret Leah had, and the only one he wanted.

She must have paused for too long. He raised his fist and Leah flinched, but instead of a punch, he threw the wad of money onto the bed. She should have just told him about seeing Cassidie, and about the cash. Leah couldn't properly explain why she hadn't, but it was too late now.

'I found that stashed in the kitchen, in a mug.'

What had he been doing, poking about in her cupboards? Concentrate, Leah told herself, it doesn't matter how he found it; this drifting off while he was talking was dangerous. She really must concentrate.

'Well?' He stared at her.

'Sorry. I meant to tell you.' His face said, *I don't believe that for one second*. Leah hurried on. 'She gave it to me.'

'When?'

'The last time I saw her?'

'Which was when?'

This was going to tip him over the edge. 'Thursday.' Three days ago.

He breathed in, then out, slowly, as if he was trying to calm himself, but Leah knew from past experience that Naz could just as easily strike when his blood was running cold as hot. You crossed him, you paid for it. When – and how – was up to him. 'You met up with her again?'

'Sorry.' Grovelling sometimes worked.

He stretched across her and picked up the curl of cash, unrolled it and started counting out the notes onto the bed. Leah felt a nerve in her neck start to tick.

'Twenty, forty, sixty, eighty, one hundred, one-twenty, one-thirty, one-forty, one-fifty, one-sixty, one-seventy?'

She nodded.

'Odd amount.'

'I had to buy a new bus pass.' He stared at the pile of notes and she stared at his dipped face. She needed to say something to bring him in on it, quickly, he wouldn't let being excluded slide; it showed a lack of respect, and Naz was all about the respect. 'I told her that I needed it for my rent. She coughed up – real easy.' Still he didn't look up. 'There's more where that came from.' Greed, it was the only appeal she could think of making.

Naz fingered the notes, thoughtfully, silently, then straightened them into a neat stack, folded them over and stood up. He slid the wad of cash into his back pocket, staring down at her as he did so. She tensed.

'Get her over again. It's time I met your new best friend.' Leah nodded and allowed herself to breathe again, thinking that it was going to be okay – this time – but Naz had one more message for her. He bent down, slid his hand round the back of her head and grabbed hold of a fistful of hair. He yanked her close and whispered in her ear. 'You and me belong together, Leah. You know that, don't you?' He twisted her hair, sending a screw of pain down her neck. 'What's yours is mine, Baby. Don't you ever forget that.'

He let go, kissed her lightly on the cheek and left.

Chapter 36

CASSIE WAS back in Oldham, back in Subway, back on Leah's home turf – dependent, yet again, on Leah's whims, but the glow of expectation at meeting up with her was rapidly being replaced by irritation. Another long, slow trip over the Pennines and another twenty-five minutes of hanging around waiting had created ample opportunity for the affection that Cassie had been feeling towards Leah to be replaced by frustration. At last Cassie spotted her crossing the road, walking slowly as if she had all the time in the world. As Cassie watched Leah amble towards the cafe, she reminded herself to be less eager, less amenable.

'You're late,' Cassie blurted out. Leah didn't seem to register Cassie's tone. She slumped down in the seat and glanced at the counter, clearly expecting Cassie to leap up and get her a drink. She could go whistle. Leah unzipped her jacket and shrugged it off her shoulders, revealing some sort of tunic. That threw Cassie.

'Sorry. I was late getting off my shift,' Leah said, then coughed.

'From work?' Cassie blurted out.

Leah looked at Cassidie, coolly. 'Yeah.' She raised an eyebrow. 'What? You assumed I was a scrounger?'

'No.' That was exactly what Cassie had assumed. 'You've just never mentioned work before.'

'Yeah, well, it's nothing to shout about. I'm a cleaner in a care home. Crap money. Crap hours. A lot of crap all round.'

'Oh.' Cassie's resolve to be tougher frayed. She went to fetch Leah a tea, at the last minute adding a couple of doughnuts to the order.

Leah wrapped her hands around her cup and drank. 'Thanks. Sorry. I'm just a bit knackered.' She did look even paler than normal, thinner too.

'That's okay. Sorry I was narky about you being late.' Cassie picked up one of the doughnuts, ripped it in half and passed the bigger piece to Leah.

The girls chewed in silence for a few moments, drawing comfort from the familiar taste of fat and sugar. Her tea drained, Leah put her cup down and splayed her fingers on the table top, inspecting them with a weary expression. The skin on both hands was flaky and dry. The creases between her fingers red-raw.

'It's the cleaning stuff – it peels the skin off.'

'Is it eczema?' Cassie asked.

Leah turned her hands over, studying the cracks in her palms. 'I dunno. It gets bad, then I have my days off and it gets a bit better.'

'They should give you gloves. And you could get some cream, from the doctor's,' Cassie suggested.

'What are you – my mum?' Leah said. Then she smiled, a small, hesitant proper smile, without the usual layers of suspicion and guardedness. She suddenly realised how hungry she was. She picked up the last doughnut and bisected it, offering the other half to Cassidie, who accepted it. They chewed in time.

'I'll never be thin.' Cassie had a sweet tooth.

Leah polished off her share. 'I never put weight on. I can eat owt.'

'Like Jack Sprat!' The minute she said it, Cassie felt like a complete idiot, quoting nursery rhymes to a girl who'd never had a childhood.

'What're you talking about?' Leah licked the sugar off her lips.

Cassie was committed now. 'It's a kids' rhyme...*Jack Sprat could eat no fat, His wife could eat no lean, And so between the two of them, They licked the platter clean.'*

Leah looked at her for a long minute, then laughed, a short, harsh bark of laughter that segued into a prolonged coughing fit. When she'd finished she said, 'What the fuck does that mean?'

Cassie shrugged and pushed the last piece of doughy sweetness into her mouth and did what she'd always been told not to do – she spoke with her mouth full. 'I think it's supposed to mean that sometimes, even when two people are completely different, it can work, because they kinda balance each other out.'

'Oh, right. I'll take your word for it.' Leah picked up her paper cup and stared into it. 'Do you want another one?' She leant back and pushed her hand into her trouser pocket, looking for cash.

'I'll get them,' Cassie immediately offered.

But Leah was already on her feet. 'No, this is my shout.' Another drink bought time, and Leah needed Cassidie to stick around for a little longer – there was an appointment to keep.

Ten minutes later, in between spasms of coughing, Leah was being entertaining. She was telling Cassie about an old woman in the care home where she worked who swore blind that she'd been a stripper in a previous life, despite the manager insisting that she'd worked as an accounts clerk in a mattress factory for thirty years. 'She gets up every now and again and starts to show off her moves to anyone who'll watch. Nipple-tassel swirls and everything. And she ain't a small lady. She says she once got picked up by an Arab at a club where she was dancing, who offered to—'

The bang was so loud that Cassie thought a car had hit the front of the cafe. Everyone jumped and reached for their hearts, their mouths paused mid-word, mid-chew. But there was no glass, no breakage, no physical impact. It wasn't a car that had smashed into the window – it was a young guy. His hand was imprinted on the window, his face was close to them, just the other side of the glass.

He looked directly at Cassie, holding her gaze for a few long seconds before he switched his attention to Leah.

Normality reasserted itself. Conversations picked up again and heartbeats slowed, as everyone realised they weren't involved in some freak 'hit-and-run' accident. When Cassie looked at Leah for an explanation, she was saddened to see that the shutter had come back down. The bloke grinned and cartoon-gestured that he was coming in. In response, Leah sat up straight and started picking at the trim on her uniform.

He strolled in and slid, in one liquid move, onto the seat next to Leah. 'Hello, ladies. How's things going?' He smiled at Cassie, keeping his eyes locked with hers for a fraction longer than was necessary.

'Fine.' Leah shuffled in her seat.

'Aren't you gonna introduce me then?' the guy mock-chided her.

Leah paused ever so slightly, then said, 'Cassidie, this is Naz.'

'Hi.' To Cassie's surprise, he reached over the table and shook her hand. Dry hands, light pressure, a slight trail of his fingertips across her palm as he withdrew his hand. There was a nice smell, something lemony-fresh and expensive coming from him. 'Lovely to finally meet you, Cassidie.' There was a pause as they considered what he meant by that, and by his choice of name for her. 'So, girls. Catching up on old times?' It seemed innocently asked, but it was such a hard question to answer. 'Plenty to talk about, I bet,' he prompted.

Leah muttered, 'Yeah.'

'And?' Naz persevered. 'Are you...bonding? Finding that you have stuff in common, despite all those years apart?'

Leah glanced at him. 'Yeah.'

It was painfully awkward. Cassie didn't know what to say or how to help, but she could tell Leah wanted away from him. In contrast, he looked utterly relaxed despite, or perhaps because of, their discomfort. It was as if he was proving he could out-chill them both.

Cassie watched Leah, waiting for her cue, but she seemed unable to break the impasse. The pause stretched and became gluey. Then Naz did something weird, and more than a little creepy. He raised two fingers to his mouth and dragged them across his lower lip, revealing his small, sharp, perfectly white teeth and pale-pink gums. His smile smeared into a leer. Then he reached out towards Leah and pressed his fingertips, hard, against her neck, on the thin blue-veined skin below her ear. It was like the signature move of a villain in a movie. But it was Leah's response that really threw Cassie. She leant into Naz's touch and closed her eyes. It was an intimate and yet, at the same time, very public display – of what, Cassie couldn't say. She looked away.

'Anyway, girls. Glad to see you getting along so well. I just wanted to pop in and say "Hi". Especially given I've heard so much about you, Cassidie. I didn't mean to interrupt. I gotta get going myself – business, you know. I'll come round later, Leah. I'll aim for about two…like we agreed.' He waited for her to nod, then switched his attention to Cassie. 'Lovely to meet you, Cassidie. Hope to see you again, real soon.' And with that, he was gone.

Both girls breathed more easily once he'd disappeared.

'Your boyfriend?' Cassie risked asking.

Leah hesitated. 'No, not really.' She didn't elaborate, but simply sat and stared at her hands. Cassie waited, fully expecting to be dismissed again, but Leah surprised her by standing up and saying, 'Don't suppose you fancy a walk?'

They sat on a bench, under a tree, in a park, a ten-minute walk away from the high street. The bench was speckled with bird shit and littered with the arrow-pierced hearts of local teenagers. Although Cassie was pleased to have been invited along, she was thrown by the change of venue and pace, uncertain, as always, of the etiquette. Leah seemed to want her there, but seemed disinclined to talk. The pressure reduced Cassie to talking crap. 'I always think it smells of cucumber.' Leah gave her a 'what the fuck' look. 'The grass.'

Cassie gestured at a lad with a bare, heavily tattooed chest on a ride-on mower, who was cutting the playing field across the way. At first glance he looked like Ryan, but on second glance he didn't, though there was a similar swagger about his movements. He steered nonchalantly, with one hand, a series of wide sweeping arcs that sent the smell of freshly mowed grass onto the breeze. They watched him in silence and he, aware, of his audience, made his turns tighter and faster and increasingly impressive.

In broad daylight, it was clear that Leah wasn't just tired, she was ill. When she coughed, which she did repeatedly, it sounded like it hurt. She was very pale, her skin almost translucent.

'Are you all right? You really don't look very well.'

Leah shrugged. 'Cheers.'

The lad on the mower seemed to tire of showing off. He suddenly revved the mower and shot away across the field, leaving a trail of grass in his wake.

'So, how long have you been friends with Naz?'

'I never said I was friends with Naz,' Leah snapped, 'he's just someone I know. We met when I was in care. Known each other ever since.' That was all she was prepared to divulge. In truth, she couldn't rightly say when Naz had gone from being an occasional shag to a fixture in her life. It wasn't a decision of her own making.

'Right.' Cassie feigned indifference. She was learning that non-committal responses were safer than questions with Leah, they seemed to provoke more information. So Naz wasn't Leah's boyfriend, and it hadn't looked like an affectionate relationship, but there had definitely been something between the two of them.

Leah started coughing again, bending over as the spasms racked her thin frame. When the coughing bout had finished, she straightened up, two bright spots of colour fading from her cheeks as she recovered from the exertion. It seemed quieter after she'd stopped.

They watched the play area, neither of them feeling inclined to talk.

It was busy. Lots of little ones with their mums and grans. There were no dads. The slide seemed to be the favourite piece of equipment, there was a queue to use it. A straggle of stocky little bodies stumped up the steps and squeaked slowly down it, egged on or ignored by their mums.

Suddenly Leah said, 'You were cute when you were little.' Cassie waited, desperately wanting more. 'You had lots of hair. Even when you were first born. People thought it was funny, how different we looked. I didn't.'

Cassie stared pointedly at the children, not risking a glance at Leah. Their dark, shared past hovered on the edge of the bright park. She waited for Leah to illuminate it for her, but she said nothing else.

In the play area one little girl was defying her mum, refusing to come away from the slide, despite being told, loudly, to *move*! The little girl put her foot on the bottom step and looked over. Her mother shouted, 'I'm warning ya. I'm not having it. Not today. I've had enough of ya already. Get here! Now!' The child bit her lip and took another step up. The little boy behind her, unsure whether it was wise to follow, hesitated, looking to his mum for guidance. She wasn't forthcoming. The children in the queue grew restless and the mums stirred nervously, unwilling to intervene. 'Off!' the woman hissed through clenched teeth, her voice curdling the atmosphere. The little girl bravely, defiantly, went to take another step. Her mum snapped. She grabbed her daughter by the arm and yanked her down the steps, her face rigid with anger. 'I said, "Off!"' A wail went up from the little girl as she was dragged away across the playground, her sparkly trainers catching and bumping on the asphalt.

Cassie looked away, upset by the violence. Leah watched, her expression impassive, her weirdly unpredictable emotions less so. Prompted by an unsettling mix of motivations, Leah then surprised them both by blurting out, 'I've got a more few pictures, at my flat – of when we were kids. Do you wanna come and see 'em?' Cassie nodded.

And so the erratic marble-run of their relationship tilted, fast, down another new, previously unexplored ramp.

Chapter 37

LEAH LED Cassie to a block of flats not far from the park. The entry system was broken, the doors ajar. Not what you'd call secure. Anyone could come and go as they pleased, but at this time of the day it was quiet. In the lobby Leah pressed the Call button for the lift and they waited, listening to the sounds of the road outside and Leah's ruttly breathing. Her colour, if anything, was worse than it had been in the park.

When the lift finally arrived, the doors opened slowly and very noisily. They had to take a step back as a young woman with a buggy came out of the lift. As she passed, she half-nodded at Leah and stared hard at Cassie, acknowledgement and hostility clearly communicated in less than half a second. Cassie felt the thud of anxiety that was ever-present within her whenever she was with Leah. As the doors ground shut, she felt committed, and a little afraid.

The lift smelt of fried food, the walls were a latticework of scratches and dents, boredom scratched into every surface. Leah saw the judgement in Cassidie's eyes. 'Yeah, I know. I normally use the stairs, but not today.' She tapped her chest. 'I'm on the seventh floor.' They watched the lights as they ascended, for want of anything better to do. The communal landing was worse. The smell hit Cassie before they'd even stepped out of the lift. Again Leah picked up the unspoken criticism. 'It's the rubbish shoot,' she said, pointing to a metal hatch in the wall. 'People chuck owt down it. Nappies. Food. They never clean it. I'm here, right next to it.' She dug her keys out of her bag and unlocked flat forty-five.

Cassie braced herself.

It was not what she was expecting.

The minute Leah closed the front door behind them, the air smelt different. It smelt clean. There was a tiny bare hall, with four doors leading off it. Leah led Cassie into a decent-sized lounge, with a big picture window. It was a sparsely furnished room – which was exceptionally tidy. There were two cushions propped neatly on the small sofa. A rug was precisely squared in front of the TV, and a table with two chairs was tucked away in one corner. There were no pictures, no books on the corner unit, no clutter, no mess. The room didn't speak of comfort. It spoke of a huge effort to make the most of a serious lack of money. But the most remarkable thing of all was that the room smelt of flowers, which was quite a feat, considering they were seventy feet above anything green or natural or floral.

'I'm going to get another drink, do you want one?' Leah asked.

Cassie didn't, she was already jittery from too much caffeine, but she said, 'Yeah, thanks', in order to be polite. She stood in the middle of the room, not wanting to impose herself on Leah's space. Leah put her bag down on the table and took off her jacket, hanging it neatly on the back of one of the chairs. 'Is it okay if I use your loo?' Cassie asked.

There was a fraction of a hesitation. 'Yeah. Just let me check it first?' Leah disappeared.

While she was gone, Cassie studied the flat, looking for clues. There weren't any. The room was as devoid of personality as it was possible to be; it could have been a room in a hotel, a cheap but well-run one, but that in itself was a revelation. The toilet flushed and

Cassie composed herself, trying her best to look relaxed. She waited and waited some more, then she heard Leah emerge. 'It's free,' she shouted. As Cassie headed for the bathroom, she saw Leah reaching for some mugs in the kitchen. A dish beside the kettle looked, for a second or two, to be piled high with the curled-up bodies of hairless baby mice. Cassie's stomach turned over. Used teabags. She was a hysterical idiot.

The bathroom was small, with the expected bathtub, loo and sink. All in pale, stained green, but scrubbed and wiped meticulously clean. The tarnished taps were shining. The towel was folded and hung up. It was immaculate. Leah's toiletries were lined up along the rim of the bath and her make-up on the shelf above the sink: cheap, own-brand shampoo and deodorant, supermarket-brand moisturiser, foundation, mascara and eyeliner. Each bottle drip-free, the lids screwed back on properly, the eyebrow-pencil sharp and recapped. Cassie thought about her own make-up, tossed into toilet bags, in the bottom of her many handbags and spread around the house. She was careless with her stuff. She threw make-up away all the time, being too lazy to squeeze a tube or sharpen a pencil.

She peed quickly and washed her hands, taking care to refold the towel and put it back precisely in the middle of the storage heater, just as she'd found it. She heard Leah cough as she passed the bathroom door. Before Cassie unlocked the door, she balanced her bag on the lip of the sink. The primer was in the bottom, still boxed, unused, bought on a whim and forgotten about until now. It was good-quality, expensive. Cassie wiped the box on her sleeve and placed it carefully on the shelf, in between Leah's moisturiser and her foundation. They had very different skin tones, but maybe that wouldn't matter. She took a breath to calm her jangly nerves and opened the door.

Leah was in the lounge, a folder on her lap. Two mugs were set on the low table. Cassie went and sat beside her. The atmosphere seemed okay. 'Thanks.' She drew one of the mugs towards her, but didn't take a drink.

Leah put the folder on the table and unsnapped the elastic straps holding the cover shut. 'I ain't got a lot.' She lifted out a sheaf of official-looking paperwork and letters, taking care to turn over the top document so that Cassie couldn't read it. 'She wasn't one for taking photos – at least not of us.' She passed three photos to Cassie.

Again Cassie experienced a weird sensation when she looked at them: a strong gust of – nothing. Though her brain registered that what Leah was showing her was evidence of her past, her heart or her soul, or whatever it was that registered feeling, didn't react. They might as well have been exhibits under glass in a museum. The photos showed a woman holding a baby, then a little girl holding a baby, then the same little girl, slightly older this time, with a toddler sitting next to her. They were blandly anonymous, they could have been anyone, though she knew what she was looking at was her – no, *their* – shared past. And yet she felt zilch. The pictures stirred nothing in the silt of Cassie's memories. Absolutely nothing. The only emotion that did eventually creep into her was embarrassment. She could sense Leah studying her reaction, waiting for her to say something.

'Thank you for showing them to me,' she said politely, stuffily, as she passed them back. Leah looked at each photo individually, keeping her own emotions to herself, before putting them back carefully into the file with the stack of papers. Cassie wondered what all the forms and official-looking paperwork related to – Leah's life after Jane, she assumed; it was a substantial wodge of documentation.

Leah pushed the file aside. Well, that hadn't gone as planned! She coughed and her chest hurt. She blamed it on her cold, but the pain wasn't just physical. The photos had had no impact on Cassidie at all. They'd reached another impasse, blocked off from each other by their different connection to the past. She had another spasm of coughing. This time the silence in the aftermath was uncomfortable.

'Leah, do you really not know what happened to her?' Cassie asked.

'No.' Leah sounded resolute, despite her wheezing.

'You never tried to find out?'

'No. I don't want to know. There's no point.' After a pause she added, 'She wasn't any good.'

'But doesn't the not-knowing mess with your head?'

'No.' Her mother wasn't the one who was messing with her head. 'Besides. It's easy enough to gúess.'

'But—'

Leah interrupted her. 'There is no *but*!' She coughed again. 'I don't know what you think you're gonna get out of trying to find her.'

Cassie tried to answer Leah honestly. 'To start with, I suppose it was just curiosity. I felt bad that I hadn't bothered to find out about her. I accepted what I got told...about everything.' Leah made a noise at this, but Cassie ploughed on, not wanting to think about the scale of the deceit perpetrated by her parents, which she still couldn't compute or comprehend. 'Getting to know you has filled in some of the blanks, but not all of them.'

'So what else do you wanna know?' Leah picked up her mug. On seeing a trail of tiny tea splashes on the table, she pulled down her sleeve and carefully wiped away the stains.

'Well...' Cassie didn't know what to ask. 'Just – more. I can remember hardly anything, not clearly anyway.'

Leah drank another mouthful. 'Lucky you.'

Cassie felt defeated. It was pointless; asking was doing nothing but damage. All she was learning was that life was unfair and messy, that beneath the surface lurked all sorts of snares and dangers, and that people lied – even the people you loved, and who claimed to love you. And with Leah, there was always that edge. Her words were rationed, doled out as and when she saw fit. Who knew whether what she was telling her was even true. Leah's motives still eluded

Cassie. The truth no longer seemed attainable to her. She wasn't even sure it was desirable any more. She gave up. She slumped back against the sofa and stared out of the window at the clear blue sky.

Leah felt compelled to fill the ensuing silence. It wasn't only her awareness that there was a trade going on – that she had to give, in order to get – but there was also a part of her that wanted to talk, wanted to reopen the old wounds, with the one person who had been there at the beginning: Cassidie. She started to speak slowly, revisiting, for the first time in years, the unpolished, jagged-edged 'facts' that were her 'legend'. Every *looked-after child* had one, an official biography that was stapled to them the moment they entered the care system. It was a label that endured throughout childhood into adolescence, and beyond. Every time you were handed on, the same sorry tale was told, with new details inked in: the educational difficulties, the attachment issues, the socialisation problems, the anger concerns. An accumulation of facts and failures that indelibly marked you as a 'reject'.

And it had all started with their useless fucking mother.

Leah took a shallow, wheezy breath and began near the end. 'She was being cuckooed.'

'What?'

Leah put her mug down and leant back against the sofa, aligning herself with her sister. 'It was the drugs in the end, that's why they took us off her. Before that, when it was just the three of us, we just about got by. She was still crap at the basics: shopping, washing, paying bills, normal stuff like that. Clueless when she was sober, worse than clueless when she was off her face.'

Cassie winced at Leah's choice of words, their direct brutality, but Leah refused to censor herself. Some cold, hard truth was what Cassidie needed.

'We were hungry a lot of the time, and it was always friggin' cold, but she didn't batter us, she wasn't a shouter, never had much of a temper on her. That was her problem. No spine. There wasn't any fight in her. She couldn't be arsed most of the time.'

Cassie could see that Leah was actually allowing herself to remember. She prompted her, nervously. 'You said she was *a cuckoo*?'

'No. I said *she was being cuckooed*. It's when they move in, start selling out of some sad sack's house or flat.'

'Who?'

'Dealers.' Leah coughed again. 'I guess it started with someone she was buying off. One day there was some bloke in the front room in a hoodie with a load of mobile phones. After that, we weren't allowed downstairs when he was there. Pretty soon he was there all the time...him, then his "mates". Loads of people started rocking up to the house, cars coming and going at all hours. The lights never went off downstairs. Fights, shouting. She let 'em, cos she had gear on tap.'

'What about us?' Cassie asked.

'What about us?' Leah shrugged. 'She forgot about us.'

'How could she?'

Leah shifted round to look fully at Cassie. 'You've never known someone who's addicted, 'ave you?' Leah had, she'd known plenty; enough to make her swear blind that it would never be her. No one had been impressed by that promise, but she had stuck to it. She was clean, and she always had been. Maybe she had learnt something from her useless, spineless mother.

'No,' Cassie conceded.

'Addicts don't care about anything, apart from their next fix.'

'But we were so little. It must have been awful, and dangerous. I was only two.'

Leah wiped her nose again. And she'd only been seven, but no one cared too much about that – not at the time, or later. No one factored that into why she might not have the best table manners, or use the right words, or have a nice, calm, affectionate nature. No one fucking bothered to wonder how a two-year-old had survived in that pit of a house, with a derelict mother and a fug of big, foul-mouthed, mean-tempered lowlifes. Nobody appreciated that it was a fucking miracle of cunning and hard graft and sleepless nights that that two-year-old had been fed and kept fairly clean, and had a few toys and a bed, and a potty, and no broken bones. Leah's breathing was shallow and fast. Remembering hurt. She'd done too much of it. Or perhaps she'd done just enough, judging by the distress on Cassidie's face.

Tentatively Cassie reached out and touched Leah's arm, gently. It was a fragile, unfamiliar gift.

Leah didn't know what to do with it – so she rejected it. She roused herself. 'Sorry, I feel proper crap. I think I need to crash.' She'd said and done more than enough for one day and she was knackered.

Cassie took the hint, she stood up. 'Of course. Are you sure there's nothing I can get you?' Without meaning to, she glanced at the bare kitchen, wondering what Leah had inside her cupboards. 'I can run down to the shop and pick up some things for you, if you want me to.'

Leah stood up slowly. 'Nah, it's okay. I'll go later.' As Cassie turned to leave Leah said, 'But if you could sub me a bit of cash, that'd be good. They've told me I can't go into work with a cold. They don't want to run the risk of the residents catching it. It can finish 'em off, so I'm gonna be short this week, and my rent's due.'

Cassie felt stupid. 'Oh, of course.' She fumbled in her bag, found her purse and pulled out a twenty. The awareness that she was standing there with a full wallet brought with it a sudden crashing embarrassment. For a split second she hesitated, unsure how much to hand over, but in the same instant she knew, with absolute certainty, that no amount of money would ever be enough. She handed over the twenty, then a tenner and then two fivers, until her purse was empty.

Leah took the cash with a muted 'Cheers'.

On the landing they said their awkward goodbyes, Cassie still struggling with her new-found concern for Leah; and Leah...well, she was just glad to have Cassidie out of her flat, and enough cash in her hand to keep Naz happy – for the time being.

Chapter 38

IT WAS Saturday morning, a lovely, high-blue-sky kind of day. Erin looked out of her bedroom window and felt restless, wanting to go out, but not knowing where, or with who. As she stood, stranded in the middle of her room, she heard the grate of the garage door. A minute later her dad emerged, wheeling his bike, clad from head to toe in skin-tight racing Lycra. He paused, with his expensive fourteen-gear bike balanced against his hip, put on his helmet, then climbed aboard. He clipped his feet into his cleats, then wobbled his way carefully past the cars, down the drive and out of sight. Erin listened and tried to locate her mum and Cassie in the house, but all was quiet. It was a pity Elmo hadn't been allowed back; he'd been good company, but apparently he'd messed something up in Cassie's room, so that made him 'canine *non gratis*'. The incident seemed to have put an end to any discussion about them getting a dog.

Erin padded barefoot across the landing and began to head downstairs. Five steps down, she was startled to see Cassie standing in the hall, near the dresser, seemingly doing nothing. Erin was about to say 'Hi', but the realisation that Cassie was doing *something* stopped her. Cassie was holding a wallet in her hands. Tom always dumped his wallet and his keys in the ugly ceramic bowl on the dresser when he came into the house, to save him losing them, *all the time*. Erin stood perfectly still and watched her sister, a bad feeling rising inside her. Cassie was passing the wallet from one hand to the other, back and forth, back and forth, as if weighing it. Erin willed her to put it back in the bowl. She didn't. After a few seconds of juggling, Cassie paused, flipped the wallet open and, without hesitating, took a wad of notes from one of the compartments. Then, to Erin's shock, she stood and counted the cash out onto the dresser. It was such a shameless thing to do. Cassie paused, as if thinking for a second, then took a proportion of the notes, folded them over and shoved them into the pocket of her jeans; the rest she slotted back into the wallet, which she closed and tossed back into the bowl. She checked her reflection in the mirror, then walked off, into the kitchen.

Erin was appalled. She sat down on the step.

The seconds ticked by, but her predicament did not improve.

It was a mixture of inbred morals and concern for Cassie that made her eventually get up, walk down the stairs and follow her sister into the kitchen. Cassie was over by the back door, eating cereal and staring out at the garden. She turned as Erin walked in, but the smile that had been about to form faded away when she saw Erin's expression. 'What?'

Erin decided it was best to get it over with. 'I saw you take it.'

Cassie put her bowl down. Her face set. She looked defiant rather than repentant. 'Leave it, Erin.'

Erin couldn't. 'But—'

Cassie cut her off. 'It's got nothing to do with you, so stay out of it.'

Erin was as shocked by Cassie's attitude as she was by the theft. 'But stealing? From Dad? Why?'

'Erin, just leave it.'

Erin moved towards Cassie. 'If you need money, I'll lend you some. I've got some cash in my room – more in my account. You can take whatever you need, but please, put what you took from Dad's wallet back.'

Cassie made as if to walk past her sister. 'No, Erin. I'm not going to do that. I don't want your money. I want *his*!'

'But why?'

'Because he's got a debt to pay,' Cassie said.

Erin felt confused, but also absolutely certain that what she'd just witnessed was wrong. 'Dad owes you money?'

'Not me.' Cassie seemed intent on leaving. As she leant across the counter to grab her jacket, Erin's eyes were drawn to the outline of the roll of cash in her back pocket.

'What're you talking about?' Erin followed Cassie out into the hall.

'Erin, for the last time. It's got nothing to do with you!' Cassie headed for the door.

Erin panicked. 'I'll tell him! When he gets back.'

Cassie spun round. 'No, you won't!'

'I will – if you don't tell me why you took it.' The girls glared at each other.

'You do that, Erin, and I'll never speak to you again.' Cassie knew it was an empty threat, but she wasn't in the mood for Erin's naïve sense of right and wrong.

But Erin was so sick of it all that she responded, honestly, without thinking about what was coming out of her mouth. 'Then it won't be any different from how it is now, will it? You've been ignoring me for weeks.'

Cassie threw her jacket down on the stairs and walked into the front room. Erin followed her, a knot of trepidation in her stomach. They faced each other, adversaries, not allies. Cassie looked at Erin with such a weird expression, a fierce mix of anger and pity, that Erin was forced to look down. She felt as if it was it her who'd done something wrong. Staring, abashed, at the chipped polish on her toenails, she waited for Cassie to explain.

It was a stilted story, which contained more accusation than confession. Erin was shocked at how far things had gone with Leah. Cassie had been living a whole other life under all their noses, without any of them realising. Erin had thought that she knew her sister; she obviously didn't. That hurt, deeply. She felt stupid for having so readily believed Cassie's claims that she'd had no further contact with the mystery woman in Oldham – that it had all died a death. Erin had assumed that Cassie's unpredictable moods were being caused by the frustration of failing to find her birth mum, not by the excitement of meeting her *real* sister. She swallowed that one down silently, painfully. Cassie actually used the words without hesitation. She kept on talking, spitting out harsh phrases, seemingly indifferent to Erin's rising panic.

'Mum and Dad lied. They pretended that she doesn't exist. All this time. Can you believe it? Even when I told them I wanted to look for my mum, even then, they kept their mouths shut. I have a sister they were *never* going to tell me about! Ever! They split us up when we were little, left her behind. Never once bothered to find out what happened to her.' Erin hadn't realised that she was shaking her head in disbelief. 'Yes, they did! Her life has been crap – and it's all their fault!' Cassie was vibrating with pent-up energy.

Erin shrank in the face of it, her mind scrambling to catch up, as her heart twisted and turned. It just didn't seem possible. It was all such a mess: everyone lying to everyone else, all of them fumbling about in the dark. What she wanted, more than anything else, was for her mum to walk into the room and take the responsibility for it all away from her. But she didn't.

'And the money?'

Cassie bristled at the mention of it. 'Is for Leah.'

Erin nodded, though she still didn't really understand. 'But if she needs some money, I can help. Like I said, I'll get some out of my account. You don't need to...take it,' she couldn't bring herself to say 'steal' again, 'from Dad.'

Cassie's mouth hardened once more. 'Erin. Stay out of it.'

'But...'

'There is no "but". You've got to let me handle this my way. Leah is my sister. It's up to me to start putting this right, and if that means Dad is a bit short, then it serves him right.'

Erin flinched. It was all wrong. *She* was Cassie's sister. Leah was a stranger. A stranger who was sucking Cassie into behaving in ways she'd never behaved before. 'Do you get on with her? You can't have much in common.' Her voice faltered.

'Other than a mother, and the first three years of my life.' Erin's heart twisted tighter. Cassie didn't notice. 'It gets a bit better each time I go over there. She's starting to talk more. But it isn't easy. She's kinda closed off, defensive about a lot of things. I think it's because of how she was brought up, on her own, in care.' Cassie paused and both girls became aware of their environment: their comfortable, peaceful home, stuffed full of family pictures and nice things. Cassie seemed to decide that enough was enough. 'Erin. You can't tell them any of this.' Erin nodded; what else could she do? 'Not yet. If Leah finds out that you...that I've said anything about her to you, or to them, then that's it. You do get that, don't you?' Erin nodded again, though she hated the thought of the secrets that were now tucked inside her. 'Good. Nothing – to no one.' Erin nodded one last time, disconsolately. 'Okay. Well, I'm off out.'

Despite the hurt cramping her soul, Erin had to ask, 'Are you going to see *her*?'

Cassie looked at her little sister. 'No. I'm just going out. I'll see you later.' The door banged shut, and Erin was left alone in a house that now had the taint of Leah trapped inside it.

Chapter 39

LEAH'S COUGH was getting better, but her chest still hurt and she still looked like shit. The first day in bed had been a luxury. The second not. Too much time on her own in the flat was never a good thing; it just made her more conscious of other people's lives. On day one she'd lain in bed and listened to people arriving and departing on the landing, catching snatches of conversation and the occasional harsh burst of laughter. On day two she'd dragged herself up and watched the comings and goings down below the flats: the girls pushing buggies, her 'neighbours' manhandling their shopping and their kids home, and a selection of identically bald men, in matching vests, being dragged across the scorched grass by their muscle-bound dogs. All of them seemed to have someone to stop and pass the time of day with.

Not her.

Naz was staying away. His version of sympathy had sounded a lot like neglect. 'I don't want your germs, thanks very much. Message me when you're proper better.'

On day three she was reduced to getting out *the file* – her only constant companion. She took it back to bed, pulling the duvet up around her, creating a nest. She knew that looking at the contents wouldn't make her feel better, it always made her feel worse.

Fourteen years of self-flagellation.

A letter sent.

A letter received.

A letter read.

Over and over again.

Every year for fourteen years – without fail.

As a child, Leah had developed a kind of sixth sense about the letters. In the weeks before the next episode from planet Happy Family arrived, she'd be plagued by an intense sense of agitation and excitement. The letters were like her own warped, very personal version of Christmas: longed for, eagerly awaited, prone to make her sick with nervous energy. But whereas Christmas was always a let-down – a half-hearted display of fake feeling – the letters were always incendiary, provoking more emotion than Leah the child, Leah the teenager, even Leah the adult could cope with. She clearly remembered turning eighteen and – despite consuming a skull-splitting quantity of vodka the night before, and waking up early on her birthday with the worst hangover of her life – her first thought had been: will the letters stop?

They hadn't. Still they came, a painful reminder of just how powerless she was.

Leah had read each of the letters a hundred times over, in what felt like a hundred different bedrooms. She'd been lying to herself when she'd said she wasn't an addict. The letters were her addiction. They were the never-ending itch that she was compelled to scratch, time and time again, reopening old wounds and raising new welts. But the pain was a release...at least it was whilst she was scratching. No addiction was without cost.

The stack of letters had travelled with her every time she'd moved on...to *something better*, to somewhere *more suited to her needs* and, towards to end, into whatever was *available at such short notice*.

There was no denying that Cassidie's black bitch of a mother had a way with words. She was able to conjure up vivid images of reassuring routines, colour and warmth, humour and happiness, the mundane and the special – very effectively, in line after line of small, neat typeface. Her descriptions of family life always sounded so real, so solid, which of course they had been – for Cassidie.

Every year a new instalment of nauseating normality would arrive, sometimes months after they'd been written. It was one of the surprising efficiencies of a chronically inefficient Social Services that no matter how often Leah moved, the letters still managed to reach her. It was as if the very people who kept failing her so miserably couldn't resist parading their success with her sister. It was as good a way of punishing her as any – more so, really. The groundings, the sanctions, the threats had little or no impact on Leah, but the letters did. They served a dual purpose. Each neatly typed missive pushed her down harder and further, ensuring that she knew her place, whilst at the same time they kept alight the roaring, tearing rage that drove her half-mad.

Because the letters – though beautifully descriptive – were also deeply frustrating. There was never enough identifiable detail in them. The bitch-mother wasn't naïve. She knew how to protect what was hers. How to build a defence, whilst seeming to build a bridge. She never gave anything useful away, no clues as to their whereabouts, no real names or even specific dates or traceable events. Nothing that could be followed up. They were a clever exercise in *Show, but don't tell*.

The file was heavy on Leah's lap – thick with a tsunami of officialese and buck-passing paperwork. Only the letters section was neat and organised. Each one carefully stored away in ascending chronological order. It made it so much easier to find her year of choice.

On her sickbed, with life going on beyond the stuffy, sealed-off box of her tiny flat, Leah selected Cassidie at seven. Her own age, at the point they were ripped apart.

At seven, Cassidie:

...is loving her ballet lessons. She's made lots of new friends. The class is so good for her confidence.

They put on a performance before Christmas, nothing too elaborate, just a small show for family and friends. She was picked to do a solo. She got very excited about it, doing lots of practising all round the house. She wanted to wear her costume all the time, even to school – she was a lion with a shaggy mane and a swishy tail.

At seven, Leah went into the unit. She turned eight there. Another birthday to forget.

It was a life lived behind glass, where she was observed twenty-four hours a day. Her every move, her every action, her every twitch assessed, as they judged whether she was safe to release back into the community. It took them nine months to decide that she was. And even then there were caveats.

At seven, Leah wasn't dancing and singing and swinging her lion-tail. She was screaming, and flailing and raging at the loss of the one person who mattered most to her.

At nine, Cassidie:

...is doing well at school. She has a lovely teacher who seems to understand her. Her teacher is encouraging her not to be afraid of making mistakes. She is thriving, loving art and literacy the most. A proper bookworm. But she still loves tearing around. Some of her energy is going into athletics. She's joined an after-school club that lets kids try out all the different events to see which they enjoy the most. At the moment it's long jump.

At nine, Leah had a chance.

The Mertons.

She was taken to a house and shown into a room that made her heart beat fast. Clean white walls. Matching bedding and blinds, covered in sprigs of blue-and-yellow flowers. An armchair, a wardrobe, a chest of drawers and, for the first time in her life, a dressing table with a mirror and a little stool with a fluffy white fur cover.

Julie, her new foster mum, stood behind her, close but not touching, and said, 'This is your room, Leah. We hope you'll be happy here. I'll leave you to have little look round. I'll be downstairs in the kitchen, if you need me. Come down when you're ready and I'll fix us something to eat.' Then she stepped out of the room, closing the door behind her.

Her own room.

Leah sat on the little stool. It creaked and swivelled. She turned a full circle – fairy steps – on the pale-blue carpet. A slow revolution, taking it all in, returning to face the mirror. She averted her eyes. Why spoil the moment? She picked up the little bottle of perfume and sniffed at it. It smelt of flowers. She didn't spray it. It wasn't hers, yet. She opened the drawer and saw that it was empty, ready for her things. She ran her hands across the cool glass top of the dressing table, her fingertips skimming the surface, fearful of leaving a mark. Then she picked up the hairbrush and held it loosely in her hands, looking at the pearly ridges on the back of it – letting hope take a small, shallow breath. Finally, she looked up.

The room reflected in the mirror was clean and shiny and pretty.

The girl in the mirror was not.

But maybe she could make her so.

Leah lifted the heavy brush and began to drag it through her hair, trying to make it look cleaner and shinier and prettier and, as she brushed, she vowed to be on her absolute best behaviour.

241

At twelve, Cassidie:

> *...found the transition to High School fairly straightforward,*
> *which was a relief. We thought she would be okay, but it is*
> *such a huge change. The school she's now attending has a*
> *good reputation for looking after their students, as well as for*
> *academic achievement. She seems to be coping fine with the*
> *work.*

At twelve, Leah had the ugliest of the three Fitzpatrick lads sucking on her neck. She'd been the last girl picked, but at least she had been picked. The noise and the sensation of him leeching on her made her stomach turn. She craned her face away from him, but not her body.

The darkness in Hulme Park was incomplete, the lights from the Mancunian Way kept it in perpetual muddy twilight. The park was busier at night than it ever was during the day. This late, it was alive with the aimless and the wilful, many of them kids like herself, absconding from whatever version of home they hailed from. The non-stop rumble of the traffic wasn't loud enough to drown out the screeching and preening of the rejected girls or the barks of laughter from the boys.

It was a community, of sorts, but a sharp-edged, uneasy one, membership of which came at a price.

The lad stopped sucking at her neck and shifted position, but he wasn't done – he was just getting started. His hand went up her T-shirt. It felt like one of those mechanical grabbers you saw at funfairs, but one that worked. He latched onto her chest and squeezed. She winced. It hurt. As he ground her nipple into her ribs in search of breast meat, she stared at the lights travelling along the motorway, tolerating his attentions.

There were worse fates than being picked last.

There was not being picked at all.

At sixteen, Cassidie:

*...has been a little stressed. The pressure of GCSEs got to her just
a bit. But she did really well in her exams, in all her subjects.
The whole family were very proud of her. We celebrated with a
family holiday away. Her good grades means that she'll be going
to the sixth form that she's set her heart on, in September.*

At sixteen, Leah moved three times.

The first move was out of her last family placement – she was
deemed a bad influence on the younger kids. The second was out
of a short-lived, supported-living flat – she wasn't a good fit with
the other residents. The third move was into a specialist unit –
admission, at last, that an actual home was never going to be found
for her.

She only sat her GCSEs because they bribed her. Cash incentives,
the last-ditch attempt to buy her a future that had long ago
disappeared down the toilet. Her resultant poor grades surprised no
one. They confirmed what everyone already knew.

Her direction was set.

Leah put the letters back into the file and closed it.

Two girls.

Two lives.

Two paths that had diverged so wildly that it had seemed
impossible they would ever cross again.

And yet they had. Leah had made sure of that.

For fourteen years the bitch-mother had done her utmost to keep
Cassidie and Leah apart.

But she'd failed.

Cassidie was hers now.

Chapter 40

CASSIE WAS back in the park in Oldham. The same bench, another day, a different cover story. Her parents assuming that she was in college; college believing that she was at her great-aunt's funeral. And Erin? Erin wouldn't know for sure where she was, but Cassie knew she'd have her suspicions. She didn't feel guilty about her deception, she felt justified. An eye for an eye, a lie for a lie, a rebalancing of the scales all round. And besides, she owed it to Leah. There were amends to be made and it was she who had to make them, no one else seemed to be willing to. Hence the money stashed away in her purse. It was only what Leah deserved, and only a fraction of what she was owed. And if it took cash to grease the wheels of their stop–start relationship, so be it.

From her vantage point, Cassie watched the road that ran along the side of the park. She knew Leah would be late, she always was. Cassie felt she was beginning to understand her a little better, but that still amounted to hardly at all, because Leah's guard was so often up. There were *so* many no-go topics of conversation. Cassie knew that Leah still held the power; she was the keeper of their past, a fact that she rarely let Cassie forget, but Cassie was beginning to notice the occasional chink in Leah's armour: momentary lapses in her fierce defensiveness, fleeting glimpses of another, softer personality beneath the rock-hard surface. And, against the odds, they were establishing a relationship of sorts, even it wasn't one that could remotely be described as affectionate or, at times, even friendly. They were certainly a long way off being sisterly.

The park was quiet, fewer mums and kids about, which was a good job, as the vandals had been out and about, and busy. There was a rash of fresh graffiti on the concrete walls of the skate-park, and broken glass glinted in the sunshine on the ground around the bins. Near Cassie's foot, the neck of a smashed vodka bottle poked out of the grass. She prodded at it tentatively with the toe of her trainer and considered picking it up, to stop any of the little kids finding it and hurting themselves, but the thought of whose mouth – or, more likely, mouths – had been wrapped around the rim stopped her; that and the fear that she would cut herself on the jagged frill of glass. The play area itself was also newly damaged. Big chunks of the spongy safety-floor covering had been gouged up, leaving a trial of black scars across the faded rainbow pattern. Cassie fought the sinking feeling that dragged at her, telling herself that she was focusing, unfairly, on the bad stuff. The park was just more messy, more well used than the ones in her home town, but the longer she sat there, the more the careless brutality of it all got to her.

It was a welcome relief when she spotted Leah heading across the grass. Anticipation warred with anxiety within her. Suddenly she felt self-conscious about the sandwiches, snacks and drinks that she'd brought with her – it was hardly *picnic-in-the-park* territory. She pushed her bag underneath the bench, out of sight. She'd only mention that she'd brought lunch if the mood felt right; she didn't want Leah thinking she was getting off on doling out charity. Leah had nearly reached the brow of the hill. As she approached, they acknowledged each other, Cassie with a smile, Leah with a dip of her head. She looked less ill than the last time Cassie had seen her, though she was puffing quite hard by the time she flopped down on the bench.

'Hey.'

'Hi. You look better.'

'Yeah. I am.'

They fell back into awkwardness. What to do with each other? It was a problem they had yet to solve. All they had in common was blood, and a mother. No shared memories, no shared experiences, no shared interests – if you discounted their growing fascination with each other.

'Are you back at work?' Cassie asked.

'Yeah,' Leah said, with a deep sigh of boredom. She held out her hands as proof. They looked shrivelled, like an old lady's. The skin was dry, stretched thin as tissue paper across her knuckles, and when she turned her hands over, palms up, Cassie was shocked to see the red-raw cracks in the creases of her fingers. Leah studied her hands impassively. 'They're wet all the time. That's what fucks 'em. Ugly, ain't they?'

Cassie lied. 'Not ugly. They just look really sore. Did you get anyone to look at them?'

Leah lost interest. 'Nah. They're not *that* bad.' She absent-mindedly scratched at the scars on the top of her left hand. 'That's pretty.' She pointed at Cassie's ring.

It was a small opal, set either side with two tiny diamonds – her Grandma Sheila's engagement ring. She had given it to Cassie when it became clear that she wasn't going to get better. Cassie hadn't wanted to take the ring, but her grandma had insisted, saying it made her happy to see Cassie wearing it. Which was all true and very heartfelt, but she could hardly tell Leah the story. 'Thanks.' She left it at that, putting her hand out of sight, by her side. A direct comparison did Leah's hands no favours.

'Nice day,' Leah observed.

'Yeah,' Cassie said.

Again the uncomfortable silence pushed them apart.

'You haven't said anything to your mum and dad about me, 'ave you?' Leah asked. The thought of Cassidie's 'lovely' parents brought up bile, but the knowledge that they had no idea where their precious daughter currently was acted as some measure of compensation. Cassidie must be getting proficient at lying.

'No.' Cassie said. Which was true, but not saying anything was driving her crazy. Everything Tom and Grace did infuriated her now. Being in the same room or, worse, trapped in the car with them for any length of time was unbearable. She couldn't stand listening to them and looking at them, because Cassie now knew they were hypocrites, and that changed everything. The urge to shock them out of their controlled, complacent little world was overwhelming. Not being able to was maddening. 'Leah, why don't you want me to tell them that I know about you? That we've met?'

'I just don't.'

Cassie heard the edge of aggression, but braved it nonetheless. 'But I'm going to have to tell them at some point.'

'Why?' Leah asked.

'Well...' Cassie floundered. 'I need to ask them why they lied about you.'

'They'll only lie again, so what's the point?' Leah said flatly.

Cassie tried a different tack. 'I just think that, if we're going to keep seeing each other...' She glanced at Leah, wanting affirmation, but didn't get it, 'well, they're going to have to know that you're in my life.'

Leah's face was blank. 'I don't see why.' The less Cassidie's parents knew, the better.

'For lots of reasons. So you can come to the house. Meet my sis— my other sister. Maybe even meet them – eventually – when you're ready. Don't you want to meet them, ask them why they didn't say anything about you?'

'No.' Leah stared out across the park. Cassie sighed. Leah turned and looked at her. 'It ain't gonna happen. I don't want to go anywhere near your house, or your parents, or your sister.' She had been, and had seen enough. For a bright girl, Cassidie could be remarkably stupid.

'Is it because you're mad at them?'

'Mad?' Leah spat out the word.

The derision made Cassie feel uncomfortable. 'Okay, "mad" obviously isn't the right word. "Angry", "pissed off" – I don't know the right word..."furious"?'

Leah watched a small bird fling itself across the sky, staring at it until it disappeared into the trees at the far side of the park, wrestling with the conflicting impulses of control and release. And as she'd found herself doing more and more when she was with Cassidie, she chose release. '"Hate". That's the word, you're looking for, Cassidie. I fucking hate your parents.'

Cassie blinked, but didn't flinch. 'I get that.'

But she didn't, because she couldn't. 'No, you don't. You love them. They love you. You can't get it. You were all I had, and they took you away from me.' The words erupted from somewhere deep inside Leah, somewhere black and bitter. 'That was it, for me. After that it was never gonna be any good. I was fucked. No one wants a seven-year-old, not even a nice one, and I wasn't nice. How could I be?' Leah lifted her chin, regaining some of her defiance. 'Do you know how many times I was moved on, altogether? Eighteen! Eighteen fucking times. Different foster families, different houses, different units – the same old shit. There was never any notice, no explanation, just another bin bag with my stuff rammed in it, and another room, another bed, following on after some other sad cunt. So no, Cassidie, I don't want to come to your nice house and meet your *nice* little sister and your *nice* parents! Thank you very much!'

Cassie wanted to shrink away from Leah's anger, but she knew she couldn't. The guilt wouldn't let her. This was the first time Leah had said anything about being in care. Cassie wanted to listen, wanted to understand. 'I'm sorry.'

'Yeah, well. It was what it was.' Leah faked a shrug, trying to haul the rage back in.

'Didn't you settle with anyone?' Cassie winced at her choice of words, waiting for Leah to take offence, but surprisingly she didn't.

'When I was nine, I had a year and a half with an older couple, in Bolton, the Mertons. They were all right. But they offed to Australia when he retired.'

'And left you?'

'Yeah. Said they couldn't take me, cos I wasn't theirs.' A clean, white room with a dressing table and a stool with a furry cover. A chance – which hadn't turned into a life, despite her best efforts to be the very best version of herself. Cassidie was looking at her now, listening, caring. It provoked another rush of painful truth. 'Once you've been in care, people can detect it on you. At school, in shops – they just know.' Leah looked out across the park. 'After that I had no chance. Teenagers. Who wants a teenager? Nobody.'

Cassie thought about Leah's scrubbed-clean, lonely flat and felt another heavy drop of knowledge fall into the gathering pool. 'So what happened to you?'

'I got sent to other placements, flats, houses. None of them worked out. I ended up in a unit.'

'I don't understand why they kept moving you? Surely—'

Leah stood up abruptly. 'They just did. That's what happens to kids that no one wants.' She stretched, as if trying to shake off the memory, putting an end to the conversation. 'I need to go to the shop. You coming?'

'Leah, wait. Sorry. I didn't mean—' Cassie's sentence was cut short by the sensation of something battering against the back of her legs.

As she jumped up and away from the bench, a volley of shouting started up. A male voice, somewhere over to their left, hollered, 'Get 'ere ! Tyson, off! I said...drop it! Tyson, drop it!

In response, Leah supplied an unbroken string of expletives. Beneath the bench Cassie saw a frenzy of white-and-brown fur and a flash of yellow teeth tangling with her bag. Instinctively she bent down and started pulling at the strap, trying to get it back, but the dog wasn't giving up without a fight. It snarled and clamped its teeth into the fabric. Cassie tugged and pulled, her heart pumping in her chest. The dog hung on.

Leah shouted, 'What the fuck!' very clearly, then, inexplicably, ran away, leaving Cassie in a bizarre, frightening tug-of-war with the slobbering slab of muscle. It went on and on. Then, without warning, the dog suddenly unclamped its jaws and Cassie stumbled backwards, bag in hand, and landed with a jarring thud on her backside. There was a gap of at most half a second, then the dog started barking again. It backed up weirdly, as if winding up itself for a full assault, then rushed at Cassie.

Just before the Staffie reached her, Leah loomed into view, yielding what looked like a tree branch. She jabbed it hard between the dog's front legs and proceeded to push and prod it away, putting herself between it and Cassie. This only served to enrage the Staffie even more. It started jumping up, snapping and snarling at Leah. After what felt like for ever, a hand finally got a grip on the dog and pulled it backwards. A lead was clipped on and it was yanked at hard, once, twice. Cassie felt blood rush up to her face, embarrassed heat replacing cold fear.

'Down, Tyson, down!' The dog finally quietened a few notches, though it was still growling and pulling. The man bent down and checked it over, then straightened up. 'Ya mad bitch! You could've killed him!' This was aimed at Leah, who was still standing, holding the branch. 'If there's any damage, I'm tellin' ya, you'll be paying for it.' The man was breathing hard with anger as much as exertion.

Leah glanced at Cassie, checking that she was okay, then back at the bloke. 'It needs fucking putting down,' she hissed.

'It's your fucking fault – leaving stuff on the floor. He's a dog, what did ya expect?' The man was struggling with the Staffie. He squared up to Leah, and Leah stepped forward.

A completely new fear raced through Cassie. She scrambled to her feet, clutching the wrecked bag to her. 'Leah, I'm okay. Let's just leave it.' She started to back away, keeping her eyes on the snarling dog.

'Yeah. I'd listen to your foreign friend, if I were you.'

Leah took another step forward and, at the precisely the same time, the guy and Cassie realised that the branch wasn't the only thing she was holding; clenched in her left fist was the broken bottle, held by its neck. Leah stared at the man, and the man stared at Leah.

'You're fucking mental!' the guy shouted, but he dropped his gaze. He turned abruptly and started dragging the dog away with him, cursing as he went. Leah threw the stick down, but she held onto the bottle until he was well away from them.

They didn't say anything to each other until they'd made it down to the play area. By unspoken mutual consent they went and sat on the swings, side-by-side, both of them breathing unevenly. They could still just about make out the man and his dog moving away along the ridge; he was shaking his head, the Staffie pulling and straining in front of him.

'Fuckin' nutter!' Leah's voice was clogged with fury and something less certain.

'It could smell the food.' Cassie examined her bag, which was covered in puncture marks and dog slobber. Thankfully her purse was still there, along with the remnants of the plastic bag; two badly squashed sandwiches, some smashed crisps and a crushed chocolate bar.

'Food?' Leah asked.

'Yeah, I brought us lunch.' The stupidity of the gesture struck Cassie and she had to swallow to stop herself blubbing. She felt shaken and suddenly very cold, despite the sun. When she glanced at Leah, she was shocked to see that she seemed to be struggling as well. She was rubbing her hands repetitively up and down her jeans, as if trying to rid herself of the whole experience.

'Are you all right? You were really brave. Thank you.'

'Stupid fucker!' Leah kept up her compulsive chafing. Cassie could hear the rasp of her skin against the denim. The swing swayed and creaked.

'Leah, it's okay. It's over. They've gone.' Cassie risked reaching out and touching the top of Leah's hand, wanting to still her agitation. Leah's hand was stone-cold. Cassie patted it awkwardly and Leah's breathing calmed, a little. The girls sat for a moment, hand over hand, fingertip to skin, old scars discernible through new contact.

Out of nowhere, a memory flooded through Cassie. A dog, barking and snarling. Sharp teeth snapping in her face. Scrabbling claws. Slobber and scratches all over her legs. Threat, fear, danger. And Leah! Leah putting herself in harm's way. Leah keeping her safe. Leah protecting her.

'It was you!'

Leah slid her hand out from underneath Cassie's and edged the swing backwards until she was standing on the tips of her toes. She set it off slowly, swinging back and forth, arcing her body, building up speed and height, back and forth, back and forth, until she was sailing high in the sky.

Beside her, Cassie sat marooned – rethinking everything.

Not her mother. Her sister.

Not maternal love. Sibling.

Not a faceless ghost. Leah.

Chapter 41

THE FLAT was filled with sunlight. Leah went straight into the bathroom and shut the door. She was badly shaken, and not just by the dog attack. She pumped soap onto her hands and began scrubbing at them under the hot tap. She needed to get clean – palms first, then the tops, then in between her fingers. The soap seeped into her cracked skin, stinging fiercely, but still she kept at it, ridding herself of the contamination. She counted under her breath, slowly. She allowed herself to get to thirty, then she reluctantly turned off the water. A trail of pink blood swirled around the sink and drained away. Though she patted her hands gently, spots of red bloomed on the towel. She folded it carefully and hung it – blood stains hidden – back on the heater. She felt calmer, more in control, but still not normal.

The dog had been a shock, but it was the emotion that the attack had released that was really freaking her out – that, and Cassidie's response. Leah looked down at her ugly, raw hands and saw Cassidie touching them as they sat on the swings. A small, simple, defences-destroying gesture. Leah brought her hands up to her face and inhaled the sharp tang of citrus, a stripped-bare, cleansing smell. It helped to ground her, and remind her to stay on task.

She picked up her phone, saw Naz's text and steeled herself.

In the living room Cassie waited, processing the same event, but with very different emotions. For the first time in months, it made sense. Her dreams weren't of her birth mother – her parents hadn't been lying about that, but they had still been wrong! The moments of kindness, affection and happiness weren't echoes of her time spent with Jane, they were memories of Leah.

It was not her mother who had danced with her, swinging her round on her hip, holding her close.

Not her mother who had looked after her when she was sick, comforting her and singing her nursery rhymes.

Not her mother who had made sure that she was fed and warm.

It was not her mother who had protected her from all the threats that had massed and gathered in their pit of a house.

It was never her mother who loved her.

It was Leah.

Seven-year-old Leah. A child raising a child. It was crazy, but it was true. The one person who had been there for Cassie had been Leah, and Cassie hadn't even remembered her. The cruelty of it was breathtaking. No wonder Leah was so angry: with her, with her parents, with the world in general. She'd shown love and bravery in the face of appalling neglect and danger, only to be ignored and rejected, over and over again.

Cassie thumped down on the sofa, took a few deep breaths and started to shift through each fragment, reassigning them, finally, to the right person – her sister.

When Leah emerged from the bathroom she was back in control. By unspoken consent, both girls moved wordlessly into the tiny kitchen; a new-found acceptance of each other's presence seemed to have taken over. Leah filled the kettle, and Cassie got out the mugs for tea. Together they made the beans on toast. They took their food through to the sitting room. They ate, balancing their plates on their knees, sitting next to each other on the sofa. The beans tasted good. It felt okay not to talk; in fact it felt safer, so neither of them did. When the meal was over, Leah collected the dirty plates and mugs. Cassie let her, knowing that she wouldn't relax until everything was washed and put away, and the tea towel was draped over the back of the chair.

When Leah walked back into the room, she went and stood over near the window. Cassie looked at her silhouetted against the sky and didn't know how to begin.

It was Leah who broke the impasse. 'Why don't we go into town?'

Cassie smiled. 'Yeah. That'd be good.' She wanted to say so much more, but all she could think to offer was, 'We could see if can we get someone to have a look your hands?'

Leah turned and shrugged. ''Kay.'

It was a start.

Chapter 42

IT TURNED into a weirdly normal afternoon. Leah seemed to want to avoid conversation, so Cassie happily went along with the quiet but companionable mood. Armed with some steroid cream from the sympathetic chemist in Boots, they drifted around the clothes shops in an anaesthetised state, picking up and putting things down with no real intention of purchasing. The piped music and presence of other people was soothing, after the violence in the park. Only once did Cassie offer to buy something for Leah, a pair of jeans that she had lingered over, but Leah shook her head and shoved them back on top of the pile, the minute Cassie started searching for her purse.

Cassie didn't push it, knowing that Leah would find the fold of notes in the cutlery drawer soon enough. Recompense by stealth – that was the way to go. Even at a dawdling pace, they exhausted the gamut of clothes shops in Oldham within the hour. Neither of them seemed to have a plan for what came next. Both of them were unwilling to say goodbye. Their dilemma was resolved by the appearance of Naz. They spotted him before he saw them. He was on the other side of the high street, outside a bookie's, talking to some lads. Leah slowed her pace and Cassie matched her. They very nearly made it round the corner and out of sight, but not quite.

'Hey!' he shouted. They stopped. He slapped hands with the lads in some styled-out, private handshake, then ambled over the road to meet them. 'Thought it was you. Bunking off again?'

Cassie didn't know whether this was aimed at her or Leah. She let Leah answer. 'We were just having a wander round the shops.' As always around Naz, she seemed tense.

'Right.' He nodded. 'I was heading your way. You got time for a drink, Cassidie? It'd be good to have a proper catch-up.'

Leah starting back-pedalling. 'I dunno, Cassidie has to get—'

Naz threw Leah a sharp look. 'I was asking Cassidie!'

Cassie cut in quickly, not wanting, for reasons she wasn't wholly sure about, to leave Leah alone with Naz in her current subdued state. 'I've got time. I don't have to be back for a while.' She wanted to prove to Leah that spending time with her was the priority, not returning to her loving, lying parents.

Naz's face lightened and he flashed a grin. 'Great. Back to yours then?'

On the short walk back he told anecdotes about people Cassie didn't know and parties Leah seemed not to have attended. Cassie was aware that Naz was bragging, but he was entertaining and funny. His previous bad temper seemed to have evaporated. When they reached the small parade of shops near Leah's flat he stopped. 'What have you got in?'

'A couple of beers, a bit of voddie left, I think,' Leah said.

'You got any Coke?' She shook her head. 'Anything to eat?' Again, that was a 'No'.

Naz glanced towards the booze shop. Cassie immediately offered to buy the supplies. She extracted a fiver from her purse and held it out to Leah, but it was Naz who intercepted it, with an OTT 'Thank *you*'. He paused, Cassie got the message and promptly offered more. Only then did Naz pass one of the notes to Leah. She stood, scratching her wrist, an unreadable look on her face, while Naz put in his order. Cassie looked away. She was fascinated by the dynamic: Leah's passivity and Naz's dominance. There was obviously some strain between the two of them. 'We'll get the snacks,' Naz announced, 'see you back at the flat.' Then he shocked Cassie by linking arms with her and propelling her along the pavement into the poky little corner shop, leaving Leah behind.

He evidently had a sweet tooth. Cassie bought the crisps and chocolate bars that he selected and they emerged back out onto the street. There was no sign of Leah, but Naz seemed in no mood to linger. As they headed for the flats they passed through the patchwork of sunshine and shadows cast by the surrounding buildings. The switch from light to dark and back again was dizzying. The entrance to the block was open, as usual. As they stood by the lift, Cassie wondered why they hadn't waited for Leah. She regretted that they hadn't.

Naz smiled at her. 'I'm really glad that you and Leah are getting on. You're good for her. I can tell.' Cassie didn't know what to say to that. He ushered her into the empty lift, 'After you.'

When they got out on the seventh floor, Cassie's vague apprehension solidified. The building was so brutally unwelcoming. She really didn't fancy having to hang around on the landing, waiting for Leah, with the dead-eyed doors and the smell of garbage, but to her surprise they didn't have to. Naz pulled a key out of his back pocket and let them into the flat. That he had a key shocked Cassie. The flat was Leah's sanctuary, it seemed completely out of character for her to let Naz come and go as he pleased. He threw the snacks and the key-ring onto the table and sat down. Cassie chose to sit opposite, not next to him.

'She shouldn't be too long.' He shrugged off his expensive-looking jacket.

'No.'

Naz seemed quite at home. 'Bit different for you, all this, I'm guessing.'

Cassie knew what he was hinting at, but didn't want to get into it. 'Sorry?'

'This.' He waved his arms around the room, but his gesture included everything that lay beyond: the other blocks of flats, the dirty landing, the tin-can of a lift, the scarred park, the shabby parade of shops, even the grey bulk of Manchester squatting in the distance.

'A bit.' She didn't want to come across as a snob.

'Ah, come on! More than a bit.'

She decided to stick to the physical geography. 'I like Manchester. It's great for shopping.' Her stupidity echoed round the room.

'Yeah. Madchester!' Naz made a mocking gesture. 'Great place,' he paused, 'if you've got cash. But Oldham is a bit of a shithole!' He watched her, waiting to see how she'd react.

Out of loyalty to Leah's home town, Cassie smiled. 'It's okay.'

Naz leant forward, picked up the tortillas and ripped the bag open. He offered her some. She declined. He grabbed a fistful for himself. 'Yeah, well, I suppose "it's okay" for some people.' He meant Leah. He threw some tortillas into his mouth, chewed and swallowed, noisily. 'She's not done *too bad* for herself, I suppose. She's got her *little* flat, her *little* job, a *little* bit of money coming in, it's quite an achievement...considering.'

Cassie left the hook of 'considering' dangling.

'She needs to have more confidence in herself, though. Have you noticed how she puts herself down all the time?'

Cassie hadn't – that wasn't what Leah did; what Leah did was disappear inside herself, which wasn't the same thing at all, but Cassie didn't argue with him. Besides, Naz didn't seem that interested in her opinion.

He flowed on. 'She thinks she's not worth anything? Now that's not right, is it? Thinking you're worthless.' He wiped his greasy fingers on the arm of the chair and Cassie winced. 'But I suppose that's what happens, when you're dragged up. No family, no rules, no respect, even for yourself.'

Cassie felt incredibly uncomfortable talking about Leah with Naz, who, from everything she'd seen, spent his time making absolutely sure that Leah knew her place. He leant back and stretched, spreading his arms and legs wide. His whole posture shouted *Look at me* and Cassie, despite herself, did just that, fascinated, repelled and unnerved in equal measure. As if reading Cassie's mind, he twisted and looked at the flat door. 'Where has that girl got to?' But the door stayed firmly, silently shut. Naz took another handful of tortillas, not noticing, or perhaps not caring, when some fell on the floor. 'You fancy one of these beers she claims she's got in, while we wait?'

Cassie nodded, as much as to break up their conversation as anything else.

He came back with the drinks: a beer for her, a glass of water for himself. She took a couple of swift mouthfuls of the cold lager, reasoning that alcohol might help to ease the awkwardness of the situation. Naz downed half of his water, his eyes studying her as he drank. 'You don't look like sisters.'

'No.' What else could she say; they didn't.

'You're very pretty.' Again there was the implication that Leah wasn't. Cassie made a non-committal noise and wondered where the hell she was. 'Different dads, obvs.' Still she said nothing. Naz warmed to his theme. 'I hate blokes like that. Having kids with lots of different women, it shows a total lack of respect...of responsibility. Mind, they let 'em, don't they?'

Cassie was thrown by his arrogance, but found herself too intimidated to say anything. He didn't seem at all bothered by her reticence.

'You see it all the time round here. Baby daddies! It's a miracle that Leah's not gone and got herself banged up, when you stop to think about it. It's what you'd expect – given her history.' He spoke as if it had nothing whatsoever to do with him.

Cassie took another swig of her drink and prayed for the sound of Leah's key rattling in the lock. It didn't.

Naz flashed her another of his smiles. 'So,' he drained his glass, 'tell me about your mum and dad.'

Chapter 43

TOM HAD been surprised when Erin asked for a lift. Apparently a group of her friends were going out for something to eat, then on to the cinema, and she'd been asked to go along. He was glad she'd been invited, even happier that she'd said yes. He glanced at her sitting next to him, then turned his attention back to the road. A touch of make-up, a pretty top and skinny jeans and a denim jacket – which was a hand-me-down from Cassie – she looked great, but she still looked thirteen, as she should. He could tell that she was nervous by the stiffness of her posture and the lack of conversation, so he stopped quizzing her about who was going and flicked on the radio, leaving her to stare, in peace, out of the window.

Erin's tentative steps into young adulthood were faltering, but they were recognisable. Tom hadn't found being a teenager a breeze, either, there had been too many unspoken rules that he'd been poor at deciphering, so he had every sympathy with Erin's uncertainty. He indicated and pulled into the filter that led on to the leisure park. Perhaps caution was no bad thing in a child. Inevitably, his thoughts went back to his reckless elder daughter. Who knew where Cassie was this evening? At work, she'd said – they'd had to take her word for that – then round to a friend's, which was no doubt code for seeing Ryan. That relationship wasn't dying a death, as he'd hoped; if anything, they seemed to be spending even more time together. His own and Grace's attempts to get anywhere near Ryan, to size him up, had failed, abjectly. The open invitation for Ryan to *call round for a beer sometime when the footie is on* had been met with a snort of derision and a closing door. They were losing their grip on Cassie. It was as if their real daughter had been replaced by a stranger, who looked and sounded like the same girl, but whose heart and soul were completely dark to them.

Tom pulled the car into a space in front of the restaurant and switched off the engine. Erin unclipped her seatbelt. 'Do you want me to come in with you?'

'Dad!' Erin leant across the handbrake and pecked him on the cheek.

'Well, have a good time. Text me if you need a lift home.'

'Thanks, but Hannah's dad said he'd drop us back.' She slammed the door and set off towards the restaurant. Tom watched and waited until she was safely inside, before he set off back home through the early evening traffic.

Chapter 44

NAZ WAS talking about BMWs. It was surprisingly soothing. Cassie sipped her beer and let his enthusiasm for torques and top speeds roll over her. He was obviously quite into his cars. She went to take another sip of her beer, but as she tilted the bottle to her lips, nothing came out.

'Want another?' Naz asked.

'Yeah, that'd be good.'

He went and fetched it. 'The last one…just for you.' He popped the cap off the bottle, wiped the rim with his sleeve and passed it to her. She took it and drank another cold mouthful, while Naz wandered over to the window and looked out. It was quiet and peaceful and Cassie realised she wasn't on edge any more. She felt relaxed, sleepy almost. She felt her eyes closing. She had to make a real effort to open them, but she found that she couldn't seem to focus on Naz's blurry outline – the sun behind him was too bright to look at. She rested her head back against the sofa, let his voice wash over her and began to drift.

The next thing she knew, Naz wasn't across the room from her, he was next to her. His voice close, whispering in her ear. She could smell him. Air, aftershave, something lemony-fresh. 'You really are very pretty, aren't you, Cassidie?' He breathed against her neck. 'Bet you get told that all the time. Lovely skin.' He was touching her arm. She let him. 'So soft.' Her head felt heavy. For a second she 'saw' Ryan's hurt face.

When Naz touched her again, she didn't feel anything.

Chapter 45

TOM LET himself back into a house that felt lifeless, because it was. He dumped his wallet and keys and wandered from room to room, unable to settle without the familiar anchor points of his wife and his daughters. Traces of their presence were everywhere: in Cassie's broken necklace in the bowl on the dresser, in Grace's hairbrush in the downstairs loo, in the girls' timetables stuck to the front of the fridge, and in the half-empty jar of Nutella with Erin's name on it on the kitchen shelf.

Tom retraced his steps through to the hall and fished Cassie's broken necklace out of the bowl. He had to sieve through the rubble of crap to find the fastener. Craning over the low coffee table in the lounge, he started to tease out the knots. It was fiddly work. The chain was delicate and the fastener had a flattened link. His fingers felt clumsy and huge. For every knot he untangled, he seemed to create a new one, but he persevered, working slowly, patiently. It took him a good twenty-five minutes, and some headache-inducing messing around with Grace's eyebrow tweezers, but in the end he managed to fix it. He held up his handiwork to admire. The little filigree disc on the end of the chain spun in the fading sunlight, sending patterns around the walls.

Tom was still sitting on the sofa with the necklace in his hand when he heard Grace swing her car onto the drive. He put it down carefully and went into the hallway to welcome her home. 'Hi. Good day?'

Grace hung up her jacket. 'Not bad. Busy. Was Erin all right when you dropped her off?'

They wandered through to the kitchen. 'Yeah. Fine. A bit – you know – but she seemed to be looking forward to it.'

'Good.' Grace stretched. 'Do you mind if we eat later? I could do with a soak.'

Tom felt foolish for wanting his wife to stay with him for a while instead of disappearing upstairs the minute she came in, but he kept his need for company to himself. 'Yeah, of course.'

As she passed by him on the way to the hall she asked, 'Have you heard anything from Cassie today?'

'No,' Tom said.

'Me neither.' She sighed and walked wearily upstairs for her bath.

Grace took her phone with her, hidden in the pocket of her jacket. She wasn't sure why she didn't want Tom to see it. No, that wasn't true; she did know. She knew he would get irritated if he caught her texting Cassie, he would see it as 'pandering' to her, but Grace couldn't relax, not knowing for certain where her estranged and enraged daughter was. Letting Cassie go – Grace wasn't prepared to do it, it felt too much like giving up. She'd heard nothing from Cassie all day, despite numerous texts and messages. It was as if her daughter had dropped off the face of the Earth. Grace set the bath running and tried again. The phone rang and rang. As punishment went, it was a singularly simple but effective one. Cassie's judgement reverberated in each dial tone. The call went to voicemail – again. As she watched the bath fill, Grace left another awkward, nervous message, though she had little hope that she would get a reply.

As she turned off the tap, she decided to make one last call.

It was unfair, sacrificing one daughter's peace in order to reassure herself about the safety of another, but it was her only option.

Chapter 46

'WHAT'VE YOU done?' Leah kicked the flat door shut behind her and dropped the shopping on the floor, ignoring the crash of the bottles. Cassidie was slumped on the sofa. Naz was kneeling next to her. Cassidie's T-shirt was pushed up, her plain white bra bright against her skin. Her jeans were unzipped, revealing a triangle of pale-blue cotton. Leah's stomach contracted.

Naz barely reacted. 'Chill!' He looked from Leah back to Cassidie. Then slowly he reached out and trailed his fingers down Cassidie's body, throat to pubic bone, demonstrating very clearly who was in control.

But a flash of hot, bright anger made Leah brave. 'I said, what 'ave you done to her?'

Naz stood up, using his height to shrink Leah back down to size. 'I said, *relax*. She'll be fine in a couple of hours, maybe a bit more.'

'You better not 'ave...' Leah couldn't bring herself to finish her sentence.

He reached out, towards Leah this time, and grabbed her. 'Now, now. There's no need to go all green-eyed. I was just having a sneaky peak. Besides, you know me, I prefer white meat to brown.'

Leah stiffened. He squeezed her breast. There was a crackle of energy about him, which she knew was dangerous. She looked past him, checking on Cassidie. Her breathing was regular and her colour wasn't *too* bad, but she was obviously out of it, utterly out of it. Her eyes kept opening, then sliding shut. 'How much did you give her?'

Naz ignored Leah's question, but at least he released hold of her. He went back to the sofa, bent down, picked up Cassidie's handbag and walked over to the table. Leah followed him. He smiled. 'Half a roofie. Or was it a whole one? You know me, I'm a generous kinda guy, especially when it comes to family. And the lovely Cassidie over there is family, to you at least, isn't she?'

Leah didn't respond.

'Aw, come on, Leah, stop sulking. It was a half. Just a little taster with her beer. She'll be fine – once she comes round.' He uncere-moniously emptied Cassidie's bag onto the table, sending her personal stuff skimming across the surface. He stirred the contents with his slim, mean fingers. With a sigh, as if he was weary of the effort, he picked up the purse, extracted the bank cards, then emptied it of cash. He left the coins. 'Mustn't be greedy. She's gonna need her bus fare back to la-la land when she wakes up.' Leah watched, unable to stop him. 'Shopping time.' He smiled, pocketed the cards and the cash and turned to leave; as he did, he planted on kiss on Leah's rigid neck. 'I might even get a little something for you. Keep an eye on her, like a good girl.'

Leah finally found her voice. 'Not her cards, Naz. Please.'

'Wot?' His tone was dark.

'If you take her cards, she'll know, and that'll be the end of it.' Leah was scrabbling for purchase and they both knew it.

He eyed her. 'Oh, it's not the end of it, Leah, nowhere near.' He tucked the cards away in his jacket pocket. 'Tell her she must 'ave lost 'em, when you were in town. She's probably dumb enough to believe you, and the roofie ain't gonna help with her memory.'

Across the other side of the room Cassidie made an odd choking noise; Leah's attention snapped back to her. Cassidie raised herself up slightly on one elbow and opened her eyes; her pupils were dark and unnaturally dilated. She seemed to be staring straight at them, like a doll in a horror movie. It was deeply unnerving, but Naz was unperturbed. No, it was more than that, he was amused.

'Ah, bless. Look at her. Two beers and she's anyone's. Good job I'm a gentleman, isn't it?' He snapped his fingers in Leah's face. 'Earth to Leah! She swung her attention back to him. 'I want her gone by the time I come back.' He turned as if heading for the door, but instead of leaving, Naz paused and looked back at Cassidie. Leah didn't like it. He walked over, hunkered down beside her inert body and took hold of her hand. For a bizarre moment Leah thought he was going to kiss it, but it was the ring he was after, not a kiss – Cassidie's ring from her grandma. He held her hand and started working the ring down her finger, tugging and twisting at it. Leah watched and hated him more than she'd ever done before.

She wanted him gone.

She wanted him away from Cassidie.

She wanted him dead.

Days, weeks, months, years of repressed emotion erupted inside her. She launched herself at his back. Bone against bone, flesh against flesh. There was a satisfying thud. Naz let out a grunt and fell sideways under the shock of her weight. Leah heard the sofa scrape backwards and felt the blunt edge of the table connect with her face like a fist.

Then it went quiet, ominously quiet.

He sat up first.

She heard him move towards her.

Curled on her side on the floor, eyes closed, Leah waited. She'd survived this before. She would survive it again. She concentrated on her breathing: shallow, regular, slow breaths.

'You fucking maniac!'

One kick. Lower back. An explosion of pain – but nothing snapped, nothing broke.

He stood over her. She braced herself for the second kick, but it didn't come – not straight away. He made her wait. Left it long enough for the hope that he might stop at that to float free. Then he let rip. Kicking, shouting, raging. Leah folded in on herself. Tried to imagine escaping down through the carpet, through the floorboards into another space altogether – one that was quiet and safe and empty. But this time the old trick didn't work. There was too much energy and violence anchoring her in the room.

When he'd had enough, he stopped. But he didn't move away. He wasn't finished.

When he spoke he did so slowly, as if she was an idiot. 'Don't you *ever* do that again. Do you hear me? Do you?' She nodded, but kept her eyes closed. He leant down, so close that she could feel his breath on her cheek, and in a cold, completely calm voice he said, 'You need to decide whose side you're on, Leah. And quickly.' He paused. Still she didn't open her eyes. 'The answer – you stupid bitch – is mine.' He straightened up. His voice returned to normal: bossy, arrogant, but no longer deranged. 'Sort her out and get rid of her. And before she leaves, get her address.'

Leah waited for the flat door to close before she opened her eyes. She lay still, feeling the pain radiate through her body. Her face was near Cassidie's feet. Cassidie hadn't moved. The fight, the beating, Naz yelling – none of it had been enough to wake her up. She was still unconscious.

Naz had done for them both.

But he hadn't got everything he wanted because, from her vantage point on the floor, Leah had a clear view underneath the sofa. And there, on the floor near the back wall, was Cassidie's ring. She stretched out, ignoring the snap and scream of the muscles in her back and retrieved it. She slid the ring into her back pocket. Fuck you, Naz.

She levered herself up slowly, using the table for support, testing out her back. It hurt, but held. Her cheek pulsed from where she'd crashed into the table. Bruises incubated beneath her skin. She knelt and surveyed the damage: the crud all over the floor, the dirty orange smears on the furniture, Cassidie's stuff scattered across the table. The smell of beer, tortillas and Naz's aftershave crawled up her nostrils.

She wanted to scream.

Even inside her flat – her small, scrubbed, bleached box, with the lock on the door and her name on the rent book – she still wasn't safe. It still got in: the chaos, the rising tide of muck, the violence. She couldn't control it. She never had been able to. She looked at Cassidie propped up on the sofa like a mannequin, still pristine amidst the mess, and felt breathless. As Leah watched, Cassidie slowly collapsed sideways, comatose.

Naz had drugged her, molested her, stolen from her and left her vulnerable, and Leah's overwhelming emotion was – revulsion. In that moment, Leah hated Cassidie. If she could have picked up her keys and walked out, she would have; walked out and kept on walking. This was Cassidie's fault. She'd been the one trying to suck up to Naz. She'd been the one stupid enough to drink the spiked beer. She was the one who hadn't left when she could have. She was the one with the looks and the money, and the lovely ring from her poor dead grandma, and the fucking mansion and the doting parents to run home to. And that was what enraged Leah. Cassidie was the one who could always leave. She could always go back to her nice, safe, predictable, secure, clean, lovely life.

Leah couldn't. This was her life.

She limped over to the window, rested her forehead against the glass and pressed, hard.

Ten minutes later Leah went into the kitchen to get a glass of water. She put it on the floor beside the sofa. Her back throbbed, a reminder

– not that she needed one – that she was answerable to Naz, and that Naz was coming back, and that when he did, she'd better have done what he said.

She tried shouting at Cassidie, but that had no effect whatsoever, and the sound of her own voice bouncing around the hollow flat was too much to bear. So she poked her, but that elicited no response, either. At last, very reluctantly, Leah took hold of Cassidie, braced herself for the pain and hauled her upright. It took all of her willpower and her strength to do it, to touch Cassidie again after all those years – skin against skin, her hands guiding her sister's body. The weight of her, flopping against Leah, was breathtaking. After a lot of awkward tugging and pushing, she managed get Cassidie sitting upright and her clothes back in order.

Leah pressed the glass of water against her lips. 'Drink,' she instructed. Most of it flowed down Cassidie's chin and soaked into her T-shirt, but at least it seemed to wake her up a little bit. Cassidie started flapping her hands, trying to push the glass away. Leah was having none of it. 'Pack it in. You need to drink.' This time Cassidie actually swallowed some of the water. Only when the glass was empty did Leah let her sit back and close her eyes.

She was mumbling, which Leah took as a good sign. 'Try and stay awake!' Cassidie nodded slowly, and for a moment she opened her eyes again, but almost immediately her eyelids fluttered and closed. 'Cassidie!' Leah yelled. Again there was a flicker of awareness before she drifted off. Leah thought about trying to make her be sick, but she knew that would be difficult. Cassidie didn't 'do' being sick. Even as a toddler, she'd try hang onto it, swallowing it down, rather than actually chucking up, so frightened was she of getting into trouble. Leah remembered shouting at her and making her cry, but washing the bedding had been such a hard thing to manage, as it had meant running the gauntlet of 'downstairs'.

The slip into the past winded Leah.

She put the glass down on the floor and sat back next to Cassidie, feeling the vibrations of an emotion that was no longer impotent rage.

Caring for Cassidie.

It was her responsibility.

It always had been.

It was what she'd done, by instinct, from that very first day when their mother had come home with the latest addition to their already dysfunctional family – not a puppy this time, but a baby. Leah had known from day one that if she didn't look after it, something bad would happen. It was just the way it was. And the more she did, the less their mother had done. Leah had cared for her little sister every day and every night, when Cassidie was crying and when she was ill, when she was bored and when she was naughty, when she was happy and normal and noisy and hard work, and all the times in between.

Leah had resisted connecting *that* little girl with *this* young woman, but some truths, no matter how hard you try to smother them, still manage to survive.

Cassidie and Cassie were, she finally recognised, one and the same.

Cassie muttered something and her head rolled from one side to the other, bringing her beautiful face next to Leah's battered one. The flat was quiet. There were alone, together, safe – for the time being. In the soft evening light, Leah looked at Cassie, searching for the little sister she'd lost all those years ago. She found traces of her in the slope of Cassie's cheek and the deep peak at the bow of her lips. Her little sister hadn't disappeared, she'd grown up.

Leah felt her protective shell crack. The layers of scar tissue that had formed after each abandonment split apart and her laminated heart gave way. It was harrowing.

She hadn't cried in years. She'd forgotten how painful it was – the bulky bitterness in her throat, the straggled breathing, the sense of letting go and plummeting wildly downwards. It was frightening. And it went on and on.

And it was her own fault.

She should have gone out and left Cassie to come round on her own. She should have walked away and protected herself. But she hadn't. For the first time in years she'd let herself care for someone else, feared for them, felt the need to protect them and watch over them, and look what had happened: she'd been disarmed. Caring was dangerous; not caring was safer. She thought she'd perfected her indifference, that it was impregnable. Her useless mother, Jane the witch, the Mertons, every 'carer' who hadn't really cared, every social worker who'd proved not to be true to their word – they'd all contributed to her cast-iron defences. And her painstakingly collected armour *had* protected her. She had learnt not to care about anyone, certainly not herself, or any supposed 'friends'; definitely not Naz, or any of the other boys and men before him. Switch off, blank out, suck it up. It was doable.

Existing, but not living.

Working, but not getting anywhere.

Eating, but not tasting.

Fucking, but not feeling.

The heart-splitting truth was that no one had touched Leah with gentleness for years, at least not without an ulterior motive. No one had talked to her and really listened, no one had truly shared anything of themselves with her – not since she had been a big sister with a little sister who needed her. Not since Cassie.

Finally cried dry, Leah wiped her nose on her sleeve and looked up. Nothing had changed. The mess was still all round her, except that now the room was tinged pink by the setting sun. She took a deep breath, gathered herself together and tried to climb back inside the small, cramped box of 'not giving a fuck'.

But she couldn't, she had unravelled too much.

Cassie stirred and whimpered and Leah patted her shoulder, reassuring her that she was not on her own. 'You're gonna be okay. It's gonna wear off. It'll just take a bit of time.' Cassie tried to rouse herself, but the drug was stronger than her intentions. She muttered something that Leah didn't catch. 'What?'

'I said...' Cassie made a concerted effort, 'I'm sorry.'

Leah didn't want to think about what Cassie was sorry for, because she knew it didn't bear comparison with her own actions, her own complicity in leaving her sister alone with Naz, knowing full well what he was capable of. 'It's okay.' Leah squeezed Cassie's shoulder and, as she did so, she noticed how badly her hands were shaking. Guilt crept through her veins, finding space alongside the sadness. She went into the bedroom and fetched her duvet, which she draped over Cassie, tucking her in, like she used to when they were little. Even in her drugged and stupefied state, Cassie managed a slurred 'Thank you'. Her head drooped again.

This time Leah let her sleep.

An odd peace settled on the flat. The only noise was the hum of the fridge and the sounds of the faceless people who lived above and below her, and all around her. The light seeped away down the walls. Time passed. And Leah sat and watched over Cassie, as the bruises on her back and her face began to bud and bloom.

It felt good to have her little sister back.

The angry burr of Cassie's phone vibrating on the table startled Leah. Cassie didn't react. Leah reached over and picked it up. The caller ID said 'Mum'. Another few seconds, then, as expected, there was the buzz of an incoming text. Cassie not responding must have given the bitch-mother something to worry about, any real mother would – Leah supposed. She sat and pondered this everyday example of maternal concern with a complex ripple of emotions. She looked at Cassie, who was still fast asleep, breathing evenly and peacefully.

Leah didn't attempt to wake her. She was warmed by the knowledge that Cassie was safe with her, rather than at home. It was comforting, and emboldening, to have Cassie in the flat, in her care, under her jurisdiction. Cassie's family would have to wait.

It was, finally, her turn.

Besides, Leah reasoned, even when Cassie did eventually wake up – and who knew when that would be – she would still have to get back to Leeds, and that could take a couple of hours, or more. By then it would be late and dark, and not safe; not for a girl travelling on her own, a girl who had no street smarts. Leah entered 1 – 2 – 0 – 4. She'd seen Cassie do it enough times to know the four-digit pass code by heart. She'd made it her business to know. The message *was* from Cassie's mother, asking what time she'd be back home. It was a nice, cheery text, 'signed' with a smiley face and a purple heart emoji. When Leah looked, there were a string of similar messages across the day. Jesus, she really was a possessive bitch. Each text flicked another drop of poison into Leah's open wounds. As she was skimming through the litany of fussing, an alert pinged up. Yet another family member keeping in touch! This time it was the bitch-sister, bragging about being out having *fun* with her friends at the cinema.

A shiver of bitterness rippled through Leah.

They were never going to let Cassie go.

Never.

Not unless she made them.

Leah scrolled through Cassie's long list of contacts: the friends and the family members who made up the wide, complex, extended web of love and support that encircled her. Eventually she found Erin's number, stored under 'Sis'. Carefully and calmly, she composed her message.

Chapter 47

ERIN AND her friends were waiting to buy their tickets for the film when her phone buzzed. A message from Cassie. She opened it, pleased and more than a little surprised that her sister had bothered to respond to her post.

The message read, i'm in Manchester with Leah having a nite out. i'm gonna stay over. Tell Mum and Dad I'm staying at Freya's if they ask. Thanx.

There was something wrong. It wasn't just the content of the message – there was something off about the text itself. Erin read it again, but it didn't feel right. Cassie never typed 'Thanx' and, given the state of their relationship at present, a 'thank you', even for providing a covering lie, was the last thing Cassie was likely to send her.

'Everything okay?' Hannah asked.

'Yeah. Fine. Can you do me a favour and get my ticket for me?' She gave Hannah her money. 'Thanks. I need to call my sister.' Erin stepped out of the queue and went to stand near one of the pillars. Cassie wouldn't actually choose to spend a whole night with Leah, would she? Erin hadn't even known Cassie was in Manchester again. How had she got there? A night out. By choice? With Leah?

And where was she going to stay? It didn't just feel wrong; it was wrong. Erin's heart sped up at the thought of it. Her phone rang. She answered it, without looking.

'Hi, Erin. Sorry to bother you, honey.' It was her mum. 'You haven't heard from Cassie, have you? She's not answering her phone, and I need a quick word with her about something.' The lightness of tone didn't disguise the concern in Grace's voice.

Erin's response was a flustered 'No. Sorry.'

'Okay, love. Don't worry about it. She's probably had to leave her phone in her locker. Enjoy the film.' Her mum rang off.

So her parents thought Cassie was at work. More lies. Erin felt overwhelmed by the sudden responsibility for her sister's safety. Knowing she'd never relax if she didn't get to the bottom of it, she called Cassie's number. It rang and rang, then clicked through to the message service. 'Cass, please call me' was all Erin could think to say.

The girls had bought the tickets and got a bucket of popcorn and some sweets. They came towards Erin, chatting and laughing, and she felt a powerful longing to be one of them, stress-free, simply enjoying a night out. Hannah passed her a ticket and they turned towards the escalators that led up to the screens, but Erin hung back.

'What's up?' Hannah retraced her steps.

Erin stumbled over her apology. 'I'm really sorry. I feel like I might be getting a migraine.' Hannah looked concerned, which only added to the pressure building up inside Erin's head. 'It's okay, you go. I just need to go home and lie down for a bit.' Even to her own ears, it sounded like a lame excuse to get out of the film – something she had a track record of doing.

Hannah still looked worried. 'But how are you going to get home?'

Erin hadn't got as far as thinking that through, but she smiled brightly. 'It's fine. My dad's coming to get me. You go. Sorry. I'll text you later.' Hannah still hesitated, trapped between contradictory impulses. 'Go! I'll be fine, honest.' At last she did.

Erin moved further away from the crowds, trying to find some space to think. Cassie was AWOL. Her mum was worried. The text message didn't feel right. But what could she do? The answer was very little, but she had to try. She sent a text. **Cassie I'm worried about you. PLEASE ring me.** She held her phone tightly and willed it to ring. She stood perfectly still as people flowed past her. The minutes accumulated. Then at 6.46 p.m. a response flashed up. **Erin, I swear to god. Just do wot I asked. I'll talk to you tomorow.** It took a huge effort not to cry. Erin turned her back on the crowds and tried to pull herself together. It was like Cassie had slapped her. In a way she had. Not telling her she was even going to Manchester, then expecting her to lie, then being foul to her, simply because she expressed some concern about what she was doing.

Erin was stranded. Trapped by the need to tell her mother *something*, and literally stuck at the cinema. For a few seconds she panicked, frozen by the scale of the lie she was going to have to tell, to cover for Cassie and to extricate herself. But cowering in the corner of a cinema lobby that had grown quiet in the lull between film screenings wasn't going to help. Erin took three long, slow, deep breaths. She decided to deal with her mum first, by text, because it'd be easier than calling her. She messaged Grace, saying she'd forgotten to tell her that Cassie was staying over at Freya's. She apologised for forgetting. She kept the message short and sent it before she could bottle out. The responding **Cheers. Thanks for letting me know** made her feel both a tiny bit better and a whole lot worse.

How to get home was the next problem.

In the end Erin decided she'd have to play the highly strung daughter card, but not straight away. Instead she wandered over to the far corner of the lobby, away from the ticket desk and out of sight of most of the other cinema-goers, where she sat on the lurid purple carpet, killing time.

It was a lonely wait, punctuated by the scraps of other people's conversations as they drifted past in waves, a steady ebb and flow.

The waiting gave her plenty of time to think about Cassie being with Leah – which she tried to do, but her imagination failed her. She simply couldn't comprehend why her sister was voluntarily choosing to be around someone so different, so unknown and, to be honest, so rough. Then there was the issue of the money. Cassie, her smart, strong-willed sister, seemed to have been totally taken in by Leah. She was lapping up her sob stories without question. Who knew whether they were even true? But Cassie didn't seem to care, she was so wrapped up in the thought of them being together when she was little. A blood-bond stronger than family – couldn't she see that Leah was playing her?

The more Erin thought about it, the more stressed she became, and the more worried. She looked at Cassie's texts again, fretting. They didn't sound like her sister, but there again, her sister wasn't behaving like her sister any more. Her phone screen faded and the words disappeared. And why pick Freya, a girl from drama club that Cassie was barely friends with? Why not Jess or Anna? Erin tried to call Cassie again, but the message told her the phone that she was calling was switched off. Cassie never switched off her phone, never. The panic escaped from Erin's chest and careered around her body.

She could think of only one person to call.

Chapter 48

THERE WAS no rush now. Cassie could sleep for as long as she needed.

It was such a pity she hadn't been able to see Little Miss Serious's distress. Leah had to make do with imagining Erin's shock and hatred at the thought of her and Cassie spending time together. And Little Miss Serious would not have liked having to lie to her parents. Serve her right. Erin's heart-shaped face and her puppy-dog eyes were imprinted on Leah's mind. She'd seen her slavish devotion to Cassie in Subway the day of their first 'meeting', the closeness between them, the love – but that was before Leah.

One real sister.

One fake sister.

It was time people knew which was which.

Erin was just going to have to learn that sometimes life took away from you the very thing you relied on, the thing that anchored and defined you. Karma really was a bitch.

Leah sat back and watched over Cassie as she slept, hope stirring in her chest. The day didn't have to be a complete disaster. If she played her cards right, things might still work to her advantage. All she needed – all she'd ever wanted – was time with Cassie, away from the bitch-mother and the wanker father and the imposter sister. And Naz's actions, painful as they were, had gifted her that.

Leah got up and went into her tiny kitchen, taking Cassie's phone with her. She flicked on the kettle. Tea would be good. Warming, reviving.

It was time for Cassie to wake up, but not for her to leave.

Chapter 49

'YEAH?' HE was on guard straight away, but all Erin could feel was relief that he was working.

'Ryan?'

'Yeah.' He sounded suspicious. Her confidence drained out of her. 'Who is this?'

'Sorry. It's me. Erin. Cassie's sister.' This was met with silence. She tried to steady her voice. 'I'm sorry to call you at work, but I wanted to know if you'd heard from Cassie tonight?'

'How did you get this number?'

'I Googled it.' Not that it mattered. 'Have you heard from her today?'

'Why?' Ryan's suspicion ratcheted up a level.

'Well. I'm...' What to tell him? *I'm paranoid...* 'I'm worried about her.'

'Why?'

How could she even begin to explain? 'She's in Manchester, with Leah, says she's staying over, all night.' That was all she needed to say.

'Ah, for fuck's sake!' Erin felt a rush of relief at his reaction. Ryan listened to her concerns and didn't interrupt. 'Okay. I'll try and get

hold of her, see if she'll talk to me, but I wouldn't hold your breath –
we've not been getting on great recently.'

'Oh.' The relief evaporated.

Ryan sighed. 'Yeah, well. Let me try and I'll ring you back. Give
me your number.' Just before he rang off he said, 'Hey. Don't worry.
She can look after herself, your sister. I'm sure she'll be fine.'

Erin appreciated the sentiment, but didn't believe it.

Chapter 50

CASSIE WAS still woozy, but she took the mug from Leah and managed to hold it level. 'Sorry. I can't believe I passed out.' Her voice was slurred at the edges.

''Sokay.' Leah had worked out what she was going to say, but first she wanted to see what Cassie remembered, and what sort of mood she was in. Embarrassment seemed to be the prevailing emotion.

'I've never done that before, ever. I'm really sorry.' She looked down at Leah's duvet draped over her knees and seemed to feel even worse.

'Not your fault. It was Naz. He's a stupid prick sometimes. I think he put a massive slug of vodka in your beer.' There was no need to say anything more. What good could come from it?

'God, I feel rough.' Cassie took a tiny sip of her drink. Leah watched her. She would be feeling awful – Leah knew.

'Drink that, then I'll make you some toast or something; that'll help.'

'No, Leah. Thanks, but I really can't face the thought of eating anything.' Cassie did, however, drink the tea, as instructed. When it was all finished, Leah took the empty mug from her.

'I'll make you another one.'

'Thanks. I'm really thirsty.' As Leah crossed the room, she heard the rustle of the duvet being pushed aside. She turned and saw Cassie make a move to get off the sofa, bracing herself against the arm, as if uncertain of her ability to stand.

'Whoa! There's no rush.' Leah caught Cassie's glance at the darkening sky and the distant lights of Manchester.

Cassie flopped back down. 'Leah, do you know where my handbag is?'

The next hurdle.

Leah turned her face away. 'Let me get you your tea, then I'll have a look for it. It'll be around somewhere.' As she waited for the kettle to boil, she kept glancing back into the room, checking that Cassie hadn't moved. She looked ghastly, but then that's what roofies did to you. It would be another twelve hours, at least, before she felt completely back to normal. Armed with the tea, and a smile, Leah came back into the room. She passed Cassie the mug, handle side facing her, then made a show of looking around for her handbag. It was a charade; she knew full well that Cassie's bag was underneath the armchair, because she'd shoved it there. The longer she hunted around, the more pinched Cassie's face became.

'I can't remember when I had it last.'

Leah pushed the bag further under the seat; perhaps the problem with the missing cards would just go away by itself. A lost bag. No one's fault.

But Cassie was starting to stress, and remember. 'We bought the snacks. I'm sure I had it when we came up to the flat. I think I put it down on the floor.' She tried to tip forward to look, but the sensation was obviously too much for her and she immediately swayed upright again.

'You stay there. I'll find it,' Leah said. After another few seconds of fake searching, she dragged the bag out. Her back went into spasm as she straightened up, but she tried not to show that she was in pain. She needn't have bothered. Cassie's priority was her stuff. 'Here it is.' Leah brushed the crumbs off it and passed it to Cassie, who clung onto it as if it were an anchor.

'It's getting late. I really should be going.' Yet Cassie made no effort to move.

'Do you feel all right?' Leah knew full well that she didn't.

'No. Not really. I'll maybe give it another ten minutes, if that's all right with you.' She still hadn't looked in her bag.

'Course.' Leah smiled. 'You can stay here tonight, if you wanna.' She watched Cassie trying to read her thoughts. All she saw was pure weariness.

'No. I don't want to put you out. I'm sure I'll be okay in a bit.' She drank another slug of tea, then put her mug on the table. Then slowly, as if moving hurt, Cassie opened her bag and started looking through it. She checked that her keys were there first. They were, clipped onto a pom-pom key-ring; then she looked for her purse. She took it out and put it on the sofa next to her keys. She carried on digging through her other stuff. Looking for her phone, Leah guessed. Maybe she wouldn't check her purse. Why should she? Why should Cassie be suspicious?

The knowledge that she had every right to be wary made Leah act. 'I really think you should eat something. I'll do ya some toast.' As she waited for the bread to pop up, she listened out for any sign that Cassie had realised her money and her cards were gone, but the room was quiet. There was no discovery, no accusations, nothing but the distant slamming of a door somewhere on the floor below and the metallic ticking of the toaster, softs sounds that were suddenly drowned out by the vibrating of Cassie's phone across the kitchen worktop. Leah snatched it up, hoping that Cassie hadn't heard it. Caller ID: Ryan – the boyfriend this time. Cassie had been away from home for less than a day and they were all panicking, like a flock of jittery pigeons.

Leah stepped away from the doorway and listened to the message. *Hi. It's me. Erin says you're in Manchester* – there was a pause – *with her. She's worried. I'm worried. Ring me. Please.* After a pause he added, *Love you.* She deleted the voicemail. Ten seconds later he texted, saying the same thing. Jesus, they were persistent. *'Her'* – the boyfriend hadn't even used her name. Well, fuck him. They had Cassie all the time, and yet they couldn't let Leah have her for one fucking day. She picked up the phone and started typing. Wreaking havoc in someone else's life was getting to be quite addictive.

She was so absorbed in causing carnage that she didn't hear the sofa creak and the sound of Cassie's footsteps cross the room.

'What are you doing?'

'Nowt.' It was too late to delete the text. Cassie held out her hand and Leah, slowly, reluctantly, laid the phone on her outstretched palm. Cassie immediately started scanning through the most recent messages. Leah stood her ground and waited, staring at Cassie's bowed head. At last she looked up. The expression of shock on her face was almost too much.

'Why?'

'They were worrying about ya.'

Cassie gave a little head-shake, trying to rejig her tumbled thoughts. 'But why not just tell them the truth? Why lie? Why be so...' She didn't supply the adjective.

Cassie and the bloody truth again, as if that solved anything. 'What? Tell them that ya were crashed out on my sofa, pissed? I'm not sure they'd have been reassured by that.'

Cassie put her hand out to steady herself against the counter top. 'She's only thirteen. There was no need to be so nasty.'

Bloody Little Miss Serious again. After everything that had happened, that's who Cassie was concerned about – her little bitch of a sister, and her lying, bastard family. Not Leah, who had taken a beating for her. Not her own flesh and blood, who was standing in front of her with a back that was fucked and a face that was smashed.

'I need to ring Erin, and my mum.' Cassie bent her head to her phone.

Leah felt a blast of fury. It was her who'd looked after Cassie. Her who'd stopped Naz doing whatever he'd been tempted to do. Cassie hadn't a clue what a narrow escape she'd had! It'd been Leah who'd made sure she didn't choke, kept her warm, brought her round with tea and sympathy, but that didn't seem to count for anything, did it? It never had. Leah went on the attack. 'And say what?' Cassie didn't respond, she just kept tapping away on her contacts. 'You're not telling them anything. I won't let ya!' Leah's voice bounced off the tight walls.

Cassie swayed. '*Let me?*' She blinked, as if trying to bring Leah into focus. 'Leah, I just need to let them know I'm all right.' She held the phone to her ear.

'Well, be my guest. Don't let me stop ya.' But Leah did want to stop her, she wanted it more than anything at that moment. She wanted the control back, she wanted her sister back. 'Don't you dare tell them that you're here. Keep me out of it.' Leah rushed at Cassie. She snatched the phone away from her. Cassie stumbled and fell forward. She crashed into the counter, then ricocheted into Leah. They bounced apart, both of them in pain, both breathing hard and fast with shock.

The sound of smashing glass was unmistakeable.

But it was more than just the phone that was broken.

Leah watched Cassie slowly lower herself down onto her knees. She picked up her phone and cradled it in her hands, as if gentleness might make it whole again. The screen was fucked, a web of radiating cracks. Cassie let out a sob. Leah had to steel herself to walk past her, out of the kitchen.

She went and sat on the chair in the corner, waiting to see how the scene would play out. It felt beyond her now. She was tired of it all: tired of Cassie, tired of trying to wrestle with so many conflicting emotions, tired of being awake, of hurting – tired of being alive. She could still see Cassie crouched low on the floor, desperately stroking the screen, trying to connect with her family – the phone was obviously not responding. After five long minutes she finally gave up and rocked back on her heels. She looked through the doorway at Leah, pleading silently. Leah looked at Cassie, huddled in a pathetic heap, and thought long and hard about passing her her own phone.

But after careful consideration, she did nothing.

Slowly Cassie hauled herself up and walked into the middle of the room. She picked up her keys and her purse and put them in her bag. Then, silently and unsteadily, she walked out of the flat, pulling the door shut behind her.

Chapter 51

Can't you leave me alone for one fuckin nite? Go find someone else to yank your prick. Im busy.

Ryan gave it ten minutes after Cassie's 'charming' message before telling Len that he was taking his break. Len shouted that he was a lazy twat, but he couldn't really do anything to stop Ryan ripping off his apron and walking out of the kitchen.

He went out into the cool evening air and called Erin. She picked up on the first ring. 'Yes?'

Ryan cut straight to it. 'Sorry. I rang and texted, but she's not coming back.'

'You spoke to her?'

'No, she texted me.'

'And?'

Ryan decided that a lie was a lot less hurtful than the truth – for both of them. 'To leave her alone. That she was having a good time.'

They were silent for a second, as they contemplated the harsh reality of Cassie preferring to spend time with Leah rather than with either of them.

'Right,' Erin said.

'You okay?' Ryan felt responsible for her, though he wasn't sure why.

'Yep.' She didn't sound it.

'Okay.' Ryan felt bad. 'Well, I gotta go work.'

'Yeah. Sorry. Thanks for trying.'

'Bye.'

'Bye.'

Chapter 52

CASSIE STOOD in the entrance lobby and scanned the area outside the flats. The dark bulk of the buildings looked familiar, but no less threatening. The effort it had taken to leave the flat and get into the lift had sapped her strength. She felt sweaty and very unwell. She leant against the doorframe, thinking she was going to faint. She took a few deep breaths to steady herself. The reality was that she was miles away from home, alone, in a way she'd never been before. The thought of pushing open the heavy doors and venturing out onto the streets was daunting, but Cassie knew that hanging around where she was wasn't a good idea, either. Every minute she delayed was another minute that she'd have to spend on her own.

Her stomach shifted. All she wanted to do was lie down and curl up somewhere safe, but she wasn't somewhere safe. She took another deep breath and told herself to stop being so dramatic. Determinedly she looped the strap of her handbag over her head and across her body, pushed open the door and set off in the direction of the shops. She wanted to walk quickly, but she couldn't. She felt awful.

Why had Naz spiked her drink? Out of nastiness? To test her? If it had been a test, she'd failed it miserably. Or had he done it just because he could – because that was his attitude towards women in general, her included? The thought of being trapped in Leah's flat, with Naz, unconscious and alone, brought on another wave of nausea. Cassie had to pause and lean against a wall for a few seconds to settle herself. She had been *so* vulnerable. If Leah hadn't come back…

But Leah's behaviour was incomprehensible as well. One minute, kind and protective – the next, wild and mean. It was as if there were two completely different versions of Leah fighting for supremacy within her, different impulses that made her impossible to read or predict. Being with her was exhausting. It was all too much.

Cassie's head hurt and it felt like her body belonged to someone else, but she forced herself to keep walking. It was like being drunk and having the hangover at the same time. She wanted desperately to be home. A couple of lads were coming towards her, hoods up despite the heat, faces obscured. Her pulse flickered. She concentrated hard on walking straight and holding her head up high. *Own your space.* That's what her mum and dad had always told her. *Don't be afraid of anyone or anything.* It was easy to do at home, but not here, not in her current state. But the lads passed her without comment or incident.

To her relief, the shops came into view up ahead. At least she was somewhere public, but she was still stranded, without any clear idea how to rescue herself. Simply to get off the street, she headed for the corner shop. The door buzzer sounded as she stepped inside and the man behind the counter looked up. It was the same little guy with the bald head and the knitted waistcoat who had served her and Naz hours ago. He nodded and went back to stacking mints on the counter display. Cassie wandered along the aisles, conscious of the mirror and the camera tracking her progress. She chose a sandwich from the fridge and a bottle of water. She was still ragingly thirsty and, much as she hated to admit it, Leah had been right: she did need something to counteract the acid in her stomach. At the till the man looked up, smiled and rang through her purchases.

'Three pounds twenty-five pence, please, Miss.'

Cassie fished out her purse and opened it. It took all of a second for her to realise it had been gutted. All the pockets were empty. No notes. No cards. Leah!

The shop assistant looked on anxiously as she stood on the other side of his counter and fell apart. She started to cry, too tired and scared and sad to stop herself. As the tears dripped off her chin, he came out from behind the display and disappeared down one of the cramped aisles. He returned a few moments later with a pack of tissues. His kindness in splitting open the pack and passing her a handful only made her cry harder.

Chapter 53

'WHAT THE fuck?' Len, the head chef, hollered, but Ryan ignored him. He ran out of the kitchen and banged through the back doors onto the car park, with his phone pressed hard against his ear. The trees thrashed in the wind, making hearing her almost impossible.

'Cassie. Slow down.' It took a few attempts before he grasped what she was saying. 'I'll come and get you. Stay where you are.' She said something about still having a ticket for the bus, but Ryan could tell by her tear-thickened, shaky voice that it was the last thing she wanted to do.

Cassie needed him to rescue her.

'Get yourself to the bus station – there'll be people around. I'll be as quick as I can. Forty minutes, tops.'

She thanked him so quietly that Ryan's anxiety about what had really happened increased.

'Keep safe. I'll be there before you know it.' He ran to his car, stripping off his chef's jacket as he went.

The guy with the dustpan on the long stick had come past Erin twice. Now he was staring at her blatantly as he wafted his brush at a popcorn spill near the entrance. Not wanting to get into a debate about why she was hanging around a cinema lobby, on her own – looking depressed – Erin removed herself to the Ladies, choosing to lock herself in the cubicle at the furthest end.

She was stuck, trapped by the lie to her parents and the lie to her friends. It was gone seven o'clock. The film wasn't due to finish until 8.40 p.m. If she rang her dad now, what could she say? But if she didn't message him, how was she going to get home? She could hardly wait for another hour and a half, then pop out of the loos and ask Hannah if she could hitch a ride. She leant her head against the cubicle stall and tried to resist the wave of self-pity that was building up in her gut. Cassie was creating headaches for all the people who loved her, and she didn't seem to care.

The only way out was another lie.

Erin started typing, going with the migraine story, but before she had chance to send it, her phone rang. This time she checked who it was before answering – Ryan.

Ten minutes later his Golf screeched to a stop outside the cinema. She got into the front seat. He didn't wait for her to put her seatbelt on before setting off.

Chapter 54

DESPITE RYAN'S breakneck driving, it still took them three-quarters of an hour to get to Oldham, then he missed the turn onto the high street and had to race round the one-way system again, before finally pulling up at the bus station.

Erin spotted Cassie immediately. She was huddled in one of the shelters, shaded monochrome by the light from the information boards. Ryan parked in the bus bay. Erin had to fight every instinct in her body in order to stay put while Ryan leapt out of the car and went to her sister. Cassie disappeared into his arms, engulfed by his embrace. Erin could hear her crying, even with the doors shut. They stood wrapped around each other, oblivious, as the traffic rolled by. Someone shouted, 'Get a room' out of an open window. They stayed glued together, until a bus pulled up behind Ryan's car. The driver leant on his horn and blasted his indignation, loudly. They split apart.

Cassie climbed in the back, Erin followed her, Ryan got into the front and they set off. Only then did Erin get her chance to comfort Cassie. She'd stopped crying, but she was still shivering. Erin wriggled out of her jacket and gave it to her sister. It wasn't going to keep her warm, but it was better than nothing, and it was all she had. Cassie put it on. 'Thanks.' Her teeth were chattering. 'What are *you* doing here?'

Erin forced a smile. 'I made Ryan bring me. I was worried.'

Cassie didn't return her smile. 'I'm sorry. The texts were from Leah, not me.'

Erin felt vindicated. 'I thought there was something wrong. Why did she send them?' She could sense Ryan listening to their conversation.

Cassie seemed to have to think before she answered. 'I'm not sure.' She paused. 'She's not what she seems. Or not what I thought she was.' Neither Erin nor Ryan said anything. 'It's been a really crap day. I'm sorry I've had to drag you into it.' They both made 'it doesn't matter' noises.

Ryan chipped in, 'Where did you call me from?'

'A shop. My phone got smashed. The man in the shop was really kind. He saw how upset I was, so he let me ring you.'

'Smashed?' Ryan asked.

'It doesn't matter,' Cassie said.

The lights blurred by, a continuous bright ribbon against the darkening sky. They were on some sort of dual carriageway, going fast.

Erin was more concerned about how ill her sister looked. 'Cass, what happened?'

'It just got out of hand. I shouldn't have stayed to have a drink with them.' Erin saw Ryan's eyebrows rise at the 'them'. 'But it's done with now. That's all that matters. And it's shown me a side of Leah I needed to see.' She pulled Erin's jacket across her body. It was too small for her. She'd grown out of it years ago.

Deep down, Erin was disturbed to acknowledge that she was pleased the night had gone wrong. Leah must have blown it by doing, or saying, something stupid. Maybe this was the end of it. She hoped so. Cassie was still shivering. The heat in the car didn't seem to be helping at all. Everything about Cassie seemed out of sync: her speech, her manner, her emotions. She started rubbing her hands together – whether she was trying to warm herself up, or rid herself of something, it was hard to tell.

'Oh!' Suddenly Cassie stopped. She sat up straight and stared down at her hands. They looked a sickly orange colour in the glow of the overhead lights.

'What's wrong?' Erin asked.

Cassie shook her head and continued to stare at her fingers. 'I can't believe she took it.'

It was the last thing she said.

After a few more miles they re-joined the motorway. Cassie's head began to nod and she slumped against Erin. Her face slackened as she fell into a heavy sleep. The only sounds were Ryan's fingers tapping out a rhythm on the steering wheel, and the whoosh of the road rushing beneath them. Erin shouldered the weight of her sister gladly, welcoming the familiar, reassuring sensation of being wanted.

It was going to be okay. Leah's hold over Cassie had been broken. Life could get back to normal. Erin closed her eyes as well, trusting Ryan to get them home safely.

Chapter 55

THE MOOD in the house pivoted when Grace came down from her bath. She walked up to Tom and slid her arms through his, pressing her still slightly damp body to his, saying nothing. She smelt of bubble bath. Wordlessly, they hugged. When she pulled away, she smiled.

'Apparently Cassie's staying over at Freya's tonight.'

'Oh. Okay.' Tom vaguely recognised the name. He thought about questioning the truth of this statement, but stopped himself. Maybe Grace had spoken to Cassie, maybe she'd texted, maybe it wasn't the truth – whatever, Grace had accepted the explanation of Cassie's whereabouts, and that was enough. She seemed to have shrugged off the tight skin of anxiety that had encased her when she'd come in, and Tom had no intentions of wrecking the equilibrium. She leant into him again and they stood embracing, relaxing into each other.

Over dinner they talked about this and that. Work, Erin, even the possibility of a last-minute family holiday. It was normal and nice. They didn't mention Cassie. Grace offered to clear up while Tom 'surveyed his plot'. The mockery was gentle, loving. The free pass on kitchen duties appreciated.

It was a lovely evening. After the harsh heat of the day, the night air felt softer, less combative. It was easier to breathe. The garden was surviving, but the long weeks of drought were taking their toll. The grass was bleached and dry, but the borders were just about hanging on, relying on their deep roots to get some sustenance. Tom wandered around in the dusk, snapping off dead stems and propping up wilting plants. He felt calm and relaxed for the first time in weeks. He was pleased to see that the apple tree was blight-free. Ambling slowly around the garden, he let his mind empty.

The sound of a phone ringing broke the peace.

He looked at the house. Grace was clearly illuminated in the brightly lit kitchen, but although the ringing continued, she didn't respond. She carried on drifting around, tidying up. It couldn't be their phone. Tom turned his attention back to his parched flower beds.

A few minutes later the ringing started again.

This time it sounded louder, more insistent.

He looked back at the house and saw Grace freeze, then turn and dash out of the room. Feeling an inexplicable surge of panic, Tom set off across the garden after her.

Something bad had happened to someone he loved.

He knew in his heart that it was Cassie.

Chapter 56

A&E WAS packed, every seat taken, every wall occupied. So many people seemed to have come a cropper, some of them quite spectacularly, judging by the bruised skin and the oddly angled limbs.

Cassie was one of them.

They spotted her immediately, crushed in among the rows of damaged bodies. The first thing that struck them was the blood; there were rusty brown splashes of it all over her top and jeans. The second was that her face was wrong. She was still recognisably their daughter, but only just. Her face was a mess, her features distorted, her beauty blurred and broken. The third thing that stunned them both was that there was a police officer sitting next to her.

The officer rose and headed towards them, sweeping away any vestiges of hope that he was there with someone else. 'Mr and Mrs Haines?' They nodded. 'I'm PC Naylor. I've been with Cassie since we brought her in.' They looked past him at their daughter. She kept her head down, refusing to acknowledge their arrival. That hurt. 'She's had an initial assessment. They're pretty confident she's not showing any signs of concussion, which is good news, obviously. We've been told to wait out here until someone's free to clean up the gash on her forehead, but, as you can see, they're busy, as always.'

'Thank you.' They responded in unison, because what else was there to say? Grace moved past the officer and sat on the seat next to Cassie, just in time to stop a man who was holding his arm to his chest like a baby from claiming it. He resumed his slot against the wall, resigned to an uncomfortable wait.

'What happened?' Grace asked. Cassie glanced at her mother, and for a second Grace was rewarded with a full view of the damage. There was a deep cut through Cassie's left brow and the skin around the eye socket was beginning to swell. The ragged edges of the wound were gaping. She had also smashed her mouth. A thick black line of blood precisely bisected her bottom lip; in fact the whole left side of her face looked like it was inflating, softening her features into those of a broken, round-cheeked doll. A tear leaked out of the corner of her battered eye: pain, shame, fear, anger? It was impossible to say. Grace reached out to take hold of her daughter's hand, but Cassie turned her face away without a word and went back to staring at the wall-mounted TV.

The officer looked from Grace to Tom. 'I haven't been able to get much out of her since we brought them in. Shock, probably.'

'Them?' Tom asked.

'My colleague's with the young man who was driving. He's just come back from X-ray. A suspected busted leg.'

'Cassie...what the hell?' Tom's sharpness drew the attention of the people in the waiting area. The intermittent crackle of the officer's radio only served to add to the excitement. Many of them stared, without embarrassment, happy to have a domestic drama to distract them from their injuries and ailments. Cassie remained silent in the face of such scrutiny. Tom turned his attention back to the officer.

'Was it Ryan...Ryan Newsome?'

'Yes.'

The noise Tom made summed up his disgust and his lack of surprise, 'What happened?'

'They were clocked speeding near the M606. When we flagged him to pull over, he didn't. He cut off down the spur road, but he misjudged the bend, took it too quickly and came off. Luckily, they didn't hit anyone else. The barrier stopped it being as bad as it could have been. We radioed for the ambulance straight away, and they were on the scene fairly quickly.'

For a second there was silence, as the reality of the situation sank in. Cassie continued to find the comedy panel show on TV more fascinating than the story of how she nearly died.

As Tom was trying to digest this new brand of awfulness, something drew the officer's attention. A nurse had emerged from behind the scenes and was scanning the waiting area. The officer summoned her over. She edged, deftly, around the sea of outstretched legs. She looked very young, and very tired. 'The Haines?' The officer nodded on their behalf. 'If you could follow me, please. I'll take you through.' She was already turning back to where she was needed.

They were both confused as to why they were being asked to go through to see Ryan, though Tom did have a sudden, very clear image of himself crashing through the curtains of a cubicle, grabbing hold of Ryan and doing something he might later regret. Cassie rose to her feet.

'No. Just your mum and dad for now – you wait there.' Cassie thumped back down onto her seat. 'It's okay,' the nurse reassured them, misinterpreting their hesitation, 'she's okay. She's obviously quite badly shaken up, but from what the officers told us, they've all been very lucky.'

'She?' Tom and Grace were confused. It seemed odd that the nurse was talking about Cassie in the third person when she was sitting right in front of them.

For a second the nurse looked as perplexed as them. 'Yes. Your daughter. Erin. She's been asking for you.'

Erin burst into tears the minute they appeared. She was sitting awkwardly on a gurney, her head held at an unnatural angle, a hospital blanket tangled around her legs. Tom and Grace were both so shocked by events that it was hard to take things in. Cassie and Ryan – with Erin, it didn't compute. And yet the nurse was chatting away quite cheerily, as if it was perfectly normal for a thirteen-year-old to be the victim of a police chase and a car crash, instead of safe, with her friends, in a cinema, eating popcorn and watching the latest Hollywood blockbuster – as she was supposed to be.

The reason for Erin's odd posture was the brace that encased her neck, a plastic-and-Velcro contraption that looked very uncomfortable. Her face was badly grazed and there was a large shadow of dirt, or oil, or bruising, on her right cheek. She was wearing a hospital gown that was tatty around the neckline; underneath, Tom caught a glimpse of her new top, now ripped and ruined. It seemed a lifetime ago that he'd dropped her off at the restaurant, looking pretty and whole. The rubber soles of Erin's beloved Converse poked out of the end of the blanket. They looked oddly everyday and out of context.

'Mum!' She sounded very shaky. Grace went and stood close to her youngest daughter, but she didn't know how best to hug her without causing her pain. Instead she took hold of her hand. Erin squeezed back, hard, which Grace took as a good sign. She couldn't be that badly hurt if she could grip that fiercely, surely. Tom took up a spot on the other side of the trolley. As he reached out nervously to push her hair away from her face, she recoiled. 'Dad, don't. My neck.' Tom paled on the inside.

The no-nonsense voice of the nurse cut through their confusion. 'This is Doctor Hassan.'

The doctor, who had appeared as if by magic, flashed them a weary smile and spoke very quickly. 'Erin has had an X-ray. There are no bones broken, but there is evidence of some ligament damage in her neck, hence the brace. Unfortunately, soft tissue takes quite a while to heal. It's going to be a case of patience and physio, I'm afraid. She must wear the brace all the time, even at night, until she's told to start scaling it back. We've put in a referral to the Outpatients department, so you should get an appointment through the post in the next few days. She was given...' he referred to the notes, 'ten millilitres of pain relief before they did the X-rays, but you'll need to get her on some paracetamol. She'll be due a dose at...' he did a quick calculation, 'one a.m., but if she's asleep, don't bother. Just give her some as soon as she wakes up. I'd keep that up for the first twenty-four to forty-eight hours and then see how you get on.' At the end of this spurt of information he flashed another quick smile. 'I'll leave you in Asha's capable hands.' And with swish of wipe-clean curtain, he was gone.

The nurse smiled, too. 'I'll let you have a few minutes together, then I'll be back and we'll get you moved out of the treatment area.' She whisked away, back into the melee of other people's demands.

'Erin, what the hell's going on? What were you doing in a car with Ryan Newsome?'

Grace cut across Tom. 'Are you in a lot of pain?'

Erin gripped her mum's hand even tighter and whispered, 'It's not too bad. Oh, Mum, it was awful. The car hit something, then it spun, round and round. I thought it was never going to stop. It felt like my neck was going to snap.'

'Erin...what were you doing in his car?' Tom asked again.

With the brace restricting her head, she couldn't turn towards her father. 'I was with Cassie.'

'So we gather.' Tom's economy of words masked a whirlpool of emotions.

But Erin was still reliving the crash. 'There was glass everywhere. Ryan was shouting that his leg was trapped. I couldn't get my seatbelt off at first. It felt like it had gone through my ribs. Cassie had blood

308

all over her hands and her face, and she was crying. Where is she? Is she all right? Mum? Where's Cassie? They took her off somewhere after we arrived. I couldn't even ring you. I think we left everything in the car.' The panic in Erin's voice escalated.

'She's all right. She's out in the main waiting area, worrying about you. She might need a few stitches, for the cut on her forehead.' Grace saw Erin's eyes widen in fear. 'But she's been thoroughly checked over and she's okay. Honestly, Erin, she's just a bit bashed up. I think it looks worse than it is.'

'And than it could've been.' Tom felt like he was wading through a deep pool of ignorance, getting further out of his depth. He'd had no idea Erin had even met Ryan, no idea they'd been hanging out together, but even that didn't make sense. Why would Cassie take her little sister with her on a date? The fact that both of his daughters had been lying to him cut deep – especially Erin. It was so out of character. Cassie's influence?

In the midst of her own frazzled emotions, Erin picked up on her father's distress. When he reached out to touch her the second time, she leant into rather than away from him. He stroked her hair silently for a few seconds, composing himself, then he tried one more time. 'Erin, honey, please, you have to tell us... What were you doing in the car with Cassie and Ryan? Where were you going?'

Erin turned her face a tiny fraction towards him, but with the brace holding her chin so unnaturally high, it was difficult. 'We weren't *going* anywhere. We were coming back.'

'From where?' Tom asked.

Erin paused, considering the price that would have to be paid for her answer. She decided, after everything that had happened, that it was worth it. 'Manchester.'

There was beat of silence.

The sounds of the hospital expanded to fill the void: footsteps, calm, reassuring voices, the crash of a trolley, the clatter of metal implements.

Tom looked at Grace and she stared back at him, as they simultaneously realised how little they knew about their daughters' lives, and how dangerous that ignorance had become.

Chapter 57

THEY DIDN'T get back home until the early hours of the morning.

Five hours. No time at all, in the grand scheme of things, and yet it felt like a lifetime to Tom and Grace. The call from the hospital, the police officer's guarded concern (and suspicion), the news of the crash, Erin's fear and, even more disturbing, Cassie's absolute, resolute silence. It was difficult to absorb the shock of it all. What was worse was that they both knew the night's events weren't the end of it, they were just the beginning.

Manchester.

Cassie's hunt for her birth mother.

This was the reckoning.

Anxiety reverberated through Tom and Grace as they crept around like burglars in their own home. Grace followed closely in the girls' wake, wanting to help, but not knowing how, as they quietly got ready for bed. Tom stayed downstairs, locking doors and turning off lights. Closing the stable door... But at least the sound of Erin and Cassie moving around upstairs was proof that his daughters were back in his care, although Tom now knew that their physical presence was no guarantee that they were truly safe.

On the way home in the car Cassie and Erin had both seemed

drugged, possibly by the pain relief, but also by the shock. Tom had watched them in the mirror. They'd not said a word, but he saw how they held onto each other, their fingers meshed tightly together. There was a pact between them, secrets shared and guarded – secrets that, in morning, would have to be faced.

Upstairs the noises faded and the house fell silent. Only then did Tom wearily climb the stairs and get into bed beside his wife. But sleep was impossible. The physical damage done to his daughters haunted him. Erin's thin frame had looked almost deformed, encased in the cumbersome neck brace, and Cassie's bloody and battered face had been barely recognisable. It was if *their* pain had entered *his* body. A few miles faster, a worse spin, a different impact and they could have been killed. The ache in his bones deepened. Ryan Newsome had very nearly robbed Tom of his family. He could, at this moment, be childless, again.

Manchester.

Tom rolled over onto his side. How had Newsome got involved in the whole adoption mess? And Erin? How on earth had Erin ended up with them? Such ignorance. What sort of father knew so little about his own children? A failing one. Tom rolled over again, binding himself tighter in the grip of his own shame.

Grace started awake in the darkness, shaken by a panic-filled dream that had felt all too real. Her heart was racing. She lay listening out for her girls, like she used to when they were little and she'd wake in the middle of the night just before they needed her, attuned to their unpredictable rhythms and irregular wants. But there were no voices, no muffled crying, no demands for attention. The house was silent. Even Tom, after hours of restlessness, seemed to be asleep. Grace tried to relax, but she couldn't, her heart rate wouldn't settle. She gave up, swung her legs over the side of the mattress and padded out onto the landing. She listened again – still nothing.

She went to check on Cassie first, climbing up to the top of the house, not counting the steps, she knew there were fifteen. Outside Cassie's door she stopped and listened, expecting the sounds of congested breathing – her poor face, it was such a mess – but all was quiet. Grace gently eased down the handle, pushed open the door and slipped inside. Cassie hadn't bothered pulling down the skylight blinds and the room was bathed in moonlight. Grace looked at the rumpled bed and immediately saw that it was empty. The splinters of fear left over from her dream dug into her. Although she knew it was pointless, she crossed the room and lifted the duvet, but of course Cassie wasn't hiding under it. She wasn't three any more. She wasn't a hot little body, curled up into a solid knot of flesh and blood, safe and sound. Grace turned and hurried down the stairs. Think logically: Cassie must be in the bathroom. But she wasn't, the door was wide open, the room empty. Grace told herself to calm down, but her fears sharpened and stung, regardless.

She pushed open Erin's door and peered into the darkness.

It took Grace a moment to realise what she was looking at it.

Erin was propped against her pillows, her head held unnaturally upright by the neck brace. The duvet was pulled up around her and her eyes were closed. She was obviously fast asleep, despite her awkward position. Lying beside her was Cassie, curled up on the edge of the bed, the duvet barely covering her. All Grace could see was the curve of her back, the soles of her feet and her mass of hair. She was tucked in beside Erin, like a boat sheltering in the lee of a harbour wall.

Grace's relief was bitter-sweet.

Her girls were home, not lost.

They were hurt, but they would heal.

But they hadn't turned to her for comfort and protection.

They had turned to each other.

Chapter 58

THE HOUSE phone was ringing again. A fresh burst of adrenaline pumped into Tom's bloodstream. He picked up on the second ring. It was a different police officer, *following up on the previous night's events.* She enquired briefly after the girls, then gave Tom an update on what they had *ascertained so far*. A statement had been taken from Ryan at the hospital. Apparently it was light on detail. He was maintaining that he'd simply been giving the girls a lift home, at their request. He was denying that he'd seen the police car and was insisting that the crash had been an accident. There'd been no trace of alcohol or drugs in his system. His mother had confirmed that he'd had her permission to drive the vehicle, although she'd been unable to provide any evidence that he was insured to do so. When asked to clarify what they'd all been doing in Manchester, and why Erin was in the car, Ryan had refused to say.

'He said to *ask Cassie* – more than once.' The officer paused as if expecting Tom, as the parent of 'said Cassie', to be able to supply further illumination on the topic, but Tom said nothing. What could he say? She went on. 'We're trying to find someone to come and take the girls' statements, sooner rather than later, but I'm afraid I can't tell you when that will be at present.' She seemed keen to wrap up their one-sided conversation. 'If you've no further questions, Mr Haines?'

'No,' Tom said. 'Thank you. We'll wait to hear from you.' He put down the phone and relayed the news to Grace. He had lied to the officer. Of course he had questions, he had hundreds of them, but Ryan had been right about one thing: the only person who had the answers was Cassie.

They climbed up to her room together. Grace knocked. Tom walked in, without waiting for a response. She was sitting on the floor, in front of her mirror, tentatively dabbing make-up onto her bruised face. Her eyes met theirs in the glass. 'We need to talk.'

She paused, mid-daub. 'Now?'

'Yes. Now.'

She carefully screwed the lid back on the tube of foundation and put it into her make-up bag, which she zipped shut. Only then did she shuffle round to face them.

Tom took the desk chair, Grace the bed. 'Cassie, what were you doing in Manchester?'

Cassie gently touched her damaged face, her fingers probing the puffy, ragged skin, playing for time. 'I wasn't in Manchester,' she said eventually.

Tom had had enough. 'Cassie! We need to know what you were doing last night? Tell us!'

Cassie lowered her hand. 'I was with my sister.'

Tom's mouth tightened. 'That's another issue altogether. What, in God's name, was Erin doing in the car with you and Ryan?'

Cassie's gaze didn't waver. She looked at her father through her normal and her swollen eye, deciding what to say. There was nothing to stop her now. No tentative allegiances to defend, no conflicting loyalties to honour. Leah had made it very clear. She'd insisted that Cassie choose: family or sister. It was a stark and unfair demand, but

Leah had made it anyway. She was never going to allow Cassie to have both. The raging black resentment inside her wouldn't permit it. The years of denial and deceit had damaged Leah too much – Tom and Grace had damaged Leah too much.

And Cassie – bruised and broken as she was by the previous night's events – was at least wiser and less naïve now. She knew, with painful clarity, that the two halves of her life were never going fit together.

It was time for the truth.

'I don't mean Erin.'

Grace and Tom stared at her, comprehension blooming on their shocked faces, as Cassie, very coldly and precisely, said, 'I was with Leah!'

Chapter 59

THUMP! JUST like that.

Their blindness was shameful.

Their culpability absolute.

Tom let out an 'Oh'. It was such a weak reaction, but he was too wrong-footed to say anything else. Leah. Not her birth mother. Her sister. His sense of failure was complete.

Grace looked at their battered daughter and felt the dam break. The pressure that had been building for weeks finally ruptured. Now for the flood. 'We can explain,' Grace said, although she wasn't at all sure that they could.

'Can you?' Cassie's gaze was frighteningly direct.

Tom faced the challenge in her eyes with something that felt very much like fear; a visceral fear that nothing he could say would ever repair the damage they'd done to their relationship with Cassie. But he had to try. He had to get her to see that they'd kept Leah's existence a secret for valid reasons. 'She was a risk to herself, and to other people.' He swallowed. 'We were led to believe that she might be a risk to you.' Cassie didn't move, didn't even blink, she simply waited for more. 'That's why we never told you about her. We thought it was for the best.' He sounded uncertain, even to his own ears.

'You thought you had the right not to tell me that I had a sister.'

Tom looked at his feet. There *had* been legitimate reasons, at the time, but they didn't seem so valid now.

Grace ran her fingers nervously along the chain around her neck. 'We know now that our decision was wrong.'

'Wrong!' Cassie snapped. The atmosphere in the room darkened. Tom and Grace waited for the explosion of her anger, but – for what felt like for ever – Cassie said nothing. The silence was worse than her letting rip.

'How did you get in touch with her?' Tom eventually asked.

'Facebook.' Cassie's voice was so quiet they had to lean forward to hear what she was saying. 'I put out an appeal for information. Leah saw it. Messaged me. Said she wanted to meet. So we met. Weeks ago.'

They hadn't even considered that Cassie might take things into her own hands; though Gail had warned them, Grace remembered – now that it was too late. Tom was struggling to let go of the version of what was *supposed* to have happened. 'We were told that she'd declined any contact.'

'Yes, well, you're not the only ones who are capable of lying.'

Grace winced, but accepted the judgement. The torrent of things they didn't know crashed down on both of them. How many times had Cassie met Leah? When had they met? Where? What the hell had been going on all these weeks while they'd been blindly, stupidly waiting for things to blow over?

Cassie's voice wobbled. 'How could you? All those years. And then – and this is what I really can't get my head round – when I started asking about my adoption, you *still* lied.'

'To protect you,' Tom said, but as he looked at Cassie's mangled face, he had to acknowledge how badly that had worked out. 'So you were with her last night?'

'Yes.'

'In Manchester.'

'She lives in Oldham.' Cassie no longer felt the need to keep Leah's secrets.

'And?' Tom prompted.

That's when Cassie flared. 'Don't you dare! You don't get to ask *anything* about my relationship with Leah. Not after what you did. You've been lying to me my whole life. You say you did it to *protect me*? Sod that! You did it to protect yourselves. I had a right to know. She was my sister. She still *is* my sister.' Cassie let her anger loose. 'She told me all about us being together, when we were little. She was the one who looked after me. You knew about that, didn't you? Didn't you? But that didn't fit in with the version of my life that you wanted to peddle, did it? So you pretended that she didn't exist.' She was shouting now. 'You knew all about her, from the very beginning. You could've taken her as well. You should have. We could've been together. Then it would all have been different... She would've been different.'

The floorboards on the landing creaked.

They all stopped.

'Erin?' Grace called. 'It's okay.'

The door swung open and Erin shuffled into the room, her gait affected by the neck brace. She was in her dressing gown, her feet bare, her hair a mess.

Cassie gestured for her to come in. 'Come on in. Sit down. You've as much right to know about this as me. We're just getting to the bit where Mum and Dad try and explain why they totally lied about Leah.'

Erin lowered herself down onto the bed, next to Grace.

'Cassie...' Tom started, but she held up her hand.

'No! Not you! I want Mum to tell it.' Tom sat back as if he'd been shoved. 'And this time, Mum, I want the truth, not some fairy story.'

They all looked at Grace.

A bird flew across the sky, right above the skylight, and for a second its shadow flitted across the room. Grace took the moment to compose herself, aware that what she was about to say would damn them, in Cassie's eyes, and yet knowing, at the same time, that it had to be told – at last.

She started at the beginning.

'It took nearly two years for us to be cleared to adopt. Even after we'd been approved, we had to wait for months and months while they looked for a match. We started to think it would never happen, that we would never become parents. Then it did. They matched us with you. It was one of the happiest days of our lives.' As she said it, she took hold of Erin's hand. The other happiest day, but that was not for now. 'The minute we saw your photo, we fell in love with you.' That much was true – totally, undeniably true. 'But there were complications.'

Cassie snorted. 'Leah?'

'Yes, Leah.' The room stilled. Grace held her daughter's gaze, waiting for the condemnation that she knew they deserved.

'So Leah *was* telling the truth. You split us up.'

Tom leant forward again as if about to say something, but nothing came into his mind that would help. Grace glanced at him, then very clearly and quietly said, 'Yes, we did.'

'You picked me and dumped her – on the basis of a photograph!' Cassie's voice was shaking with emotion.

Once again Grace answered very quietly, but very clearly, 'No.'

'What?' Cassie's eyes widened.

'When they first started talking to us about adopting you, they told us about Leah. We were shown the reports on her. They told us about her problems, the psychological damage that had been done to her by the neglect she'd suffered – that you'd both suffered.'

'She was just a little girl,' Cassie threw at them.

Grace nodded slowly. 'Yes. I know. We knew that it wasn't her fault.'

'She was my sister.'

'Yes.' Grace drew a shallow, quick breath. 'That's why we went to see her.'

Cassie struggled to form the next question. 'What're you talking about?'

Grace took a deep breath. 'We went to visit her.'

Cassie looked from Grace to Tom and back again, unaware that she was slowly shaking her head back and forth in disbelief. 'And?'

And it was one of the hardest things they ever had to do.

Grace could still very clearly remember the unfurling of hope in her heart on seeing Cassidie's photograph, the belief that their worn-thin dreams might, just might, become a reality. Then the shock when Steph dropped the bombshell of a sister – an emotionally fragile, older sister.

They had felt tricked.

'I know it's a huge thing to throw at you, but we do have a responsibility to try our very best to keep siblings together, wherever possible. It's so much better for them in the long term. I know it's a lot to ask, but I wouldn't be doing my job properly if I didn't raise it with you, on behalf of both the girls.' As Steph talked, the excitement that had ignited inside them guttered. They heard Steph out. They had to. She gave them no choice. They listened to her carefully worded description of the challenge that Leah represented, the damage that had been done to her, the need for patience, and time, and above all unconditional love. Love, Steph tentatively suggested, that they might be able to provide.

'But this isn't what's been agreed.' Tom said. 'We applied for one child. A girl, under five. That's all we're cleared for. This isn't the plan.' Steph shuffled in her seat and shifted her gaze to Grace, which irritated Tom, hugely – a confirmation of the stereotypes: the caring mum, the hard-ass dad. Steph should've known better.

She sighed and sat back in her seat. 'I completely understand your hesitation. And I know it's a lot to ask. I just wanted you to be aware of the situation, of the option...of trying to keep them together.' She was beginning to give up, Tom could hear it in her voice and, ashamed as he was, he felt relieved.

'She's seven, you say?' Grace spoke softly.

They both stared at her.

'Nearly eight,' Steph said. She leant forward again, her hand poised over the file, ready to divulge more.

'And how bad are her behavourial problems?' Grace asked.

They went to see Leah a week later. Grace quietly, implacably insisted that they must. 'She's Cassidie's sister. We have to. We owe her that.' Morally, Tom agreed and so he acquiesced, but privately every fibre within him wanted to avoid going anywhere near the child and the problems she represented.

Steph drove them to the meeting. It was a long, conversation-starved journey into the hinterland of north Manchester. After getting lost in the maze of very similar-looking streets, they eventually parked outside what looked like an average house. Well, almost. The locked gate was the first clue. The high, solid fence, the second. The lack of an identifying number or name, the third. They were let in by a woman with a tired face, a resolutely cheery manner and a bunch of keys.

Each step took them further away from normality.

The weird mix of homeliness and high security continued inside the house. There were keypads on most of the doors and wire-mesh glass in the windows, but there were also kids' drawings Blu-tacked to the walls and plenty of toys dotted around. A fluffy pink slipper lay abandoned on the floor in the hallway, along with a scooter. There was the strong smell of toast and cleaning fluid. It was an unnerving concoction.

Tom and Grace entered a side room, breath held, but it was just a lounge with a selection of saggy chairs and sofas and a bookshelf crammed full of picture books. Oddly, the curtains were drawn, which blocked out the sunlight and made the room gloomy. They sat together on one of the sofas. Grace shrugged off her jacket. Tom kept his on. The woman, Nina, welcomed them and explained a little about her role and the 'nature' of the children who spent time in the house. She spoke clearly and honestly, and Tom saw Steph wince, more than once. Conflicting priorities, he presumed. Steph was keen to encourage them to keep an open mind. Nina keen to make them fully aware of what they might be considering taking on. 'Might' – even that was too strong a word. They were here to reassure themselves that they had given *consideration* to adopting both girls, but that didn't mean they were seriously considering it. At least he wasn't, and Grace said she wasn't, although her insistence that they come was confusing. It was almost as if she wanted the shame and pain of their rejection of Cassidie's sister to be as deep and absolute as possible. They could have said 'no' straight away, should have done, but they hadn't, and now they were about to be tested – and shown to be wanting.

Nina was still talking about the therapies they employed and the progress they were making with Leah. 'As you can imagine, there were huge trust issues initially – there are with all our children – but I think she's beginning to feel safe with us, and that's lessening her anxiety. The flare-ups are far less frequent.'

'What causes her "flare-ups"?' Grace asked.

'Well, there seem to be two main triggers. Personal space, for one; if the staff come too close, too quickly, that frightens her – especially male members of staff. Leah still doesn't really like to be touched, by anyone and...' there was a noticeable hesitation, 'her interactions with other children can still be a little...problematic. The separation has been very hard on her.'

The reference to Cassidie hung in the air.

'Problematic, how?' Tom asked.

Nina looked at them, gauging how much honesty was appropriate. 'She tends to hone in on the little ones, gets a bit obsessed. It's not always appropriate. When staff intervene, Leah can sometimes react. There's been some physical aggression. Kicking, nipping, the occasional bite. It's never aimed at any of the other children,' she clarified quickly. 'But, as I said, we're having far fewer incidents than when she first arrived. She's learning to control her anger and her grief – with help. She's doing very well, really, for a little girl who has been so severely neglected. But...' she grew brisk, 'I really think the best thing is for you to meet her.' And with that, she got up and walked out.

Tom's stomach contracted. Grace stared at her clasped hands.

The wait was agonising.

A few minutes later they heard the sound of a woman's voice in the hallway and Nina re-entered the room. She walked over to the far wall and pulled on a cord. The curtains parted, revealing not a window, but a floor-to-ceiling one-way mirror with a view into the adjoining room. The door in the other room opened and they watched as a young woman walked into the brightly lit lounge, followed by a small, thin, white child, who went to sit on the facing sofa, as instructed. The young woman kept up a stream of chatter while she opened a toy chest and started pulling out drawing paper and pens and some simple boxed games. Tom and Grace could hear every sound.

'What would you like to do today, Leah? Draw, play Snails' Race again?' The woman sat next to the child and arranged the playthings on the table, trying to attract her attention. 'Leah?' There was no response. 'I'm sure we've got Hungry Hippos in here somewhere, as well. What about that?' The child didn't react. Tom and Grace both stood up. They walked slowly towards the glass, drawn by an awful curiosity. Intuitively, they positioned themselves on either side of the mirror, hiding themselves at the edges.

Pale-blue eyes, white, almost translucent skin, her hair cropped into a severe fringe. Thin arms. Bony knees. Everything about Leah seemed washed-out and fragile. Everything except her expression, which was steady and unsettling. To Tom, she looked far older than seven. Her face had the same pinched toughness about it that he saw on the teenage girls who hung about in the centre of town. She was like a tiny, thin, hard-faced woman. To Grace, she looked like a ghost-child, a faint, watered-down version of what a normal little girl should look like, behave like, be like. Neither of them could see her as the sister of the smiling, healthy toddler that their hearts had already embraced.

Cassidie attracted attention.

This child repelled it.

'She can't hear or see you. We use the viewing room to observe their progress – it's much less intrusive. Play is, unsurprisingly, one of the things many of our children struggle with. They just don't know how to do it, especially children like Leah, who have had caring responsibilities thrust on them far too soon. But as you can see, she's coping well with the one-to-one attention. That's another thing that can be quite alien to them – positive attention. It can be overwhelming, when they're not used to it.'

In silence Tom and Grace watched, fascinated.

After a few seconds Grace looked away, ashamed at her confused and conflicted response, but she was immediately drawn back to studying the scene being enacted a few feet away, on the other side of the glass. She watched the efforts of the carer to engage the child, and the child's steadfast refusal to be engaged, and the closer Grace looked, the more she saw. She noticed that the child was growing agitated. She kept clenching and unclenching her small hands, rocking ever so slightly in her seat. And Grace saw her glance from the woman to the mirror and back again – furtive, restless looks. Grace suddenly knew, with absolute certainty, that the child was aware she was being watched. At the exact moment this thought came into Grace's head, the child stood up and walked towards the mirror.

Tom and Grace both took a step backwards. The child came right up to the glass and stared through it, ignoring the efforts of the carer to distract her. There were a few agonising moments when they all watched, transfixed by her small, sharp little face – so close to them, and yet so separate. Her breath misted the glass. Her eyes stared intently, at nothing. Then she jerked her head back and smashed it against the mirror – hard. The thud went through their hearts.

There was a second of shocked nothingness, then a fluster of action.

Nina ran out of the room, the young woman scrambled to her feet and moved towards the child. She didn't flinch. She merely tilted her head back on her thin, pale neck. Thud! Her forehead bashed against the glass again. The noise was worse the second time. Instinctively Grace stretched out her hands to stop her, but her fingertips smashed into the glass and bounced off. A painful juddering sensation ran up her arms. Please God, not a third time. But thankfully the carer got hold of the child just in time and pulled her backwards.

Nina ran into the playroom and dropped on her knees beside the little girl, who was now twisting and screaming in the young woman's arms. The noise filled the viewing room, amplified and distorted by the microphones. The desire to turn away from the thrashing child and stricken faces of the adults was strong, but far stronger was the awful compulsion to watch.

Steph finally realised that she needed to *do* something. 'Sorry. This is really very distressing. I think it best if we leave, give them some space to help Leah calm down. They'll take good care of her, I'm sure.' She ushered Tom and Grace out. They did not resist.

Tom heard the screaming in his head for days afterwards.

The small pinched face on the other side of the glass stayed with Grace for ever.

The possibility of them adopting Leah was never raised again.

They were culpable.

Grace knew it. Tom knew it.

They had rejected Leah.

But…had it been the wrong decision?

They couldn't say.

'She spent the rest of her life in care. Eighteen different placements – never in one place long enough to feel safe, never mind loved. That's what you condemned her to. What? Why the sad faces? You didn't know?' The acid in Cassie's stomach churned. 'Well, I guess that's because you never bothered to find out, did you?'

Grace hung her head. 'No.'

Tom tried to speak again, but to his dismay, Cassie wouldn't let him. 'No! Mum!'

Grace was forced to try and defend them. 'What your dad was going to say was that we did try to keep in touch with her. We wrote a letter to her, every year. She never replied. We took that as a sign that she didn't want any contact.'

Cassie was shaking her head, disbelief and distress contorting her already-smudged and swollen features. Grace suddenly stopped talking, rose from the bed and left the room. In her absence they fell silent. Cassie's head hurt. Too much had happened, too fast, in the past twenty-four hours. It had left her feeling unhinged. She tried to rest her chin on her hand to ground herself, but it was too painful; every part of her body felt tender and bruised. The three of them sat, tense and unspeaking, isolated by their own turmoil, until Grace's footsteps sounded again on the stairs. She came back into the room with her laptop.

Grace opened it and tapped at the keyboard. When she'd found the letters, she crossed the room and placed the laptop on Cassie's knees. 'They're all there.'

Cassie's eyes shuttled back and forth as she read. A click, a skim-read, another click, another skim-read, then another and another. Her expression became clouded with confusion and doubt. She held a tissue against her leaking, damaged eye and read on. No one risked interrupting her. At last she looked up. 'Leah never said anything about any letters.' Leah had been crystal-clear that when Tom and Grace abandoned her, that had been it. And yet here they were: a catalogue of Cassie's life across the years, full of the painstaking details of a happy childhood, all addressed to Leah. 'Maybe she didn't get them?'

'Maybe,' Grace said. 'But we sent them. Every year.' Tom was grateful for the *we*. Then Grace risked another small, defensive statement. 'According to Social Services, they were collected. But she never responded.'

More lies. From her mum or from Leah? Despite her rage at her parents, Cassie's gut said 'Leah'. The bulging file, full of paperwork, in Leah's flat? Cassie's head throbbed. She shoved the laptop aside

Tom risked opening his mouth. 'They told us that when they got in touch with Leah – when they were trying to trace your biological mum – she flatly refused to have any contact with us...or you.'

'That's because she hates you.' Neither Grace nor Tom knew how to respond to that. 'She's furious: at everyone, but most of all at you.'

'It sounds like she's had a very difficult life. It must have affected her,' Grace said.

'You think! She has every right to be angry. What happened is so unfair. Me and her, we're so different, and we didn't have to be.' The momentum seemed to be draining from Cassie. She reached up and cradled her swollen cheek, and Grace ached to be able to comfort her. She took a chance and sat down on the floor next to her daughter. Cassie didn't move away. It was progress of sorts.

'How often have you met up with her?' Grace asked tentatively.

'Enough.'

'Enough to…'

'Get to know her.' Cassie stalled. They waited for her to go on. 'Or I thought I did.' They all noted the qualification.

'So what is she like?' Tom asked.

'Like I said: angry…and scary, and unpredictable, but she's brave, and she can be funny. She works. She's got a flat. She's got a life. But she's so on her own.' Cassie rocked slightly as she spoke.

'So you've made a connection?' Grace said.

'We already had a connection. She's my sister!' The distress was drowning out Cassie's anger.

'But what happened last night? If she's so special, why were you in such a state when we picked you up?' They had forgotten that Erin was even in the room.

Cassie shifted, uneasily. 'Nothing. Nothing that matters now.'

Erin couldn't let that stand. She couldn't bear the thought of Leah being Cassie's sister. All it had done was bring trouble. She hated the way they were all heading in totally different directions since Leah had crashed into their lives. It had to stop. 'That's not true. I've never seen you so upset. Something happened.'

Cassie seemed to be wrestling with conflicting loyalties. 'It just went wrong.'

'How?' Erin again.

Tom and Grace were surprised by her persistence, but grateful. This had to come out.

'It got a bit out of hand. Leave it, Erin.'

Erin paused, her face giving away the stress she was feeling, but she pushed on. 'What do you mean? How did it get out of hand? And what about the money?' Cassie glared, but said nothing. Erin turned her attention to her parents. 'Leah's been taking money off Cassie. Quite a lot.'

'Has she?' Tom asked, nervously.

'Not taken. I gave her it. She needed it, and we owed her. It was the least I could do.' Tom and Grace exchanged a look, which Cassie intercepted. 'Don't! We have enough. She's got nothing.' The thought of Leah's small, bare flat came back to her.

'Let's not worry about that now.' Grace wanted to take the tension down a notch.

But Erin was suddenly relentless. 'She got Cassie to steal for her.'

'She did not!' Cassie started up as if she was going to fly at Erin.

'Girls, girls! The money doesn't matter. Please. We can sort it out later.' Grace positioned herself between her daughters. 'What I still don't understand is why last night ended up the way it did. And why you were there, Erin?' Grace looked from one daughter to the other. They simply stared at each other, a deluge of things left unsaid surging between them.

Erin spoke first. 'I thought I was helping Cassie, but it seems she doesn't want my help.' She made to leave.

Cassie was angry with her, but she hated the thought of her leaving. 'Erin!' She couldn't bear to lose both her sisters.

Erin stopped at the door. 'What?'

'Don't go!'

'Why not? You obviously don't need me, or trust me any more. I'm sick of lying for you. If you want to spend your time with someone like her, rather than with me, then go ahead. I've had enough.'

Cassie brushed past Grace and grabbed hold of Erin's arms. 'I'm sorry. I don't know what else I can tell you.'

Erin's chin lifted and, despite the tears, she said very clearly. 'How about the truth?'

Chapter 60

THE SMELL of the kitchen was comforting. They sat together at the table. Tea, thick slices of toasted white bread, butter and blackcurrant jam. You can't cry and eat. Tom and Grace hung back, letting the girls talk.

Cassie took a small bite of toast and chewed it cautiously before she spoke. 'She must have gone through my purse when I was asleep. I didn't realise at first. She took my cards as well as the money – or he did. I cancelled them this morning.' This to her parents. 'I'm sorry, I should have done it sooner, but with everything that happened last night... I don't know if they'll have used them. I'm really sorry.'

'She took Grandma's ring as well, didn't she?' Erin asked. Cassie nodded miserably.

There was so much that Tom and Grace didn't know. Tom tentatively patted Cassie's hand. She didn't seem to notice, but it brought him a tiny shred of comfort.

'The money, I can maybe understand, but not Nana's ring.'

'He?' Tom asked.

'Leah's got this friend, more a boyfriend – he's called Naz. Him and Leah have an odd relationship. I'd met him a couple of times before. He's very confident, cocky. I thought he was okay.'

The new, assertive version of Erin asked, 'But he isn't?'

Cassie shook her head. 'He came back to the flat with us yesterday. We had a drink. Not a lot. Not enough to make me feel as out of it as I did. I think he spiked mine with vodka. I felt really drunk, really quickly. I must have passed out.'

Tom felt a wash of iced water sluice through him. Cassie had been alone and vulnerable, miles away in Oldham, while he had been wandering around worrying about his sodding lawn, oblivious. No, not even oblivious; actually relieved that his unsettling, combative eldest daughter wasn't coming home.

Cassie continued with her staccato retelling of events. 'One minute I was sitting talking to him, the next I woke up feeling crap and he was gone – but Leah was there. I didn't know what time it was or how long I'd been asleep. To start with, she was nice, normal, like she'd been earlier in the day. There was a dog that attacked us in the park.' Grace bit her lip, her tea and toast forgotten. 'Leah chased it off. She was really brave, actually. We talked afterwards – kinda made a breakthrough. Or I thought we had. Anyway, that doesn't matter now. When I came round, she got me some water. She looked after me, was kind...but then she went really weird when I said I needed to ring home.'

'Weird, how?' Erin again.

'She got mad, really irritated. She acted like me ringing you guys was somehow letting her down. She didn't like it at all when I said I wanted to go home.'

'Did she try and stop you?' Tom asked.

Cassie was struggling to tell them what had happened, because she wasn't sure she was remembering it clearly herself. She certainly didn't understand why it had gone so badly wrong, so quickly. 'No, not really. I'm not sure what she wanted, really. But the mood in the flat changed. I saw the texts that she'd sent to Erin and Ryan. She didn't like that, either. Then my phone got smashed. She wouldn't let me use hers to ring you. She just sat in the corner, refusing to acknowledge that I was even there. It was like she'd disappeared inside herself. I just wanted to get out of there. I didn't realise the money and the cards were gone until I got outside. That's when I rang Ryan, from the shop.'

'And you rang Erin?' Grace asked, grieving all over again that, even at such a low point, Cassie had chosen to call her sister rather than her parents.

Erin answered, without breaking eye contact with Cassie. 'No, Ryan and me had been calling each other. I didn't buy the text about staying at Freya's. We'd both been trying to get in touch with Cassie, to check she was all right. I was worried; we both were. I made Ryan pick me up from the cinema. I really didn't give him a choice. All he was trying to do was help.' At this, Cassie nodded. Erin suddenly turned her attention to Tom. 'You shouldn't be mad at Ryan, Dad. It really was an accident. I think he panicked when he saw the police car. He'd never to do anything to hurt Cassie. He just wouldn't.'

As Erin was talking, Tom had a sudden very clear flashback to the day Ryan dropped Cassie off at the house – the tenderness he'd witnessed, the closeness between the two of them. How wrong he'd been all this time, thinking the threat to their family was Ryan, when all along it had been their own avoidance of the truth.

'We can speak to the police about it, when you make your statements,' Tom told them.

'Do we have to?' Cassie asked.

'Yes. You both do. If nothing else, you have to let them know that Ryan was only doing as you'd asked. It sounds like you owe him that.' Cassie nodded. 'And you can tell them about the theft, and about this Naz character. He sounds dangerous.'

'No,' Cassie said firmly. The consequences, if she spoke about the money and the cards going missing, would be bad – the police at Leah's door, invading her flat, searching her things, accusing her, provoking her. Who knew what might happen? She couldn't bring herself to do it. Stupid as it seemed, she still wanted to protect Leah. And there was Naz. Cassie didn't want to risk any retaliation from him. She simply wanted never to have to see him again.

'But if she took your cards and the ring, that needs reporting,' Tom said carefully.

'Dad. No. Please. I want to leave it. Forget it ever happened. That any of it ever happened.'

Tom and Grace didn't need to weigh up the issue for long. The theft wasn't their primary concern; getting Cassie back was. 'Okay.' Tom nodded. Cassie gave a small lopsided smile, which struck at Tom's heart. But they weren't out of the woods yet, the big question still hung over them – Leah.

Again it was Erin who asked what they were all thinking. 'What are you going to do now? Are you going to stay in touch with her?

'No,' Cassie said firmly.

'No more seeing her?' Erin asked.

'No,' Cassie said flatly.

'So this is the end of it?' Erin pressed.

'Yes,' Cassie said miserably.

Tom and Grace sighed inwardly with relief. Erin smiled, and Cassie started to mourn.

It didn't take too much persuasion to get Cassie to go back up to her bedroom to rest. The showdown with her parents and her sister had exhausted her.

She climbed the stairs slowly. Telling the truth had not made her feel lighter. What she felt was the opposite of relief – a new type of sadness weighed her down, one that was as tender and bruised as her face. She left her bedroom ajar, pulled off her jeans and slid under the covers, too worn out to bother getting properly undressed. She lay on her back. Her face was too sore to lie in her natural position, on her side. She could hear Grace and Erin talking in the room below. It was a reassuring sound. Her eyes drifted round the room. Little darts of lights were flashing around the walls and ceiling of her room, bright slivers of silver that swam and rippled like tiny fish. She looked round for the source of the reflections and found it in the old toy hippo that sat on her bedside table. Draped over its gappy-toothed mouth was her necklace, the one that had got broken during the awful fight with her dad at Flo's party. It was fixed, untangled, whole again. Her dad? The little filigree disc was spinning in the sunlight, casting reflections around the room. Cassie lay back and watched the light-show, until her eyelids grew heavy and she drifted asleep.

She's hot, sweaty and very uncomfortable, but there's something about the place she's in that is reassuring.

It's a box, with a lid, which is closed above her head. She could push it open, but she chooses not to. She's on her knees. Through the gaps in the sides of the box she can see rows and rows of photos of people she thinks she knows. They pulse in and out, as if they're alive and breathing. One mum, another and another; one sister and another. One dad and another. A never-ending whirl of faces, some smiling, some scowling.

Her arms are full of hard, plastic animals. She scoops them up from the floor of the box, but each time she does, they disappear and reappear at her feet. She picks them up again, and they disappear again.

The lid suddenly lifts, but instead of light, darkness fills the box.

She is frightened.

She tries to make herself as small as she can, tries to bury herself underneath the animals. Their hard little legs and snouts dig into her, their trunks and teeth bite her flesh. It hurts. They're not good camouflage. Some part of her knows that the old trick of the blind not being seen doesn't work, but she tries it anyway.

Even with her eyes closed, she can sense the hoods bending low over the box. She feels their presence. There's a meaty, nasty smell, a change in the air, a sense of threat.

Hands reach into the box, searching for her. They grab at her. Bone and muscle connecting with her soft flesh. Relentless fingers and sharp nails.

Then...there's a different touch.

Someone is lifting her up.

Someone she trusts.

Someone whose face she can't see, but who makes her feel safe nonetheless.

Chapter 61

FOUR WEEKS later, Erin was home alone.

It was a normal weekday afternoon. Her mum and dad were at work, and Cassie was staying late at college for a catch-up class. The brace had come off – for good – the week before, and her neck and shoulders were feeling much better; and you had to know where to look, to see Cassie's scar. Ryan was still in his leg-cast, and would be for a good while longer, but he was up and hobbling about, and no longer a pariah within the family. Everyone was exactly where they should be, doing exactly what they should be doing, with who they should be. It made Erin feel good. She changed out of her school uniform into shorts and a T-shirt and went back downstairs to get a drink, before starting on her homework.

Leah was standing in the kitchen.

The shock made Erin drop the beaker she was holding. It smashed, sending shreds of sharpness skidding across the floor. Her first thought was 'Run!', but she couldn't. She was barefoot, stranded in a sea of glass. Leah tilted her head to one side. A small, tight smile flickered across her lips as she realised Erin was trapped.

Erin finally found her voice, though it was not the one she wanted. 'How did you get in?' Her words wobbled.

Leah wandered casually round the kitchen island, as if she had every right to be there. She came as close as she could to Erin without standing on the glass. 'You left the door open. Are you always that stupid?'

Erin felt her face flush. 'You need to leave.' Even to her own ears, she sounded pathetic.

Leah nodded slowly, as if giving the suggestion some actual thought, before pulling out one of the stools and climbing up onto it. A better vantage point. She stopped nodding. 'Yeah, well, that's not gonna happen.' She turned towards Erin, crossed her legs and began swinging her foot back and forth, within centimetres of Erin's body. 'Erin, poor little Erin, you still don't get it, do you? I don't do what I'm told. Haven't you worked that out yet?' Leah pushed the toe of her trainer against Erin's ribs. 'I do whatever I want, and what I want at the moment is to talk to Cassie.' Each word was accompanied by a jab of her foot.

Erin hated being touched by her. She kept her head down and stood there like a little kid taking a kicking. It was humiliating. This was her home, her kitchen, her life, and yet Leah had simply walked in and taken control.

Leah snapped her fingers in front of Erin's face. 'Erin! Erin! Anyone home? Is Cassie here?' Erin said nothing, which was a mistake, because she saw the anger flare in Leah's eyes. 'Erin! Where is she?'

'Out.' Was she being brave...or stupid? Probably both.

Leah's tone changed, the mockery disappeared and was replaced by something more complex. 'Stop pissing me about, Erin. I need to talk to Cassie. Where is she?'

Erin's ingrained hatred of Leah knitted together tightly enough for her to put up some resistance. 'Like I said...she's out.' She saw a tiny change in Leah's expression, a glimmer of desperation beneath the scowl. Perhaps she wasn't as Teflon-coated as she pretended to be. It was enough to make Erin feel bolder. Who was Leah after all? A nobody, barely scraping by in life. She acted mean, but what did it amount to really, except a foul mouth and an inflated sense of her own importance. Erin wasn't going to let her come between her and Cassie, not again. She lifted her chin. 'She won't talk to you. She doesn't want anything to do with you – not any more. Not now she knows what you're really like. You blew it. So, like I said, you need get out. Now!'

Confusion and anger wrestled within Leah. It had taken a lot for her to come and speak to Cassie, more than Erin could ever know, and yet here was Erin telling her to fuck off. Erin was a mouse; timid, squeaky, as irritating as all fuck... she wasn't supposed to have sharp teeth. Leah couldn't get her head round the change in her. 'You don't fucking know what Cassie wants!'

Erin actually smiled. 'Yes, I do. We're close. We always have been.' It was a direct provocation. Leah flinched and Erin saw it. 'And you're never going to change that. Cassie talks to me, tells me things – her secrets, her feelings, what she really thinks about people, including you. That's what sisters do. And right now, she hates you. She can't stand the thought that she's related to you. It makes her want to scrub her skin off. She wants to forget all about you, that you even exist. So why don't you go and crawl back under whatever stone you came from and leave me and *my* family alone.'

Leah was staggered by the vehemence of Erin's outburst and – though she was loath to admit it – she was also scared that what Erin was saying was true: that Cassie hated her and wanted nothing to do with her.

What happened next was a blur – a rush of air and swearing and anger.

Leah leapt off her stool, determined to shut Erin's flapping mouth. As she lunged, she caught sight of the chunk of glass sitting on the counter top. Instinct made her pick it up. A second later she cannoned into Erin, pushing her backwards. Erin staggered and cried out. They crashed into the wall, rebounded, then collided with a chair. Erin ended up sprawled in the chair, with Leah kneeling on top of her, shouting, 'Shut up, you snotty little bitch. Shut the fuck up!' Her hands gripped Erin's shoulders like claws. 'You're not her sister. I am! Where is she? Tell me where she is, or so help me God...' Erin's neck hurt with each shake and there was a biting pain in her left shoulder, but she bravely kept her mouth shut. Leah's tears of rage and frustration were her reward. 'Where is she?' Leah screamed.

'I'm here,' Cassie said. The shaking stopped. The room stilled. Cassie was standing in the kitchen. 'Get off her. Now!'

For a second, all movement ceased. They froze in their respective positions: the victim, the aggressor and the saviour. Then slowly – because what choice did she really have? – Leah did as instructed; she clambered off Erin as if dragging herself out of a deep hole.

'Jesus, Leah, what have you done?' Cassie said quietly. The room was a scene of carnage, dusted in glass and blood. They all watched as more drops seeped from the soles of Erin's feet and a rose-red bloodstain bloomed and spread like a corsage across the left side of her T-shirt. Cassie's shocked face swung back towards Leah. 'Get out!'

Leah grabbed hold of a chair-back to steady herself. 'Cassie, please?' she pleaded. Erin looked up, taken aback by the change of tone. It was like someone else's spirit had taken over Leah's body – someone human and afraid. 'Cassie, please, I just wanna talk to you. I need to talk to you.'

But Cassie couldn't hear Leah – didn't want to any more – her focus was on Erin. Leah had hurt Erin. That was the end of it. Cassie walked across the debris, indifferent to the glass crunching under the soles of her shoes, towards her sister. 'Are you all right?' She crouched down in front of Erin, creating a barrier.

'I'm okay.' Erin was, now that Cassie was there.

Cassie reached up and touched her sister's hair and, without turning round, she said, 'I told you to get out of our house.' Flat, cold, hard syllables, leaving no room for uncertainty.

Leah hesitated. 'This wasn't me.' It was, but it wasn't what she'd intended. She hid her hand behind her back. The lump of glass felt heavy and sharp against her palm. She hadn't really meant to hurt Erin, not intentionally anyway; no, what she really wanted was to *be* Erin.

Cassie stood up and faced Leah. 'It never is your fault, is it, Leah? Nothing ever is. It's always someone else's.'

'But it wasn't...'

Cassie put her hand up, warding off Leah's words. 'Shut up! Just shut up. I've had it with listening to you. You do nothing but lie, and steal and take, and hurt people. I don't want to hear any more of it. Get out of this house – before I call the police.'

'Cassie, please?' In her desperation, Leah sounded like a child.

But Cassie was stony-faced. 'No. Enough! Shut up and leave. I don't want to hear from you ever again. Never. Do you hear me? That's it. You and me are finished. Get out.'

Leah swayed slightly and seemed to be about to try again, but Cassie's expression stopped her. She turned away, crossed the kitchen and went out through the back door. Cassie and Erin watched as she walked round the side of the house and out of sight.

Leah set off back to the high street towards the solitary bus stop. Erin! What a bitch, what a little bitch. Shows you. You shouldn't judge a person by what they looked like, or acted like. Butter wouldn't melt. Yet Cassie loved Erin. Loved her more. Loved her most. Loved Leah not at all. Fuck 'em. Fuck the lot of them, with their big shiny house and their money, and their tiny, tidy minds. Fuck 'em, fuck 'em, fuck 'em, fuck 'em. Leah gulped some of their precious, clean air into her creased, dirty lungs. It was a stupid idea going to their house. Even if Erin hadn't been there to screw things up, Cassie still wouldn't have listened – wouldn't have cared. Not really. She should've known better. She did know better. Jesus, she was a dumb fuck.

A woman with a pair of the biggest motherfucker scissors Leah had ever seen was snipping away at some dried brown flowers on a plant in her front garden. She stared as Leah walked by, an expression of alarm stapled on her face, the scissors paused mid-air, mid-snip. Uncharacteristically, Leah looked away. She hadn't the energy.

Half an hour later, sitting on the bus, she finally breathed out. She leant back in her seat and watched the scenery change, becoming more recognisable with each mile: darker, harder, messy, busier. She was heading back where she belonged. The chink of light that Cassie had represented was extinguished – for good. The thought was depressing, but at least it was definite. Hope was a fucking tiring, confusing, hurtful, ultimately useless emotion. She was better off without it. She would go back to her flat, where she would wait, not knowing what the fuck she was going to do. Naz would come round, when he wanted something, and she would let him in. And life would go on, just like before, until it didn't. That was the plan – such as it was. The thought of it made Leah feel less shaky, but also vaguely sick.

Her situation was clear.

No more stupid fantasies.

Cassie had made her choice – and it was not Leah.

It was Erin.

She needed to forget that she'd ever had a sister.

She needed to forget that she'd ever been a sister.

She was on her own.

Chapter 62

THEY DECIDE to take the narrow stairwell rather than face the confines of the lift. The sounds and smells of the building are horribly familiar. Cassie's last, disastrous visit feels a lifetime ago, but the memories are still sharp and clear, the environment still alien and unwelcoming. There is nothing to soften the hard edges of Leah's world. The floors are unforgiving, the walls gouged and badly scratched. It's unremitting. Grey paint, grey skies and the occasional grey person, toiling down past them with grey, suspicious eyes.

As they plod up the stairs, Cassie focuses on her parents, trying to read their thoughts in the hunch of their shoulders. Her dad is transmitting fake calm, her mum nervous energy; both of them are emanating a quiet, grim determination to get this over with. Cassie's own feelings are clawing at her insides, scrambling over each other for supremacy. Fear is winning. She has not seen Leah for months, not since she broke into the house and attacked Erin. Absence has not made her heart grow stronger. Cassie is genuinely terrified of seeing her sister again. Leah is nothing like her, and never will be. She isn't normal and civilised and predictable. She's wild and unreadable, seemingly incapable of kindness or affection. What she has proved herself very capable of is manipulation, lies and rage.

Common sense, self-protection, loyalty to Erin, a renewed belief that Tom and Grace have her best interests at heart – everything is telling Cassie to stay as far away from Leah as possible.

Yet here they are.

The phone call from Social Services had shocked and unsettled them all.

Gail rang, out of the blue, and said they'd been approached by Leah – that she'd asked for permission to contact Cassie.

'Really?' Grace had failed miserably to disguise her dismay at the news.

Gail picked up on her tone. 'Sorry, I thought you'd be pleased. I know it all came to a bit of a dead-end last time we tried.'

Grace recovered, slightly, reminding herself that Gail was unaware of the incident at Leah's flat, the theft, the car crash, the break-in. They hadn't told her about any of it, wanting nothing more than to close in on themselves. The girls had recovered well from their physical injuries, but the after-effects of their contact with Leah still lingered. Her shadow was slowly beginning to dissipate, but they were not the same family they had been; there had been too much hurt and deceit all round for that. As Gail chattered on, Grace felt awkward not telling her about what had happened, but she didn't, there was still a need for some omissions. Cassie had insisted that they say nothing, and Grace wasn't about to break a confidence with her eldest daughter any time soon.

'Do you know what she wants?' Money? Another attempt to win Cassie over? Threats? Whatever it was, Grace was frightened that it was going to do more harm.

'No,' Gail said, 'but it'll come through Letterbox – the usual protocols. I'd recommend that you read the letter before you pass it on to Cassie. It's better to be on the safe side. I'm sure it'll be fine, but it never does any harm to be cautious about contact at the beginning – at least until you've worked out people's motivations.'

Grace was uncomfortably aware that it was much too late for such sensible precautions. Gail wished them well and rang off, unaware of the anxiety she'd just provoked.

Grace and Tom waited on tenterhooks for the letter to arrive.

It did, five days later.

It was lying on the hall mat when Tom came downstairs for breakfast. A perfectly ordinary-looking white A4 envelope that might as well have been an incendiary device. He picked it up and put it away in his briefcase. A Tuesday morning was not the time to tackle this. He took it into work with him, not even telling Grace that it had arrived.

At lunchtime Tom put on his coat and scarf and headed to the canal, the envelope tucked inside his jacket pocket. It was a mockingly clear, bright, cold day; a beautiful day for walking or cycling, but not for sitting. His bench was empty. He drew the envelope out and, with cold fingers, clumsily unpeeled the tab. Inside was a smaller, cheaper, buff-coloured envelope on which was written one word: CASSIE. The handwriting seemed shocking personal. It disturbed Tom, deeply. It was the closest he'd come to actually having contact with Leah. Up until that point she'd only ever been a dark shadow that stalked his life. The uneven block capitals, penned in black Biro, forced him to think about her as a real living, breathing person. He didn't want to, but the physical reality of the letter made him; it demanded that he acknowledge her existence, and her power. He stared at the envelope and wondered at her motivation for contacting Cassie. Why now, when they'd thought it all over and done with? What else could she possibly have to throw at them?

The envelope was lumpy. Tom squeezed it, trying to guess the contents. He turned it over. It was sealed with two raggedly torn pieces of sticky tape. He weighed the letter in his hand. With every fibre in his body he wanted to throw it in the canal and let the scummy water swallow it up. If he got rid of it, he could get rid of Leah. It was a neat, appealing equation. He had the right, hadn't he – the right and the responsibility to protect his daughter? Again?

A sudden loud splash made Tom look up.

A pristine white swan (the same swan as on his previous visit?) had crash-landed on the canal. It folded away its wings, shook its head and fixed Tom with its glassy eyes as it glided towards him. When it reached the weed-choked bank, it stopped and began dipping its head smoothly in and out of the black water, sifting for food. Tom watched it, feeling the cold of the bench creeping up into his bones. After a few minutes the swan stopped, stretched out its long neck and silently, effortlessly slid away.

Tom put the letter back into his pocket.

Tom and Grace told Cassie about the letter after dinner that evening. They watched her struggle to control the emotions that chased across her face at the mention of Leah. Tom went to fetch the envelope and put it on the table in front of her. She eyed it nervously, but didn't pick it up.

'We were advised to open it first, before we gave it to you, but we thought that wasn't right. It's addressed to you. It's your letter. It's for you to open – if you want to.' They really were trying to learn from their mistakes.

Cassie picked it up. 'Why now?'

'We've no idea.' Grace said.

'I suppose I'd better open it.' She seemed very reluctant.

'You don't have to.' Tom said, hating Leah for messing with his daughter.

'No. I do.' Cassie ripped open the envelope as if speed would lessen the pain. A photo fell out, face-down on the table, along with a folded piece of paper and a wad of toilet roll. Cassie flipped over the photo. It was the one Leah had taken from her the day they first met: Cassie and her birth mum; but when Cassie picked it up, she realised it wasn't only her picture, because stuck to the back of it was another print, the one of her birth mother with both of them. Tom and Grace both craned forward, curiosity proving stronger than sensitivity. Cassie pushed the photos aside, indifferent, or at least feigning indifference. She unfolded the piece of paper. Her face flickered as she stared at it.

Grace's anxiety climbed. 'What does it say?'

Cassie let the paper drop onto the table. Just a single word, carved out in graceless block capitals: SORRY. Hesitantly she picked up the lump of tissue and unwound it. Bedded inside the wad of loo roll was her grandma's ring. Cassie took it, slipped it back onto her finger and stared at it.

Which is why – despite everything that has happened, despite her parents' very valid concerns, and despite Ryan's and Erin's downright opposition – they find themselves climbing up a grey, depressing stairwell, heading back towards Leah.

Because Leah *is* Cassie's sister. Nothing will ever change that. They're connected by blood. Cassie can't forget that, never will forget that. And, if she's learnt anything over the past year – and she has – it's that families aren't always nice and neat, that love isn't always expressed politely, and that care isn't always soft and sweet. Sometimes a sister looks and acts like Leah, not Erin.

And there is no denying the past.

It was Leah who had saved Cassie when she was a baby. She was the one who had cared for her – the only one. Somehow she managed to protect her from the squalor, the neglect and the dangers that surrounded them. She was the one who put the needs of her baby sister before her own, providing food, warmth, protection, even love and affection, in circumstances that would have overwhelmed most adults. She was a better mother to Cassie than their real mother ever was.

Seven-year-old Leah had empathy and loyalty, and huge reserves of resilience and ingenuity. She only changed because they were ripped apart.

So if twenty-two-year-old Leah's behaviour is erratic and incomprehensible, and sometimes plain scary, it isn't her fault. She's faulty because no one ever truly tried to mend her, at least not enough to succeed; not her mother, not Tom and Grace, or any of the subsequent long list of professionals, carers and guardians who were supposed to be on her side. Little wonder she's nothing like Cassie. How could she be? But she is still Cassie's sister. The letter was Leah's way reminding her of that. Cassie has to find out why she sent it.

They make it to the seventh floor, where they gather on the landing, catching their breath. There are six identical doors, each as blank and utterly anonymous as the next: a letterbox, a spyhole, a scratched lock. Behind number forty-five is Leah. Even at this late stage, they're unwilling to announce their presence. They stand close together and whisper about who should knock and what they should say. In truth, Tom wants to turn round and creep, like a coward, back down the dirty stairs and out of the depressing building, back to their clean lives, but Cassie is resolute. It's shaming and inspiring, in equal measure. Despite Tom's pleas that it's safest if he knocks and speaks to Leah first, Cassie is adamant that it should be her.

'The only person Leah trusts, even a tiny bit, is me. If she opens the door and sees you, she's going to slam it in our faces. It has to be me.'

It's hard to argue with her logic, but it still makes Tom feel inadequate that his seventeen-year old daughter is more in control of the situation than he is. 'Okay,' he concedes, 'but if she's at all aggressive, we're leaving.'

Cassie makes a non-committal noise; and Grace, who knows her daughter well, squares her shoulders and accepts that, whatever happens in the next few minutes, it isn't going to involve leaving quickly or cleanly. They crossed more than miles and demographics when they set foot inside the building, they crossed the barrier between their lives and Cassie's past.

Time's up.

Cassie steps forward and knocks, and Tom and Grace fall in line behind their daughter.

There's no response. Nothing. Only the rapid thudding of their hearts. Cassie waits, then knocks again, not louder or longer, just the same two short, firm raps. Still nothing. They listen for sounds from the other side of the door, but there are none. Perhaps she's left, Cassie worries. Perhaps we can still reverse away from this, Tom prays. She's there, on the other side of the door, Grace is certain.

Then the lock rattles, the door opens and Leah stands in front of them.

Something has happened. Cassie can see it immediately. Leah looks different. She's fatter, her face fuller and her cheeks plump. All the definition is gone, replaced by a pale, smudgy softness. Even her eyes have changed – they've grown smaller, the dark glitter dulled. Tom needn't have worried; this young woman looks incapable of sharpness or anger, never mind violence.

She isn't what they were expecting. It's disorientating.

'Hey,' Leah says. If she's shocked to see them, she does a good job of covering it up. She tugs at the edges of her hoodie, trying to pull it together across her chest, but it's too small. 'Why are you here?'

'I got your note.' Leah doesn't say anything. 'I wanted to say "thank you" for sending my ring back to me. And I thought it was maybe a sign...that you might want to see me.'

Leah doesn't move. She looks at Cassie, and Cassie holds her nerve and looks straight back. Tom and Grace stand, surplus to requirements, witnessing the silent conversation.

Cassie tries again. 'And I wanted to come to say "sorry". For last time. For how it ended. It wasn't right.' Leah blinks, but she doesn't move. Cassie holds her voice steady. 'Are you okay?'

Leah shrugs and finally breaks eye contact with her. She glances at Tom and Grace, a swift, utterly dismissive appraisal. The flatness of her expression is absolute. It's as if she's looking through them, rather than at them. It's no less than they deserve.

'This is my mum and dad. They wanted to meet you. Could we maybe come in, just for a few minutes?' Cassie ventures. Leah doesn't respond. Cassie perseveres, 'We won't stay long. Please, Leah.'

Still Leah doesn't move. She stands, a lumpen sentry, on the threshold to the flat. They wait.

Leah looks at Cassie and at her shiny, polished parents standing there, a mere foot away from her life. Is she going to let them in? She doesn't know. She still blames them, still wants to wreck something of theirs, but she doesn't have the energy. She can see now that they come as a sealed unit, that this is what a proper family looks like; this is how it functions, where its power comes from – they stick together. Leah knows she will never be able to peel Cassie away from them. She's not even certain she wants to any more. Together they are strong and she is weak.

She is also painfully aware that she's poised on a knife-edge. She knows that whichever way she falls, she's going to get hurt; the question is: how badly? Behind her, in the jaws of the flat, lies impossible. She knows that if she closes the door on them and goes back inside, something bad is going happen, if not this day, then the next, or the next – because that's where her life is heading, it always has been. In front of her stands a chance of changing that, but at what cost? She knows that if she invites them in, she'll lose. They'll take over, of that she's absolutely certain. They'll crush her with their knowledge and their words and their swift, assured actions, and they'll take away from her the only thing that matters. And for that she hates them – all of them, even Cassie.

Or she would, if she weren't so damn tired. Leah has no anger left and as, she's discovered, without her anger, she is nothing. The last month is proof of that. She's useless, inadequate, pathetic and so, *so* lonely. She wishes she could just stay there, at the door, with her head leaning against the frame, balanced in the void.

But they're waiting.

She turns abruptly and heads back into the flat, thereby issuing an unspoken, unwilling invitation to follow her – which they do, filing in, one after another: Cassie first, backed up by Tom and Grace. They walk through the tiny hallway and step into the living room. It's bare and yet messy at the same time, a palette of beige and brown. The thing that strikes Cassie immediately is the smell. Gone is the astringent, floral scent of disinfectant, in its place an oddly sweet, almost fetid smell hangs in the stale air. The ceiling light is on, despite the light flooding in through the window, and through the smeary glass the compact sprawl of Manchester is visible, but it isn't the view that catches their eye.

The room isn't empty.

On the floor, in front of the unlit fire, there's a baby.

A newborn baby, soft-skulled, thin-skinned. It's sleeping peacefully, covered by a grubby baby blanket, which rises and falls gently in time with its breathing. Tom, Grace and Cassie stop and stare. Leah walks round the child and goes over to the far side of the room, where she stands, silhouetted against the window, her arms folded across her soft, unreliable body. 'She's called Lola.' Her voice is full of compressed distress. 'I came to tell you, but you didn't wanna know.'

'When?' But as soon as she asks, Cassie knows. That was why Leah came to the house. It wasn't to hurt Erin. It was to tell her that she was pregnant. 'Oh, Leah.' Cassie feels a thick, sticky guilt seep through her. It extinguishes the last remaining flickers of fear.

'Don't bother!' Leah musters up a tiny spark of anger. 'You don't get to pretend you care.' At the sound of a raised voice, the baby starts to stir. Her eyes flutter open, revealing glossy black pupils. Her arms and legs begin to wave. They all watch as her tiny feet lift and kick and get tangled in the fringe of the blanket. In frustration she starts to cry. Leah shrinks further into herself with each high, harsh, angry yelp. She's done it now, there's no going back. She looks at her daughter, then at them, wanting...what? She doesn't know – for things to be different, to be better, or at least not worse; or maybe just to be on the other side of the room.

No one moves.

The baby stops crying for a moment.

They all wait.

It takes three short, desperate gulps, drawing in the stale air, then it starts crying again, louder, more insistent, more desperate.

Leah doesn't respond, she can't. She retreats further away from the child – safer for her and for her daughter. But there is nowhere to go. She's trapped, her back pressed against the glass and the city beyond. Confession time. 'They've been round already, asking questions. They know about Naz. I 'ave to prove he isn't staying 'ere. How can I prove he isn't here? He isn't. Not most of the time. I don't want him here. But I can't stop him. He was supposed to piss off out of it when I got pregnant. But he keeps coming.'

The baby's crying is relentless and heart-piercing. They all look at her lying on the floor, but no one dares make a move. It's painful to be so powerless.

Leah stares at her daughter. When she speaks again, it's as much to herself as to Cassie. 'No matter how hard I try, I can't keep her clean, not properly clean. She's always spitting up her milk, shitting in her nappy. The smell – it gets everywhere, on her clothes, on her bedding, on her, on me. I can't stand it. I can't. I just wanted someone to love, someone who was mine. I thought I'd be able to look after her, love her, properly, but I can't. I can't.' She looks away and her voice grows quiet. 'I don't think I should have her. I can't do it on my own.' Tears slide down her cheeks and drip off her chin, unchecked. Slowly she turns her back on her own daughter. She leans her forehead against the window and closes her eyes.

In that instant Grace and Tom see a pale, unloved little girl – the child who raised their child.

'You're not on your own,' Grace says, compelled by the pressure in her chest to offer hope.

Leah does not respond.

She is done.

She has lost.

It's a vicious cycle and she's not strong enough to break it. She must let her daughter go. It's almost a relief to finally admit defeat and give up, but oh, it hurts – hurts all over, hurts as bad as when they took Cassie away. Leah presses her forehead against the glass and silently begs for them just to take her daughter and leave.

Cassie takes a step towards the child. 'Can I pick her up?' Leah can't bring herself to say 'yes', but she doesn't say 'no'. Cassie kneels down. 'Shush, it's okay. I'm your Auntie Cassie.' She brushes her fingertips against the baby's cheek, soothing, tentative, a gesture of comfort and love. 'It's going to be all right,' she whispers. The crying grows softer, less insistent. She slides her hand underneath the child's head and carefully picks her up. The weight and the warmth of her are intoxicating. She is Cassie's flesh and blood. Her niece. Her family. She gets to her feet, cradling the baby against her chest, and slowly, carefully carries her over to her mother.

THE END

A new mother is a vulnerable thing, full-hearted, thin-skinned, best watched over, for fear of damage.

And this young mother is alone.

She is disarmed, weakened, prone to dark thoughts and even darker emotions.

The sudden, shocking imperative to care is intolerable. The responsibility of becoming a parent overwhelming.

A newborn baby is not a soft, biddable, calming healer. It's a hungry beast, full of raging needs and demands. It consumes, leaving no oxygen to breathe, no place to hide, no time to think.

This new mother wants so desperately to respond to her child's incessant cries, but she can't. She wants to rise, meet and conquer its ferocious tyranny, but she is too weak and too alone. It's too much. Her longed-for child is placing too much pressure on the fragile carapace of her soul. She is cracking and buckling under the strain.

This baby was supposed to make everything all right. It was supposed to make up for the past; make her happy, and whole, and strong.

It has not.

It has broken her.

It is not a new beginning.

It is another dead-end.

She wanted a child to love.

She wanted her child to love her back.

All she has ever wanted is a family of her own.

But one vulnerable new mother and one tiny, screaming, fatherless newborn do not a family make. Together they are not enough.

It is not the child's fault. It's hers. She is useless. At the most basic of human functions – the loving and raising of a child – she is failing, miserably.

She stands, defeated, accepting the inevitable, as the chance of love and happiness slips through her fingers, into the hands of others.

She is desolate.

But this time she is not alone.

She has someone who understands.

Someone who cares.

Someone who might be able to make a difference.

She has a sister.

It might, just, be enough.

Acknowledgements

ALL BOOKS start somewhere – this one began in a warm kitchen, on a dark night, with two complete strangers who kindly shared with me their personal, very bumpy path to becoming parents. So my first thanks go to Heidi and Wendy, for their generosity, open-heartedness and their wicked sense of humour.

Then there is Kath, my primary reader. Writing is solitary exercise and you're lucky if you find someone who wants to share the experience with you. Kath is my writing companion and my friend, and I'm truly grateful for her involvement in my writing.

Thanks are also due to my editors at Corvus, Sara and Susannah. They have both exercised their considerable patience and their sharp critical faculties on this book. Respect to Mandy, the copy editor, as well; she laid bare just how innumerate I am, and how addicted to 'that'! This book is better for all their efforts. In fact, the whole team at Corvus has been as good as their word in supporting my first steps in what I hope is going to be a long career as a published writer. Professionally I also benefit hugely from the support and advice of Judith Murray at Greene and Heaton. As my agent she is a useful and necessary guide to the often slightly 'odd' world of publishing.

My family matter and I thank them for loving me. In a book about sisters a special 'shout out' must go to my sister, Sue. She has been a one-woman sales and promotion department for my writing. And I'm proud to say she's about to join the quiet, dedicated, under-appreciated army of foster carers who make such a difference to so many children's lives.

Cheers, as always, to my friends, Sam, Kath and Joss, who have played their part in the keeping me sane. I thank them for supporting me, running with me, laughing and crying with me. A special mention also needs to go to Linda, for her strength.

All books are dreamed up, written, fretted over, re-written and edited somewhere... This one spent quite a lot of time in No.54, Fulneck, the café with the best scones in Yorkshire. Thank you Ann, Amy and Neil for the good food and the support.

And lastly I would like to thank every book blogger, librarian and reader who mentioned, reviewed, recommended, bought, borrowed and lent out my first book, *The Second Child*. A book that is not read might as well be blank.

Book Club Questions

What happens after the last chapter? (Please feel free to let me know your ideas via Facebook or Twitter for a sequel!)

Did you find the ending hopeful or depressing? Satisfying or frustrating? Why?

Did the story make you question how well you know your own children? Do you always know where they are, who they are with, what's really going on inside their heads?

Grace falls in love with Cassie at bath time. '*The simple pleasure of being close to Cassidie's warm, soap-clean body was so powerful that Grace had to take a few deep breaths to steady herself. The years of aching for a child melted and pooled in her heart.*' What is your first memory of falling in love with your child?

Who is the strongest character in the book for you and why?

Who is the most loyal character in the book?

Do you agree with the author's premise that our early beginnings fundamentally shape who we become as adults? What passages in the book demonstrate this childhood influence most clearly?

Do you believe we can retain early childhood echoes within ourselves?

Would you be happy for Ryan to go out with your daughter? Why? Why not?

Who is to 'blame' for Leah and the way her life turns out?

What are Leah's strengths – as a child and as an adult?

Could you adopt another woman's child?

What do you think the book has to say about adoption and the support, or lack of support, for struggling birth parents and adoptive parents?

If Cassie had been your daughter how would you have handled her wish to find her birth mother?

Can a child be 'unlovable'?

Who has the ultimate right to decide what's best for a child?

When does a child become an adult?

The author states that 'one vulnerable new mother and one tiny, screaming, fatherless newborn, do not a family make.' What does make a family in your opinion/experience?

Is *The Forgotten Sister* the story of a vicious cycle?

Who is 'the forgotten sister'?